$\mathcal{I}$7. 30

10
F

Endocrinologic and Morphologic Correlations of

THE OVARY

The Florentine Conference

Endocrinologic and Morphologic Correlations of

THE OVARY

The Florentine Conference

Compiled and Edited by

PROFESSOR WLADIMIRO INGIULLA

Professor and Chairman
Clinica Ostetricia e Ginecologica
Universita di Firenze
Firenze, Italy

and

ROBERT B. GREENBLATT, B.A., M.D., C.M.

Professor and Chairman
Department of Endocrinology
Medical College of Georgia
Augusta, Georgia

CHARLES C THOMAS • PUBLISHER
Springfield • Illinois • U.S.A.

Published and Distributed Throughout the World by
CHARLES C THOMAS • PUBLISHER
Bannerstone House
301-327 East Lawrence Avenue, Springfield, Illinois, U.S.A.
Natchez Plantation House
735 North Atlantic Boulevard, Fort Lauderdale, Florida, U.S.A.

With THOMAS BOOKS *careful attention is given to all details of manufacturing and design. It is the Publisher's desire to present books that are satisfactory as to their physical qualities and artistic possibilities and appropriate for their particular use.* THOMAS BOOKS *will be true to those laws of quality that assure a good name and good will.*

D
612.62
END

Printed in the United States of America
N-1

CONTRIBUTORS

ARCHIE A. ABRAMS, M.D.
Assistant Professor of Obstetrics and Gynecology
Boston University School of Medicine
Boston, Massachusetts

ROBERT CONIFF, M.D.
Department of Internal Medicine
Geisinger Medical Center
Dannville, Pennsylvania

A. C. CROOKE, M.D., F.R.C.P.
Director of the Department of Clinical Endocrinology
The United Birmingham Hospitals
Birmingham and Midland Hospital for Women
Birmingham, England

P. ALESSANDRO DALL'OLIO S.J.
Direttore dell'Istituto Stensen
Firenze, Italy

RALPH I. DORFMAN, PH.D.
Director, Institute of Hormone Biology
Visiting Professor of Pharmacology
Stanford University School of Medicine
Palo Alto, California

R. FORLEO
Professor
Clinica Ostetrica e Ginecologica
Della Universita Firenze
Firenze, Italy

BRUNO LUNENFELD, M.D.
Director, Institute of Endocrinology
Tel-Hashomer Government Hospital
Professor of Endocrinology and Head of Department of Biology
Bar-Ilan University
Ramat-Gan, Israel

VIRENDA B. MAHESH, PH.D., D.PHIL.
Professor of Endocrinology
Medical College of Georgia
Augusta, Georgia

Jorge Martinez-Manautou, M.D.
Research and Instruction Department
National Medical Center, I.N.S.S.
Mexico, D.F., Mexico

Paul G. McDonough, M.D.
Associate Professor of Obstetrics and Gynecology
Medical College of Georgia
Augusta, Georgia

Irma D. Pico, M.D.
Research Fellow
Department of Endocrinology
Medical College of Georgia
Augusta, Georgia

Robert H. H. Richter, Ph.D.
Director of Laboratories
Department of Gynecology and Obstetrics
Medical School, University of Berne
Berne, Switzerland

Harry W. Rudel, M.D.
The Population Center
The Rockefeller University
New York, New York

Kenneth Savard, D.Sc.
Professor of Biochemsitry
Professor of Medicine
University of Miami School of Medicine
Miami, Florida

Ian F. Sommerville, M.D., Ph.D.
Director, Endocrine Unit
Chelsea Hospital for Women
Institute of Obstetrics and Gynaecology
London, England

G. I. M. Swyer, M.D., D.Phil., F.R.C.P.
Department of Obstetrics and Gynaecology
University College Hospital
London, England

Adriana Buzzati-Traverso
Director, International Laboratory of Genetics and Biophysics, Naples
Professor of Genetics, University of Pavia
Naples, Italy

Other Participants:

Piero Donini, M.D.
Instituto Farmacologica Serone
Roma, Italy

P. K. Siiteri
University of Texas — Southwestern Medical School
Dallas, Texas

Luciano Martini
Istituto di Farmacologia e Georopia
Milano, Italy

P. Quinto
Clinica Ostetricia e Ginecologica
Bologna, Italy

PREFACE

T HE CONFERENCE ON OVARIAN physiopathology held in Florence was organized by Professor Ingiulla, Director of the Department of Obstetrics and Gynecology, University of Florence. The faculty was recruited from many countries of Europe and North America. The registrants, many of whom participated in the conference both directly and indirectly, came from many parts of the world. Because of the wide interest in the subject matter, Professor Ingiulla felt that the proceedings should be published and asked me to edit the work. The manuscripts were updated and edited to permit each participant to use his own characteristic terminology and spelling. The inclusion of the discussions by the various panelists, frequently providing more heat than light, is a particular feature of this book. The international flavor of the proceedings underscores the universality of problems concerning ovarian physiology and chemistry. It is my pleasure to acknowledge the cooperation of Professor Ingiulla's assistant, Dr. Forleo.

ROBERT B. GREENBLATT

Medical College of Georgia
Augusta, Georgia, U.S.A.

FOREWORD

THE PAST DECADE HAS witnessed an upsurge of interest in the ovary. The whole field of gynecologic endocrinology has been revitalized; old concepts were reexamined and new concepts were evaluated in the face of new evidence. The Florentine conference was organized so that knowledgeable men in this field could be brought together, present their views, reason together, and throw some light on many of the complexities concerning ovarian physiology and chemistry. With this in view I asked Dr. Greenblatt to lead off with the histopathology of the ovary and to relate morphology to clinical disorders and endocrine chemistry. His emphasis on the significance of the various components of the ovary is quite in keeping with the newer concepts of the role of the follicle, the corpus luteum, and the stroma in steroidogenesis. Of vital interest is Dr. Greenblatt's conception of the role of follicular atresia in the ovarian economy and the dynamic potential of the dormant stromal cells in contiguity with the corpus atreticum. This introduction paved the way for Dorfman's brilliant exposition on ovarian steroidogenesis. He opened for us exciting gateways in the field of steroid metabolism. He gave us a new perspective of estrogen and androgen synthesis.

With characteristic elegance and clarity Sommerville related practical experience of the laboratory to the clinic. He demonstrated the pitfalls, and the importance of selecting and interpreting laboratory results. Mahesh's ingenious procedures in studying ovarian steroidogenesis clarified many poorly understood mechanisms, particularly as they are related to hirsutism. With the foregoing studies, the presentation on hirsutism and the Stein-Leventhal syndrome afforded all of us a better understanding of the relationship of ovarian morphology and ovarian steroidogenesis to clinical manifestations. The panel discussion that followed served to emphasize the many gaps in our knowledge, and was particularly highlighted by Siiteri's explanation of "secretion rates" and why a new look into the value of urinary assays is in order.

The second part of the conference was confined to discussion of contraception and the effect of steroids on ovarian function. The case for the "classic" pill was ably presented by Swyer, while Richter and Abrams defended the case for the "sequential" pill. A revolutionary concept in conception control was introduced by Rudel and Martinez-Manautou, who described the administration of a daily "mini-dose" of progestogen.

Following this, clarification of the mechanisms of action of the various regimens used in contraception was attempted. Though the elucidation of the *modus operandi* left many loopholes, much was learned. The moral aspects and the social impact of the pill were approached from many angles. The enlightened views of Father Dall'Olio, as representative of the "new thinking" by many in the Catholic Church, were heartening. The panel seemed to say that in a changing world, what was morally wrong in yesteryears may not be so tomorrow.

Lastly, the techniques available for stimulation of the ovary were meticulously presented by Crooke. He equated hormone response in search of the ideal ovulatory-stimulating dose. Lunenfeld followed with a resume of his wide experience with human menopausal gonadotrophins in problems dealing with gonadal inadequacy. Of great interest was the demonstration of the ovulatory-inducing ability of a chemical agent, clomiphene citrate. Greenblatt's original observations on the ovulatory-inducing properties of this agent will be a landmark in gynecology. Our own studies parallel and confirm the usefulness of this drug and we agree with his conclusion that clomiphene should be tried before resorting to gonadotrophins. The presentation of Savard's *in vitro* studies following ovarian stimulation with gonadotrophins was most timely. By demonstrating a separate role in steroidogenesis for the various compartments of the ovary, he neatly tied into one package what we set out to do, that is to cleave ovarian morphology and ovarian chemistry for a better understanding of ovarian physiology.

I am grateful to my illustrious colleagues for their contributions, and particularly to those who participated in the panel discussions and thus helped immeasurably in crystallizing our knowledge of the complexities of ovarian function.

W. INGIULLA

Clinica Ostetrica Ginecologica
della Universita di Firenze
Florence, Italy

CONTENTS

14. The Use of Human Pituitary Gonadotrophin in some Aspects of
     Ovarian Pathology
            A. C. Crooke 210

15. The Use of Human Menopausal Gonadotropins in Gonadal Pathology
            B. Lunenfeld 225

16. The Induction of Ovulation with Clomiphene
            Robert B. Greenblatt, Irma Pico and Virenda B. Mahesh .. 251

17. Biogenesis of Steroids in the Human Ovary
            Kenneth Savard 264

18. The Stimulation of Ovarian Function (Panel Discussion)
            W. Ingiulla, Moderator 274

     Contributors and Discussants Index 289
     Author Index 291
     Subject Index 297

Endocrinologic and Morphologic Correlations of

THE OVARY

The Florentine Conference

Chapter 1

ENDOCRINE HISTOPATHOLOGY OF THE OVARY

ROBERT B. GREENBLATT and PAUL G. McDONOUGH

EVERY GONAD HAS THE POTENTIAL to develop into an ovary or a testis. Because of this, the vagaries of ovarian histopathology are frequently great. A brief review of current concepts in gonadal embryology should prove helpful in understanding the multifaceted aspects of ovarian chemistry and physiopathology. At approximately six weeks of embryonic life the undifferentiated gonad consists of an external layer of coelomic epithelium (mesothelium) covering an internal blastema of loosely arranged mesenchyme.

Lack of testicular elements in a gonad by the seventh week of embryonic life may be taken as indirect evidence that the anlage is destined to be an ovary. At approximately seven weeks, germ cells migrate into the potential ovary. This migration from the yolk sac endoderm has been traced by the characteristic staining properties of these cells. The complete differentiation of the ovary depends upon the arrival of sufficient numbers of viable germ cells. When migration is successful, clusters of epithelial-like cells (cortical sex cords) appear beneath the coelomic epithelium. They extend through the underlying mesenchyme and embrace the primordial germ cells (gonocytes). These embracing cells are thought to give rise to future granulosa cells of the ovary. The remaining mesenchyme of the original ovarian anlage develops into ovarian stroma and theca cells. Vestigial structures frequently found in the medulla of the ovary represent either remnants of medullary sex cords or of the primitive mesonephric tubules.

Genetic sex determination is present from the time of fertilization. Anatomically the two sets of accessory ducts are similar in human embryos throughout the second month of intrauterine life. However, regression of the heterologous accessory ducts does not occur until postgenetic differentiation of the gonad has been accomplished. During embryonic life there is therefore a long period of sexual neutrality. This concept explains the great variety of sexual anomalies observed clinically and facilitates the interpretation of endocrine histopathology of the ovary.

Gonadal differentiation occurs during the period of so-called sexual dimorphism. Whether differentiation of the gonadal anlage into an ovary or testis depends on some "gonadal inductor" or represents the resolution of competitive interplay between the medullary and cortical regions remains

3

unsolved. It has been conjectured that the struggle between cortex and medulla for dominance is a prime factor in gonadal differentiation. If the cortex is favored, an ovary results; if the medulla gains preeminence, a testis develops. The experiments of Jost, and clinical experience seem to indicate that in instances where gonadal differentiation fails and neutrality is preserved, the accessory reproductive structures are "permissibly" female.[5] That is to say in the absence of any testicular or ovarian elements in the gonad, the gonadal accessory ducts will develop along müllerian or female lines. The implication is that the differentiated testis secretes a factor which stimulates male accessories to develop and causes regression of female müllerian elements. In the absence of such a factor male structures do not develop, but rather the müllerian or female elements are permissibly preserved.

The prime example of gonadal neutrality is gonadal dysgenesis. The indifferent gonad is made up of cortical and medullary portions. Proponents of the corticomedullary inductor theory of gonadal differentiation would

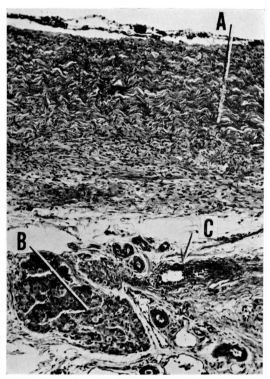

FIGURE 1-1. Photomicrograph of histologic section of a streak gonad showing the three basic constituents: stroma (A), Leydig cells (B), and mesonephric elements (C). (Reproduced from Greenblatt, R. B.; Vazquez, E., and De Acosta, O. M.: *Obstet Gynec, 9:* 258, 1957.)

regard any cortical superiority as a portent of a potential ovary. The cortex of the rudimentary gonad is made up of fibrous connective tissue not unlike ovarian stroma. In the medulla mesonepheric elements and nests of Leydig cells are frequently found (Fig. 1-1). The salient feature of this "neutral" gonad is the lack of germ cells. The privation of germ cells is difficult to explain. Where a sex chromosome anomaly is present it may be assumed that the migration failure is on a genetic basis. However, where no morphologic alteration in sex chromosomes is evident, we can only assume that some extrinsic factor prevented normal gonocyte migration or the genetic defect, though present, is not recognizable by present investigative methods. Gonadal dysgenesis with an XY sex chromosome pattern, though few in number, suggests that extrinsic teratogens may play a role in certain instances of gonadal failure. Of course, it is always possible that normal migration did occur, but the germ cells found the environment unsatisfactory for normal development. As with most biological phenomena, failure of migration or germ cell development is not an all-or-none phenomenon. Figure 1-2 shows a histologic section of the gonad of an eight-year-old child with classical stigmata of gonadal dysgenesis who had an abnormal sex chromosome karyotype (XO/XXX). Some primordial follicles are seen in the gonadal

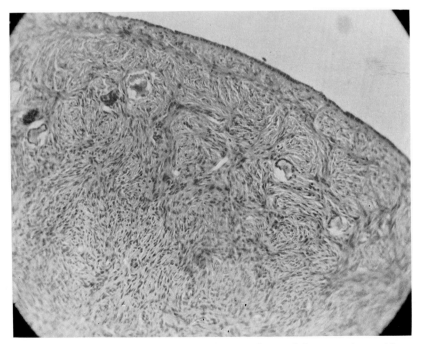

FIGURE 1-2. Photomicrograph of histologic section of gonad from patient with gonadal dysgenesis (XO/XXX) showing some primordial follicles in cortical portion. (Reproduced from Greenblatt, R. B.: *J Clin Endocr, 18*:277, 1958.)

cortex. Some individuals with postpubertal ovarian failure may represent still another variant of the same basic mechanism. The ovaries of such persons are poorly endowed with primordial germ cells that are rapidly expended.

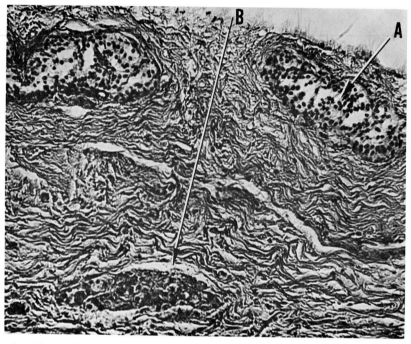

FIGURE 1-3. Photomicrograph of gonad from eunuchoid female with primary amenorrhea showing nests of cells resembling noncanalized seminiferous tubules (A). Note islet of Leydig cells (B). (Reproduced from Greenblatt, R. B.; Carmona, N., and Higdon, L.: *J Clin Endocr, 16:*235, 1956.)

The spectrum of altered gonadal morphogenesis is further illustrated by Figure 1-3. This histologic section is from the gonad of a tall eunuchoid female with primary amenorrhea and clitoral enlargement. Located in the periphery of a luxuriant ovarian stroma were nests of cells resembling uncanalized seminiferous tubules. Deeper in the gonadal stroma were clusters of Leydig cells. This patient had a normal female sex chromosome karyotype. In a measure this gonad is a link that bridges gonadal dysgenesis with complete gonadal dimorphism as represented by an ovotestis. The true ovotestis (Fig. 1-4) is defined as containing both testicular and ovarian elements. It probably represents a static state, where neither ovary nor testis became the dominant structure. Equally perplexing are those cases of asymmetrical gonadal differentiation that have a rudimentary gonadal streak on one side, and a testis on the contralateral side. The gonadal accessories in these cases are usually female, in spite of the presence of a testicle. The microscopic study of such gonadal structures points out the extremes of sexual bipotentiality present in the human gonad. If we remember that this bipotentiality is present in every gonad, we can understand the occurence of ovarian tumors as the arrhenoblastoma.

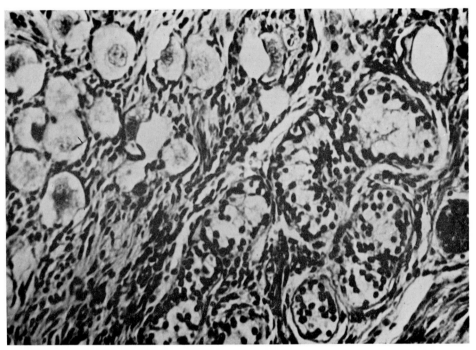

FIGURE 1-4. Photomicrograph of histologic section showing typical ovotestis. (Courtesy of Henry Turner — Reproduced from Greenblatt, R. B.: *Recent Prog Hormone Res.* 1958, p. 335.)

For many years we felt that different portions of the ovary possessed different functions.[3] Ryan succeeded in separating the granulosa layer from the theca layer of the follicle and demonstrated the potential of the isolated granulosa and theca cells to metabolize various hormones.[15] Structurally and functionally, the ovary may be divided into four units: follicle, corpus luteum, stroma, and corpus atreticum. We should like to stress the importance of the reactivated corpus atreticum with its garland of specialized stromal cells. The prime role of the developing follicle and the corpus luteum in ovulation has led us to overlook the endocrine potential of the atretic follicle.

Follicles are continuously undergoing atresia from birth until complete follicular exhaustion. The endocrine role of these atretic follicles is poorly understood and needs to be further explored. When subjecting histologic sections of a normal ovary to a Sudan III stain, very little lipid material is found in the granulosa cells of the mature graafian follicle but is abundant in the theca interna. However, sections of a newly formed corpus luteum demonstrate on Sudan III staining, that the luteinized theca interna maintains its sudanophilic property while now the luteinized granulosa cells exhibit high lipid content. The considerable difference in lipid content of the granulosa cell prior to and after ovulation is shown in Figure 1-5.

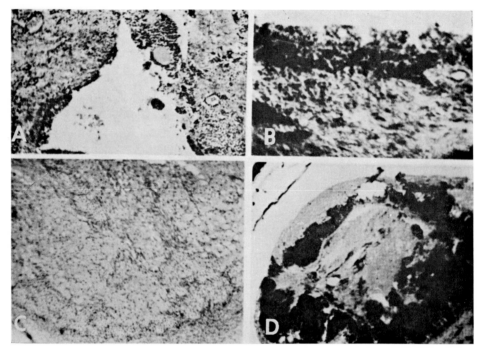

FIGURE 1-5. Photomicrographs illustrating lipid content of granulosa cells of graafian follicle before and after ovulation. (A) Graafian follicle, H.E.; (B) wall of graafian follicle, lipid stain; (C) corpus luteum, H.E.; (D) corpus luteum, lipid stain. (Reproduced from Greenblatt, R. B.: The adenohypophysis and ovulation. *Fertil Steril, 8*:537, 1957.)

In recent years, histochemical methods have been devised to demonstrate the activity of several enzymes involved in the synthesis of steroid hormones.[1,2] These staining techniques demonstrate intense enzymatic activity not only in the theca interna, the luteinized granulosa cells, the hilar cells, but also in the cells abutting the atretic follicle (Fig. 1-6). The granulosa cells exhibit increasing enzymatic activity as they develop from the follicular cells of the early graafian follicle into the lutein cells of the mature corpus luteum.[2]

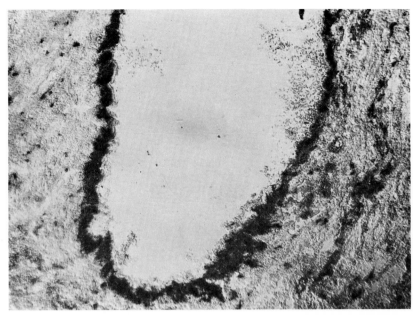

FIGURE 1-6. Histochemical preparation from ovary showing marked glucose-6-phosphate dehydrogenase activity in theca cell of an early atretic follicle. Note stromal cells with similar enzymatic activity.

Developing follicles which are not destined to reach full maturity and form corpora lutea undergo a process of atresia. As the gräafian follicle undergoes regressive changes, the ovum with its cumulus of granulosa cells undergoes degeneration. The atretic follicle which is thus formed eventuates into a corpus fibrosum and is gradually displaced toward the medullary region of the ovary. The stromal elements in direct contact with the atretic follicle frequently show evidence of hyperplasia with or without luteinization (Fig. 1-7).

In vitro studies have shown that the stroma of the ovary can produce estrogens and androgens.[10,15,19] The steroidogenic activity of the stromal component, however, seems to be minimal in normally menstruating women, while its endocrine potential may be marked during and after the menopause. The significance of cortical stromal hyperplasia is not yet fully elucidated, but it has been found to be twice as frequent in cases of breast and endometrial carcinoma as in control cases.[8,11,16,17] Sometimes the markedly hyperplastic ovarian stroma in cases of hirsutism and in cases of Stein-Leventhal syndrome contains nests of large, lipid-rich polyhedral cells (Figs. 1-8 A and B). The role of the luteinized cells in the ovarian stroma is little understood. It is our belief that these nests are related to the reactivated garland of theca-like cells contiguous to the atretic follicle.

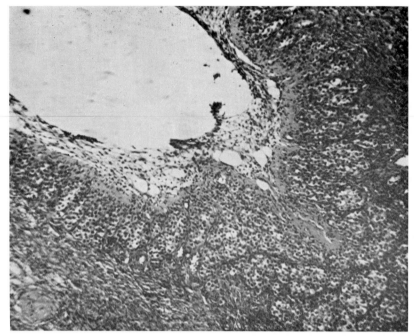

FIGURE 1-7. Atretic follicle showing marked theca cell hyperplasia and luteinization.

Recently, Scully and Cohen performed histochemical studies on the human ovary and they reported[13] finding "enzymatically active stromal cells." These are closely related to the luteinized thecal stromal cells and may not appear dissimilar to stromal cells that are morphologically indistinguishable from neighboring cells without enzymatic activity.

During histologic examination of ovaries, it is not infrequent to find small nests of epithelioid cells arranged in a mosaic fashion in the ovarian hilus. These cells received little attention until Berger (1923) described them under the name of "sympathicotrophic gland" of the hilus and stated that they are homologous to the interstitial cells (Leydig cells) of the testicle. The significance of the cells still remains unclear. It is possible that these Leydig-like cells are capable of producing a variety of steroid hormones. *In vitro* studies have shown that the tissues of the ovarian hilus possess a steroid metabolic pattern resembling that of the stromal component.[10] It is interesting to note that Hawkins and Lawrence[6] reported a case of hilus cell hyperplasia which showed a significant decrease in androgen, progesterone, and estrogen following extirpation of the lesion. Hilus cells may be found in large number in some hirsute women. Sometimes they form multiple nests (hilus cell hyperplasia), or they may represent the chief component of a virilizing tumor of the ovary.[9] Collections of Leydig cells are found in the majority of dysgenetic gonads, but are seldom associated with androgenicity and probably represent vestigial remnants of the primitive undifferentiated gonad.

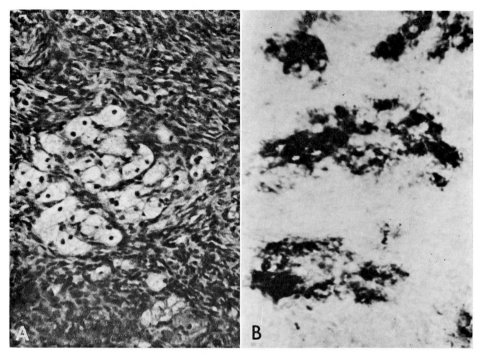

FIGURE 1-8. A. Photomicrograph of histologic section of ovary from a hirsute patient with polycystic ovaries. B. Sudan III stain shows rich lipid content of these luteinized large pale polyhedral stromal cells seen in A.

In the past few years we have encountered several patients who, to all intents, could be regarded as belonging to the category of the Stein-Leventhal syndrome. We present such a patient who had primary amenorrhea, marked hirsutism, enlargement of the clitoris, and mild voice changes. After subjecting her to a battery of hormonal assays, a definite diagnosis could not be made. Laparotomy was done and the typical large pale ovaries described by Stein were found; a wedge resection was performed but menstruation did not follow. Histological study revealed collections of large cells in the medulla displaying a vesicular nucleus and a prominent nucleolus. (Fig. 1-9). Another patient presented herself with a more or less similar picture but in whom the histopathologic study of the resected wedges of ovarian tissue showed a considerable number of hyalinized atretic follicles (Fig. 1-10). The stroma cells in immediate contact with these hyalinized bodies were sudanophilic. The histologic picture was reminiscent of the

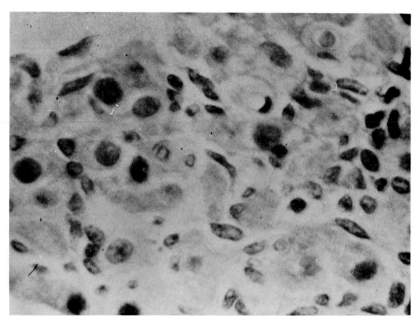

FIGURE 1-9. Photomicrograph of histologic section of ovary from a case of virilism and large pale ovaries. Note large cells with vesicular nuclei and prominent nucleoli found in ovarian medulla.

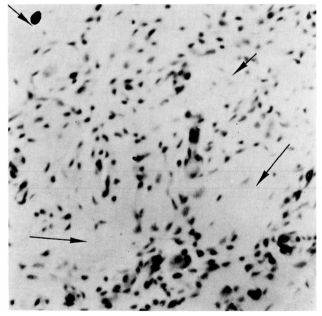

FIGURE 1-10. Photomicrograph of histologic section of ovary from a virilized patient demonstrating the presence of many hyalinized atretic follicles and increased numbers of hilar cells which proved to be sudanophilic.

hyalinized tubules and collections of Leydig cells seen in Klinefelter's syndrome.

Morris and Scully drew attention to certain tumors (cystadenofibromas, Brenner tumors, and certain ovarian carcinomas) which may be associated with clinical manifestations of hyperestrogenism, or rarely, of virilism, although they are ordinarily considered as having no functional capacities. The estrogenic function of these neoplasms is thought to be due to the activity of the stromal tissue in relation to the epithelial component of the tumor.[9] The theca-like stromal cells seen in such cases have been found to be rich in lipid content.[13]

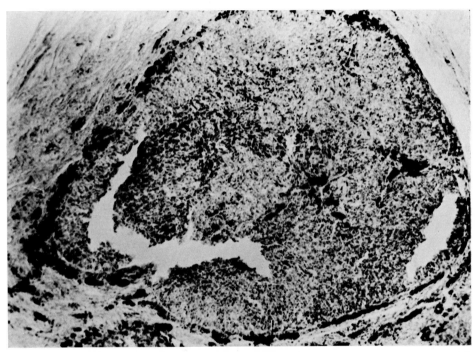

FIGURE 1-11. Photomicrograph of granulosa-cell tumor (Sudan III stain). Note rich lipid content of stroma in juxtaposition to tumor cells. (Reproduced from Greenblatt, R. B.; Greenhill, J. P., and Brown, W. R.: *Amer J Obstet Gynec, 37*:929, 1939.)

The granulosa-cell tumor is an uncommon feminizing neoplasm, but one is constrained to ask what role the granulosa-like component of the tumor actually plays in the production of feminization. When histologic sections are subjected to lipid stains, it is the tissue in immediate contact with the granulosa cells that takes a deeper lipid stain than the granulosa-like cells themselves.[4] It may be that incretory activity is stimulated in those cells which are in contact with the granulosa component. From the amount of lipid deposition in the theca as opposed to the granulosa cells of the developing follicle it may be conjectured that the cells in juxtaposition to the mass of granulosa cells in the tumor tissue are responsible for the feminizing nature of granulosa-cell tumors (Fig. 1-11). This concept finds further support in the study of granulosa-theca cell tumors. Figure 1-12 shows that it is the stromal elements in between the masses of granulosa cells that exhibit the marked sudanophilic property. The arrhenoblastoma, more clearly than its counterpart, points to the importance of the interstitial cells with their characteristic rich lipid content, as the important incretory component of the neoplasm.[4,7] Figure 1-13 shows an arrhenoblastoma composed mainly of strands and columns of cells with several groups of interstitial cells rich in lipid material.

FIGURE 1-12. Photomicrograph of histologic section of granulosa-theca cell tumor of ovary showing characteristic rich lipid content of theca component. Sudan III stain. (Reproduced from Greenblatt, R. B.; Greenhill, J. P., and Brown, W. R.: *Amer J Obstet Gynec, 37*:929, 1939.)

Because of the proximity of the gonadal ridge to the mesonephros and the adrenal anlage, adrenal rests are occasionally found in the dysgenetic gonad (Fig. 1-14 A and B) as well as in the broad ligament and ovary. Tumors of adrenal rest origin are as a rule richly sudanophilic and have

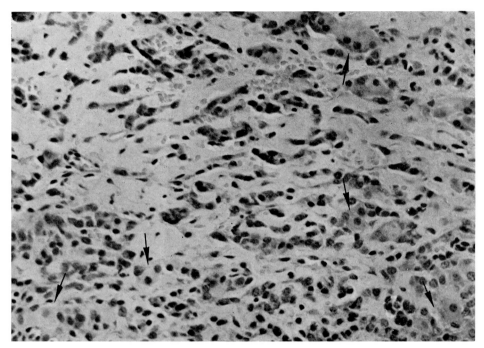

FIGURE 1-13. Photomicrograph of histologic section of arrhenoblastoma with large pale interstitial cells, which on Sudan III stain, showed rich lipid content.

virilizing properties. Although the presence of Reinke crystalloids and/or the arrangement of the tumor cells about nonmedullated nerve fibers may be of help in some cases, it is quite difficult at times to differentiate a Leydig-cell tumor from an adrenal-rest tumor of the ovary (Fig. 1-15).

Gonadoblastoma may contain germ cells, theca-Leydig and Sertoli-granulosa cells.[12] In a sense they recapture the embryonic development of the ovary. These tumors have been classified by Teter according to above composites.[20] The most common of these, gonocytoma III, is better known as gonadoblastoma. It consists of germ cells and in addition Leydig-theca, and granulosa-Sertoli cells may be found. The gonadoblastoma occur occasionally in rudimentary streak ovaries. Calcification is one of the hallmarks. A gonadoblastoma occurring in the rudimentary streak of a twenty-one-year-old female with gonadal dysgenesis is illustrated by Figure 1-16. Large germ cells are surrounded by Sertoli-granulosa-like cells.[18] In some reported cases there has been evidence of androgenicity and in others estrogenicity.[10] This is probably related to the predominance of specific cell types.

The endeavor to relate specific function of various ovarian components continues. The development of more sophisticated research techniques such

The Ovary

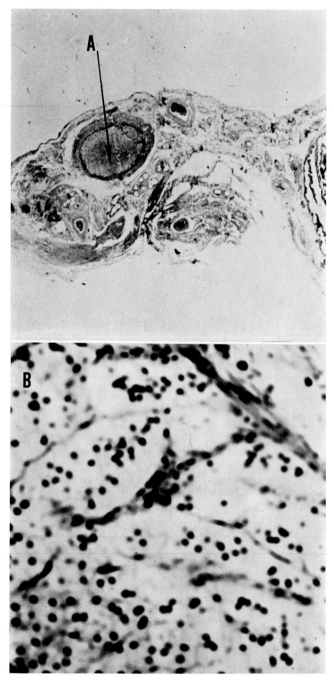

FIGURE 1-14. Photomicrograph of histologic section of a rudimentary gonadal streak showing A, adrenal rest, and B, high-power view of section shown in A.

as quantitative and qualitative enzyme studies, microdissection of ovarian components, improved cytochemical methodology, and hormonal assays of incubated ovarian slices and homogenized ovarian tissue may lead to a more definite understanding of the relationship between morphology and function.

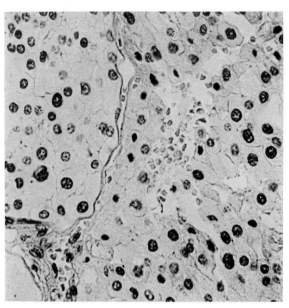

FIGURE 1-15. Photomicrograph of histologic section of ovarian tumor composed of adrenal-like cells (hypernephroma).

DISCUSSION

DR. INGIULLA: Dr. Greenblatt, do you think it is possible to have an ovulation without subsequent transformation of the follicle into a corpus luteum? What do you think of those descriptions made by Dubreul of the plissé follicle, in which ovulation had taken place but not the subsequent transformation into corpus luteum? Do you accept Dubreul's concept of the plissé follicle? Have you ever had occasion to observe a corpus luteum in which the ovum was still contained?

DR. GREENBLATT: The plissé follicle may represent ovulation without subsequent corpus luteum formation. There is no evidence, however, for such a sequence. We have seen a corpus luteum with a captive ovum in rabbit ovaries. I have been looking for this in human ovaries but have never found it. After the administration of Pergonal® or human gonadotropins, or clomiphene, pseudo-corpora lutea may result. I am not sure that they necessarily signify that an ovum has escaped. I think the true corpus luteum

The Ovary

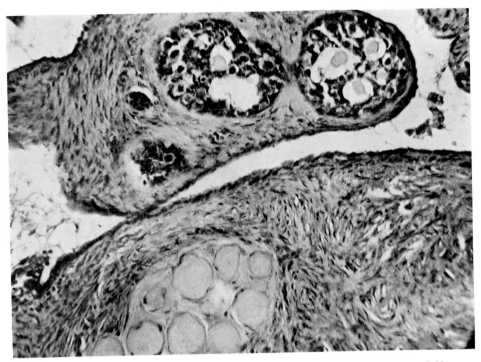

Figure 1-16. Photomicrograph of histologic section of gonadoblastoma. Note calcific concretions and folliculoid nests of neoplastic cells. (Reproduced from McDonough, P. G.; Greenblatt, R. B.; Byrd, J. R., and Hastings, V. E.: *Obstet Gynec, 29:*54, 1957.)

usually implies the escape of an ovum and the conversion of the collapsed follicle into a new gland of internal secretion, the corpus luteum.

Dr. Ingiulla: If an ovary doesn't work, is full of atretic follicles, would stimulation with HMG cause hirsutism instead of stimulating the ovary toward normality?

Dr. Greenblatt: I believe HCG may have this property. It may be that HMG (human menopausal gonadotropin) has the same capability. Various gonadotropins can stimulate the regressing theca cells to activity, especially the dormant tissue cells contiguous to corpora atretica and regressing follicles.

Dr. Ingiulla: Do you think that the dehiscence of the follicle and the migration of the ovum are due to chemical phenomena or to physical phenomena of superficial tension?

Dr. Greenblatt: Many explanations have been given for the migration of the follicle to the surface of the ovary. Three or four follicles are stimulated to activity each cycle. They all progress to a certain degree of maturation. Many follicles are called upon, but only one goes on to ovulation.

The Bible says, "Many are called, but few are chosen." What directs one follicle to the surface? What causes the dehiscence of the capsule and what expels the ovum? It could be a question of intrafollicular tension. There may be a lot of enzymes at play, responsible for dehiscence and lysis of the capsule. The explanation must remain speculative for the present.

DR. INGIULLA: What significance, if any, can be given to light-colored cells that are sometimes found in the stroma of ovaries from women with uterine fibromyoma?

DR. GREENBLATT: Yes, we've seen these cells, hypertrophic pale stromal cells in the ovaries of women with a variety of disorders. I think these pale cells do have a hormonal function; they have significance, but their presence in the ovary is not particularly related to uterine fibromyomas.

DR. SAVARD: Do you think that the corpus luteum, formed from elements derived from the theca, and from the granulosa, preserve different steroidogenic functions?

DR. GREENBLATT: Yes, to my way of thinking the corpus luteum has two separate functions. The developing follicle with its rich theca interna was an estrogen-producing gland. Once it becomes a corpus luteum, the theca interna continues with its estrogen production. The luteinized granulosa cells now take on the production of progesterone. Dr. Ryan separated the granulosa cells from the theca and by incubation studies found that the granulosa cells produce Δ^4 compounds like progesterone; whereas the theca interna produce the Δ^5 compounds like dehydroepiandrosterone. So that the corpus luteum, made up of two different types of cells, may well preserve separate steroidogenic functions.

DR. CENTARO: Do various histopathological types of micropolycystic ovaries exist? If so, is classification possible?

DR. GREENBLATT: Polycystic ovaries are seen in various endocrinopathies such as Cushing's disease, hypothyroidism, congenital adrenal hyperplasia, acromegaly as well as the Stein-Leventhal syndrome. If an endocrinopathy exists where the pituitary-ovarian axis has been disturbed, resulting in some menstrual disorder, polycystic ovaries are commonly seen. We have two types of polycystic ovaries, the large polycystic ovary and the small polycystic ovary. Yet they may have similar functions. It is difficult to make a definitive diagnosis purely on histologic basis alone.

DR. SOMMERVILLE: Is there a histological possibility of distinguishing or recognizing the Stein ovary, since there are polycystic ovaries found in patients who have no particular disturbances or who have a syndrome different from the Stein one?

DR. GREENBLATT: I do not feel that the histopathology of the Stein-Leventhal syndrome is specific. When we examine the wedge resection histopathologically, we can only say it is suggestive of Stein-Leventhal syndrome. But the same histopathology may be seen in simple secondary amenorrhea, and in oligomenorrhea. There are pathologists who will categorically say, "this is a Stein-Leventhal ovary," or "is not," but I am not so certain of it.

DR. KRAWCZUK: How can we prove the presence of certain hormones in the cells of the ovary? Are there histochemical or cytochemical methods to find these elements?

DR. GREENBLATT: The histochemical methods may suggest the site of action of hormonal activity but not the actual hormone itself.

DR. KRAWCZUK: Do all ovarian cysts—those commonly called retentive —always have a functional significance?

DR. GREENBLATT: No, I don't think retention cysts necessarily have function. The granulosa lining these retention cysts are frequently atrophic or mostly exfoliated. There are instances, however, where menstrual disorders have been associated with retention follicular cysts. Retention cysts, in most instances, have very little function.

DR. NEWTON: What is the role of the capsule in ovarian pathology?

DR. GREENBLATT: I'm afraid we've paid too much attention to the capsule of the ovary; we've made it into an important structure. I fear that too many textbooks still talk about the thickened capsule hindering ovulation. This concept has been destroyed by a series of studies performed in my department where patients with large pale ovaries and thick capsules had one ovary removed and the other allowed to remain intact and untouched. Ovulation invariably occurred from the contralateral ovary despite its thickened capsule. In the Stein-Leventhal ovary, it is reduction of ovarian mass by 50 per cent (whether this was accomplished by wedge resection of either ovary, or removal of one ovary alone) that changes the dynamics so that ovulation can take place. I believe that in the presence of adequate gonadotropins, thickness of the capsule is in inverse ratio to the frequency of ovulation; that if ovulation fails to take place, the capsule gradually thickens from disuse; and that frequent ovulation attenuates the capsule.

DR. INGIULLA: The removal of one ovary provokes ovulation in the other remaining ovary that has the Stein characteristics. He has given a particular interpretation for this. But there are also observations of ovulatory resumption in Stein cases after appendectomy, which permitted these ovaries just to be looked at. What do you think about this?

DR. GREENBLATT: Yes, I think this confirms what I said, that the patient with a classical polycystic ovary with a thick capsule may occasionally ovulate under stress conditions in preparation for a laparotomy. The administration of cortisone to some of these patients will also permit ovulation to

take place despite the thick capsule. So that every once in a while a patient with a classical Stein-Leventhal syndrome who has not menstruated
in two or three years may show a fresh corpus luteum at laparotomy. Along
with the stress of hospitalization there may be an increased corticoid output, which indirectly may facilitate the ovulatory process. Wedge resection in these cases may fail to reveal any other evidence of a previous ovulation; there may be no corpora albicantes anywhere in the ovary. This
accounts for the occasional patient with a typical Stein-Leventhal syndrome
who says that she has had one child, or even two children. So that infertility is not the *sine qua non* of the Stein-Leventhal syndrome. Some of
these patients, under certain types of stress, whether it's laparotomy or just
hospitalization, may experience an occasional ovulation. When the patholo-
gist reports histology incompatible with a diagnosis of Stein-Leventhal syndrome because there is evidence of a past ovulation, such as a corpus albi-
cans, I feel that this is not a valid reason to say that this is not a Stein-
Leventhal ovary.

DR. FURUHJELM: How can you explain the urinary output of estrogen
by the tumor cells of the granulosa?

DR. GREENBLATT: You would have to prove to me that it is the tumor
cells of the granulosa that produce the estrogens. I still think it is the cells
in contact with the granulosa cells—the specialized stromal cells in the immediate environs—that probably are producing estrogens. It is very difficult
to separate these cells from one another; it is not like stripping a follicle
and obtaining the granulosa cells of the follicle, or stripping the lining
of a corpus luteum and studying the tissue. In the tumor, we can only subject these histologic sections to various enzyme and fat stains, and assume
from such studies that the granulosa plays little role except with the so-
called luteinized granulosa-cell tumor (folliculoma lipidique). Luteinized
granulosa-cell tumors have been reported which proved markedly feminizing or masculinizing. It is the luteinized granulosa-cell that I think has the
function. Some of the luteinized tumors described by Lécène had a secretory endometrium. There have been typical granulosa-cell tumors where
the patient was not feminized, nor was there evidence of increased estrogen secretion. The granulosa cell itself is a poor producer of estrogens.

DR. SWYER: Can you tell us why in some Stein-Leventhal cases, the
wedge resection does not cure amenorrhea? Is a differential clinical and
histopathological diagnosis of these cases possible?

DR. GREENBLATT: Wedge resection fails in some cases of so-called Stein-
Leventhal syndrome. Perhaps the diagnosis was incorrect and the enlarged
polycystic ovaries were merely a manifestation of an endocrine imbalance
involving primarily the thyroid, or adrenal, et cetera. In these cases the

ovaries look alike; histologically we cannot tell them apart. The adrenal suppression tests may be able to pinpoint the cases of ovarian origin, i.e., the real Stein-Leventhal syndrome.

Dr. CENTARO: What is the importance of the hormonal content of the cystic liquid in the micropolycystic ovary.

Dr. GREENBLATT: The microfollicular cysts have been aspirated by various investigators and subjected to analysis. The results vary tremendously in different laboratories. Dr. Mahesh, in our laboratory, found that some of these cysts contain large amounts of 17-OH-progesterone, a forerunner of other steroids. Others have found various steroid hormones, varying from the Δ^4 compounds to the Δ^5 compounds. These points will be discussed further on.

Dr. MIRAGLIA: Some information on relaxin: its origin and its relationships with progesterone.

Dr. GREENBLATT: Relaxin is wonderful for the guinea pig; it's specific there, we don't know what role it plays in the human being. Relaxin has been made available for experimental purposes. We could not find a specific function for the relaxin that was made available to us. I am sure that one cannot extrapolate the results obtained on the pelvic ligaments of experimental animals with that which happens in the human. Whether the cervix relaxes with relaxin, or whether dysmenorrhea disappears with relaxin is doubtful. The placebo in our studies did as much. We have abandoned the clinical use of relaxin. Relaxin is thought to be a water soluble ovarian hormone.

Dr. SPANIO: When the androgenous fraction, presumably of ovarian origin, is greatly augmented do you think that they may derive from the presence of hilar cells similar to Leydig.

Dr. GREENBLATT: I believe, with Dr. Savard and others, that the ovarian stroma under various conditions is capable of producing androgenic hormones. In some cases of hirsutism there is frequently found a nest of large pale stromal cells which probably are functional. I'm not sure whether the vestigial Leydig cells that we sometimes see in the ovary have any function.

Dr. SPANIO: What is the significance of luteinized cysts?

Dr. GREENBLATT: Luteinized cysts are present in choriocarcinoma and in hydatidiform mole, sometimes a persistent corpus luteum becomes cystic and may be associated with amenorrhea and/or bouts of protracted uterine bleeding. Luteinized cysts may be induced with clomiphene, by gonadotropins of human origin (especially when followed with human chorionic gonadotropin). Lutein cysts have been found at laparotomy in patients with delayed menses. Some patients with amenorrhea and especially the patient with pseudocyesis, in whom the hypothalamic-pituitary axis is so deranged that there is thought to be persistence of LH stimulation, the corpus luteum remains active and cystic for a long period of time.

DR. SPANIO: Is a differential diagnosis possible for the granulosa and theca tumors before surgery?

DR. GREENBLATT: No, I don't think it's possible nor is it necessary to differentiate them before surgery. If an ovarian mass is present and there are signs of feminization, I think an incretory tumor should be suspected. I don't know how we would be able to differentiate them hormonally. It may be that the theca-cell tumors have a higher level of estrogen production. Do not forget that in every granulosa-cell tumor there are thecal or stromal elements that behave like the thecoma. The levels of estrogen output vary tremendously in granulosa-cell tumors as well as theca-cell tumors.

DR. SAVARD: Are there data on the hormonal function of the gonadoblastoma?

DR. GREENBLATT: Gonadoblastoma may well be a variant of the dysgerminoma. Teter in Poland has classified them into four different types depending on the degree of calcification and on the arrangement of the cells. The gonadoblastoma, like the dysgerminoma, has very little hormonal production, if any. Most of these patients seem to be neutral from a clinical appearance. It is true that some dysgerminomas and maybe some of the gonadoblastomas produce gonadotropinlike substances similar to the choriocarcinomas, except that the levels are very low. From the point of view of estrogens or androgens, or progesteronelike substances, most gonadoblastoma are inert; some cases however are accompanied by signs of feminization, others by masculinization. In Teter's view, tumors containing predominantly Sertoli-granulosalike cells (gonocytoma II) are feminizing. On the other hand those consisting chiefly of theca-Leydig type cells (gonocytoma IV) are usually masculinizing. Gonocytoma III (gonadoblastoma), containing the above cell types plus germ cells, is in most instances clinically neutral.

REFERENCES

1. DEANE, H. W.; LOBEL, B. L., and ROMNEY, S. L.: Enzymic histochemistry of normal human ovaries of the menstrual cycle, pregnancy, and the early puerperium. *Amer J Obstet Gynec, 83:*281, 1962.

2. FIENBERG, R., and COHEN, R. B.: Oxidative enzymes in luteinization. A histochemical study with special reference to persistent follicular cysts and the stromal theca cell. *Obstet Gynec, 28:*407, 1966.

3. GREENBLATT, R. B.: Histologic changes in the ovary following gonadotropin administration. *Amer J Obstet Gynec, 42:*983, 1941.

4. GREENBLATT, R. B.; GREENHILL, J. P., and BROWN, W. R.: Variation of lipid content in certain ovarian tumors. *Amer J Obstet Gynec, 37:*929, 1939.

5. GREENBLATT, R. B.: Clinical aspects of sexual abnormalities in man. *Recent Prog Hormone Res, 14:*335, 1958.

6. HAWKINS, D. F., and LAWRENCE, D. M.: Virilizing ovarian hilus cell hyperplasia with special reference to hormone excretion. *J Obstet Gynec Brit Comm, 72:*285, 1965.

7. HUGHESDON, P. E., and FRAZER, I. T.: Arrhenoblastoma of ovary. *Acta Obstet Gynec Scand, 32 (Suppl 4),* 1953.

8. McMANUS, R. G., and SOMMERS, S. C.: Breast cancer prognosis and ovarian cortical stromal hyperplasia. *New Eng J Med, 246:*890, 1952.

9. MORRIS, J. McL., and SCULLY, R. E.: *Endocrine Pathology of the Ovary.* St. Louis, Mosby, 1958.

10. NOALL, M. W.; ALEXANDER, F., and ALLEN, W.: Dehydroisoandrosterone synthesis by the human ovary. *Biochem Biophys Acta, 59:*520, 1962.

11. NOVAK, E. R., and MOHLER, D. I.: Ovarian stromal changes in endometrial cancer *Amer J Obstet Gynec, 65:*1099, 1953.

12. SCULLY, R. E.: Gonadoblastoma. A gonadal tumor related to the dysgerminoma (seminoma), and capable of sex hormone production. *Cancer, 6:*455, 1953.

13. SCULLY, R. E., and COHEN, R. B.: Oxidative-enzyme activity in normal and pathologic human ovaries. *Obstet Gynec, 24:*667, 1964.

14. SHIPPEL, S.: Ovarian theca cell. IV. Hyperthecosis syndrome. *J Obstet Gynec Brit Emp, 62:*321, 1955.

15. SMITH, O. W., and RYAN, K. J.: Estrogen in the human ovary. *Amer J Obstet Gynec, 84:*141, 1962.

16. SOMMERS, S. C., and TELOH, A. H.: Ovarian stromal hyperplasia in breast cancer. *Arch Path (Chicago), 53:*160, 1952.

17. WOLL, E., *et al.*: The ovary in endometrial carcinoma with notes on the morphological history of the aging ovary. *Amer J Obstet Gynec, 56:*617, 1948.

18. McDONOUGH, P. G., *et al.*; Gonadoblastoma. *Obstet Gynec, 29:*54, 1967.

19. RICE, B. F., and SAVARD, K.: Steroid hormone formation in the human ovary: IV ovarian stromal compartment formation of radioactive steroids from acetate 1-14C and action of gonadotropins. *J Clin Endocr, 26:*593, 1966.

20. TETER, J.: The Mixed Germ Cell Tumors with Hormonal Activity. Presented before the Joint Meeting of Pathologists and Endocrinologists, Copenhagen, December, 1962.

Chapter 2

METABOLISM OF OVARIAN
STEROID HORMONES

RALPH I. DORFMAN

T HIS CHAPTER WILL PRESENT an overall biochemical view of ovarian steroid hormones including types of steroids present and certain aspects of biosynthesis. The pertinent information is presented by one table and eighteen figures.

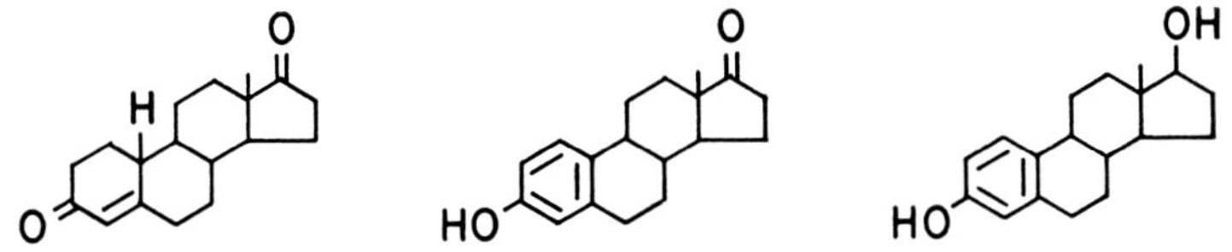

19-NORANDROST-
4-ENE-3, 17-DIONE   ESTRONE   17β-ESTRADIOL

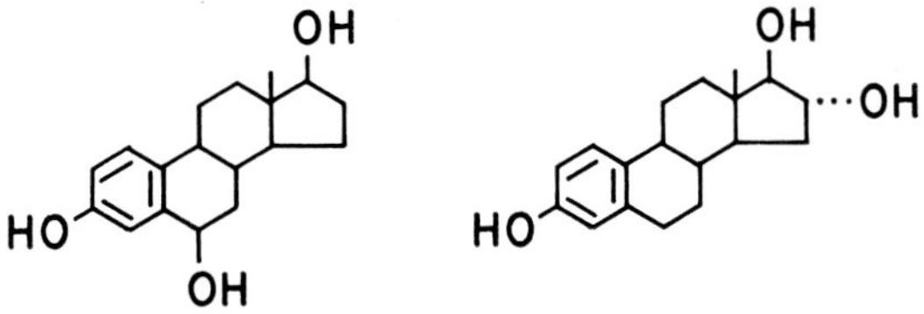

6β-HYDROXY-
17β-ESTRADIOL   ESTRIOL

FIGURE 2-1. C_{18} steroids in the ovary.

Figure 2-1 summarizes the ovarian C_{18} steroids which include primarily the estrogens of the ovary. Estradiol-17β is the most active estrogen of the group and it is quite likely that the concentration of this estrogen in plasma really determines the significant estrogenic activity at various target tissues. Estrone is a companion estrogen to estradiol-17β and probably is active to the extent that it is reduced by a proper 17β-dehydrogenase to estradiol-17β. The compound 19-norandrost-4-ene-3, 17-dione is a neutral compound, not estrogenic, but is an intermediate in the biosynthesis of estrogens from androgens, and in fact it has been isolated from the ovary of the mare and is indicated as a possible biosynthetic intermediate in a number of species, including man. The estrogen 6β-hydroxyestradiol-17β is an ovarian estrogen considerably less active than estradiol-17β. The introduction of additional oxygen functions into the estrone or estradiol-17β molecule usually results in compounds with decreased biological activity. This rule seems to hold at least for classical estrogenic activity such as the direct effects on the vagina and the uterus.

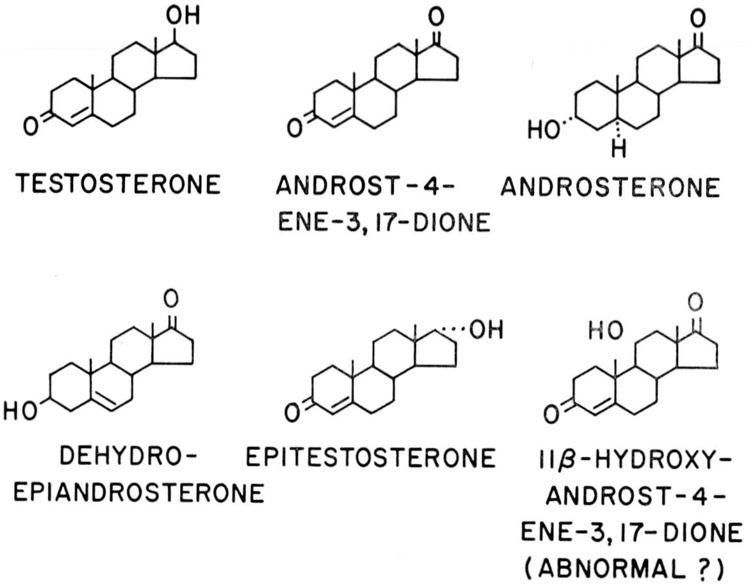

TESTOSTERONE   ANDROST-4-ENE-3, 17-DIONE   ANDROSTERONE

DEHYDRO-EPIANDROSTERONE   EPITESTOSTERONE   11β-HYDROXY-ANDROST-4-ENE-3, 17-DIONE (ABNORMAL ?)

FIGURE 2-2. C_{19} steroids in the ovary.

The ovary produces C_{19} androgens (Fig. 2-2). Androst-4-ene-3, 17-dione, testosterone and dehydroepiandrosterone, either free or sulphated, are the most important quantitatively and on the basis of androgenic activity. The compound 11β-hydroxyandrost-4-ene-3, 17-dione has been found to be ovary-associated in certain adrenal-rest tumors.

Testosterone is the most active androgen in humans and the "effective plasma concentration" of this steroid in effect determines the total androgen acting at the target tissues. This point may be illustrated by the details of the following patient. A seventy-one-year-old woman had become intensely virilized although she had normal values for total and individual 17-ketosteroids. In spite of this normal total 17-ketosteroid value of about 12 mg per day, her plasma testosterone value was twenty times that of a normal female and three times greater than that of a normal man. The removal of a hilus cell tumor of the ovary fully corrected the clinical difficulties, did not change the 17-ketosteroid titer in the urine, but decreased the plasma testosterone to 0.05 μg per 100 ml, a normal value.

Epitestosterone is of interest since, although it is only a small per cent as active as testosterone by conventional androgenic assays, it is about one-third to one-fifth as active as this highly active androgen on the hypothalamic center of the five-day-old rat. The biological importance of epitestosterone is not as a classical androgen but may have some as yet undefined function in the regulation of sexual cycles or the negative feedback control system involving the hypothalamic-anterior pituitary-ovarian complex. Epitestosterone is also known to increase in the urine of hirsute and virilized patients sometimes more convincingly than the increment in testosterone.

Androst-4-ene-3, 17-dione and dehydroepiandrosterone are weak androgens, perhaps biologically unimportant except that they may serve as biosynthetic substrates for the formation of testosterone either in steroid-producing tissues or peripherally.

Androsterone is also a weak androgen and no specific, important biological function can be suggested.

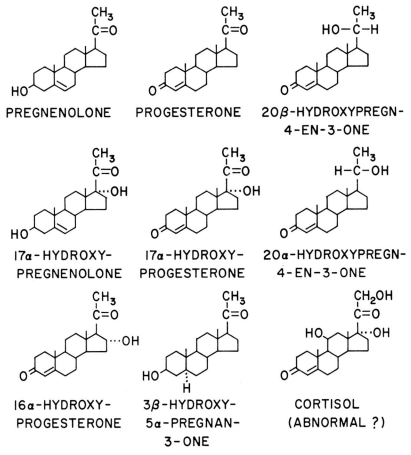

FIGURE 2-3. C_{21} steroids in the ovary.

The outstanding C_{21} steroid (Fig. 2-3) is progesterone and pregnenolone is the immediate precursor. The stereoisomer 20β-hydroxypregn-4-en-3-
one and 20α-hydroxypregn-4-en-3-one may have some special biological
activity other than that associated with the weak progestational activity.
These 20-reduced derivatives of progesterone can also be considered to be
a reserve form of progesterone since they are easily convertible to the hormone progesterone by a single oxidative step. 17α-Hydroxypregnenolone
and 17α-hydroxyprogesterone are intermediates in androgen biosynthesis.
Cortisol has only been associated with certain human adrenal-rest tumors
of the ovary and need not be considered as a normal hormone product of
the ovaries.

The C_{27} steroids of the ovary are presented in Figure 2-4. Figure 2-5 illustrates the biosynthetic sequence to the formation of pregnenolone. The
pathways indicated involve in one case the 22R-hydroxy derivative of cholesterol and in the second instance an initial 20α-hydroxylation of the same
substrate. In either case the second step involves the formation of 20α, 22R-
dihydroxycholesterol and finally oxidative removal of isocaproic aldehyde
leaving pregnenolone. It is quite likely that gonadotrophic hormone stimulates steroid biosynthesis of hormones by increasing the overall reaction of
cholesterol to pregnenolone. More specifically, the gonadotropins seem to
induce 20α-hydroxylase, the enzyme which introduces the 20α-hydroxyl
group into cholesterol.

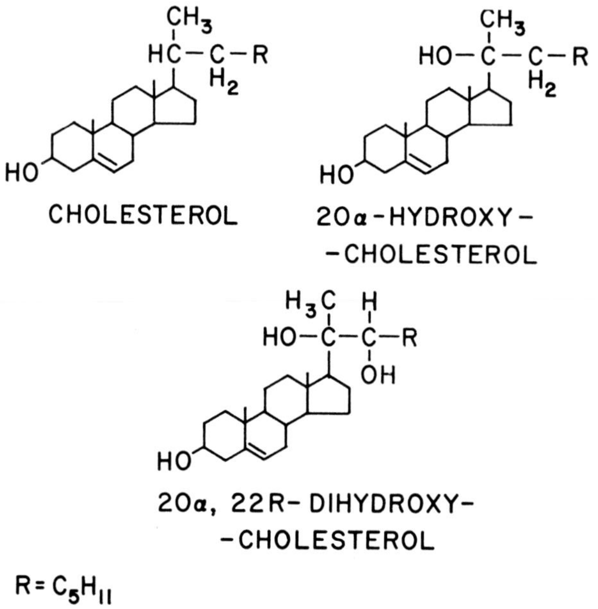

FIGURE 2-4. C_{27} ovarian steroids.

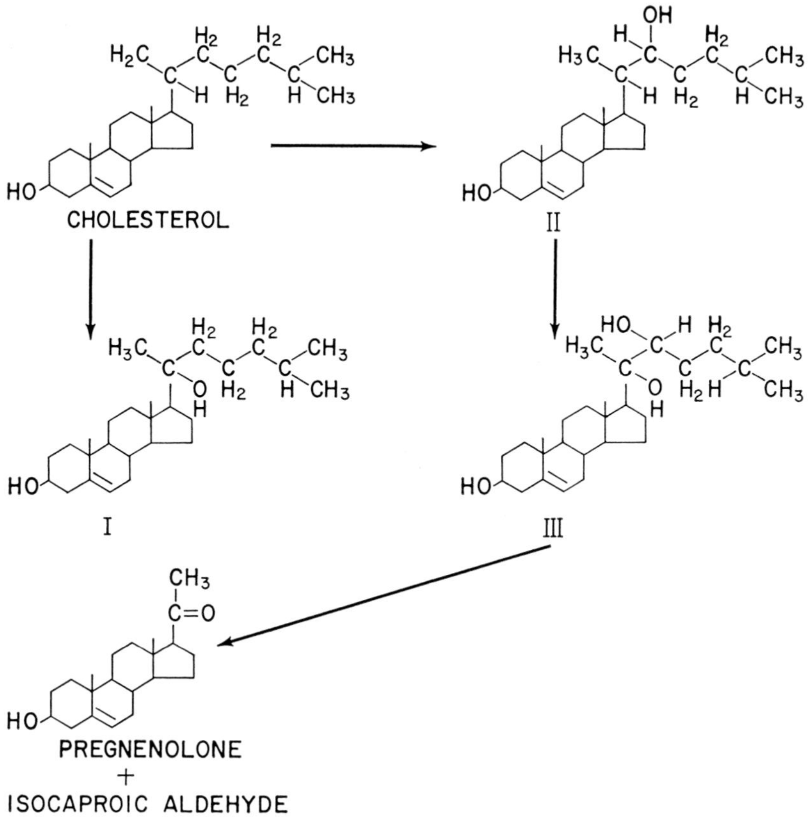

FIGURE 2-5. Biosynthesis of pregnenolone.

I. 20α-hydroxycholesterol.

II. 22R-hydroxycholesterol.

III. 20α, 22R-dihydroxycholesterol.

Figure 2-6 describes an experiment in which pregnenolone was added to an incubate of a bovine corpus luteum. The presence of both 20α-hydroxycholesterol and 20α, 22R-dihydroxycholesterol is indicated, and the addition of pregnenolone inhibited the reaction leading to an accumulation of these two intermediates.

Whole homogenates of bovine corpus luteum carry out the enzymatic conversion of cholesterol to pregnenolone (Fig. 2-7). On fractionation of this homogenate we find the enzyme system to be present about equally in the mitochondrial, microsomal, and soluble fractions. This is in contrast to the findings in rat and rabbit testis where the enzymatic activity was concentrated in the mitochondrial system.

Three enzymatic steps have been demonstrated for the formation of pregnenolone, two hydroxylations and the last a desmolase reaction. To

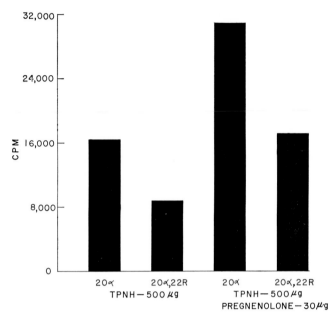

FIGURE 2-6. Influence of added pregnenolone on the accumulation of 20α-hydroxychol-esterol-^{14}C (20α) and 20α, 22R-dihydroxycholesterol-^{14}C (20α, 22R) in a bovine corpus luteum incubate with cholesterol-^{14}C.

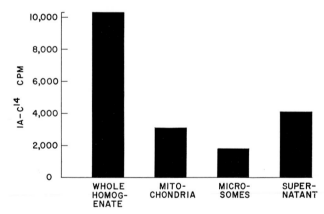

FIGURE 2-7. Distribution of cholesterol side-chain cleaving enzyme system in a bovine corpus luteum homogenate.

elucidate the mechanism of the biosynthesis and the role of the gonado-trophic hormone in these reactions, it is of considerable value to purify the biosynthetic enzymes. One such effort is indicated in Figure 2-8. This enzyme has been purified by successive steps through acetone precipitation, ammonium sulphate precipitation and twice through calcium phosphate gel. The specific gravity of the desmolase was about three for the extract derived from the acetone powder extract subjected to 100,000 g centrifugation. The final purification by the procedures indicated in Figure 2-8 yielded a product with a specific activity of about twenty-three but the overall yield had decreased to about 10 per cent.

The more formal presentation of steroid hormones by the ovary is presented in Figures 2-9 through 2-16.

It already has been pointed out that cholesterol is an important precursor, if not the obligatory one of pregnenolone. Acetate is the obligatory precursor of cholesterol and Figure 2-9 illustrates that each carbon of the steroid is derived either from the carboxy or methyl carbon of acetate. The formation of pregnenolone and progesterone has already been illustrated in Figure 2-6.

The biosynthesis of androgens proceeds by various routes from pregnenolone and progesterone. The pathway illustrated in Figure 2-10 describes the sequential formation of 17α-hydroxyprogesterone, androst-4-ene-

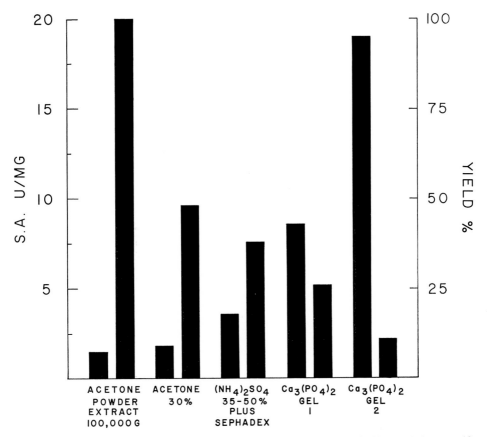

FIGURE 2-8. Purification of pregnenolone synthetase. Bar to left indicates S.A. (specific activity) units/mg. Bar to right indicates per cent yield of enzyme.

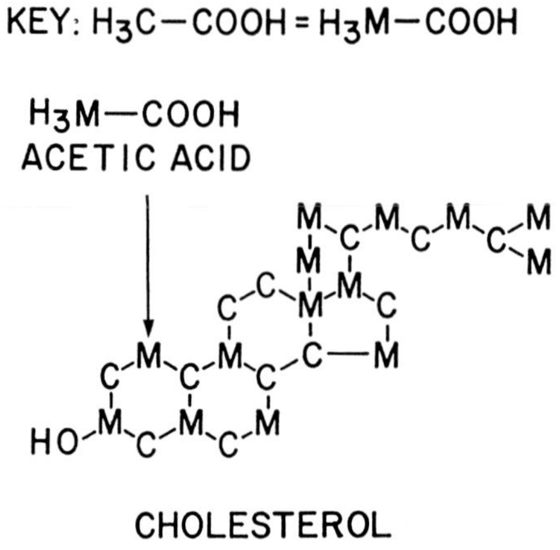

KEY: H₃C—COOH = H₃M—COOH

H₃M—COOH
ACETIC ACID

CHOLESTEROL

FIGURE 2-9. Origins of carbon atoms of cholesterol.

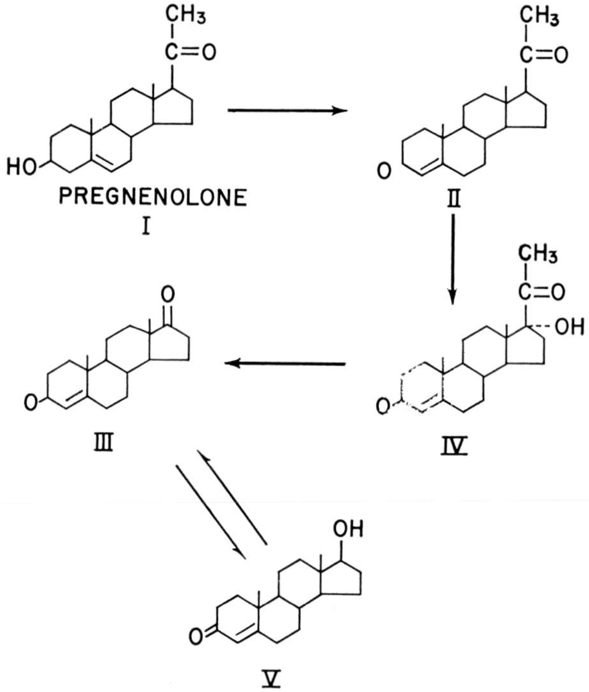

PREGNENOLONE
I

II

III

IV

V

FIGURE 2-10. Biosynthesis of androgens through 17α-hydroxyprogesterone.

II. Progesterone   IV. 17α-hydroxyprogesterone
III. Androst-4-ene-3, 17-dione   V. Testosterone

3, 17-dione, and testosterone, the most potent androgen. Androst-4-ene-3, 17-dione and testosterone may also be derived through a pathway involving the prior formation of dehydroepiandrosterone (Compound III, Fig. 2-11). This rather weak androgen may undergo oxidation to androst-4-ene-3, 17-dione or formation of the sulfated ester. The latter steroid is essentially inactive as an androgen. The transformation to the free dehydroepiandrosterone may, however, be readily accomplished in various tissues. This mechanism has certain similarities to that of the glucose interrelationship with glycogen. In both instances an inactive form of a useful and required biological material can be made readily available in an active form when needed.

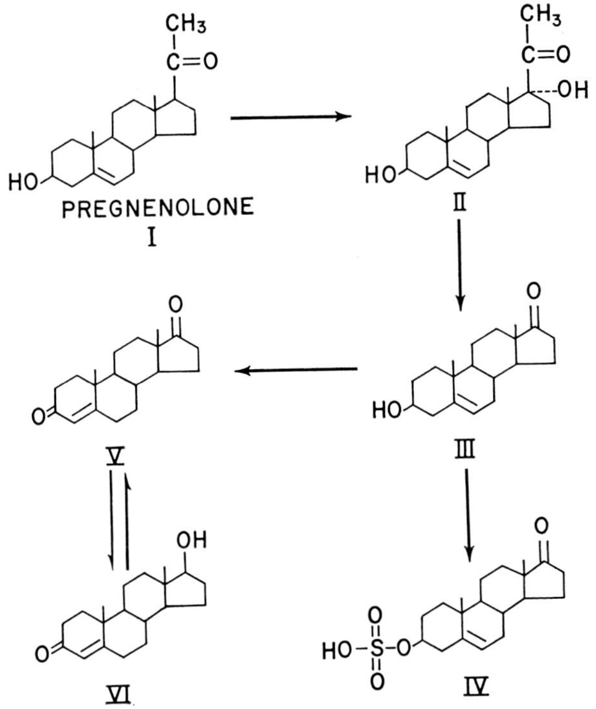

FIGURE 2-11. Biosynthesis of androgens through 17α-hydroxypregnenolone.
II. 17α-hydroxypregnenolone   V. Androst-4-ene-3, 17-dione
III. Dehydroepiandrosterone   VI. Testosterone
IV. Dehydroepiandrosterone sulfate

Estrogens are formed from androgens. No other biosynthetic route is known. Testosterone, androst-4-ene-3,17-dione, and dehydroepiandrosterone are the principal precursors of the estrogens. Thus, there seems to be a logical sequence from progesterone and/or pregnenolone to a C_{19} (androgen) intermediate, to a C_{18} steroid, an estrogen.

The removal of carbon atom 19 and aromatization of ring A are the key steps in estrogen formation. It is still difficult to say which is the primary route by which the transformation occurs. For that reason the various possibilities are described.

Testosterone is the substrate which first undergoes hydroxylation at carbon 19. This new compound, 19-hydroxytestosterone, may undergo oxidative removal of formaldehyde with the formation of estradiol-17β (Fig. 2-12).

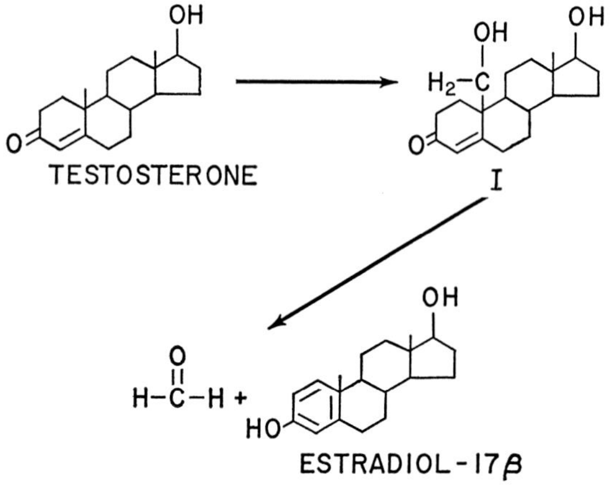

FIGURE 2-12. Biosynthesis of estrogens through 19-hydroxy-C_{19} steroids.
    I. 19-hydroxytestosterone.

Estrogen formation may proceed by a modified biochemical procedure in which 19-hydroxytestosterone is oxidized to 19-oxotestosterone and the removal of carbon 19 occurs in the form of formic acid and estradiol-17β is biosynthesized.

A third alternative for the formation of estradiol-17β from testosterone involves the successive oxidative steps from 19-hydroxytestosterone to 19-oxotestosterone and finally the 19-carboxytestosterone. This latter acid is decarboxylated and carbon dioxide liberated with the formation of 19-nor-testosterone. This latter compound then undergoes aromatization probably after 1, 2-dehydrogenation. Estradiol-17β is the final product.

A summary of experiments dealing with ovarian steroid hormone biosynthesis is presented in outline form in Figure 2-15. The central substance is acetate which is convertible to many steroids. This does not mean, of course, that the transformation is a direct one. In each instance the biosynthetic pattern is through definite intermediates.

In addition to experiments involving acetate as the substrate, Figure 2-15 illustrates the products obtained when other substrates are employed.

This figure illustrates again what has been discussed previously with respect to the movement of steroids in the biosynthetic pathways. It illustrates that cholesterol is the precursor of the C_{21} steroids and that there is a progression to the C_{19} androgens and finally to the C_{18} estrogens.

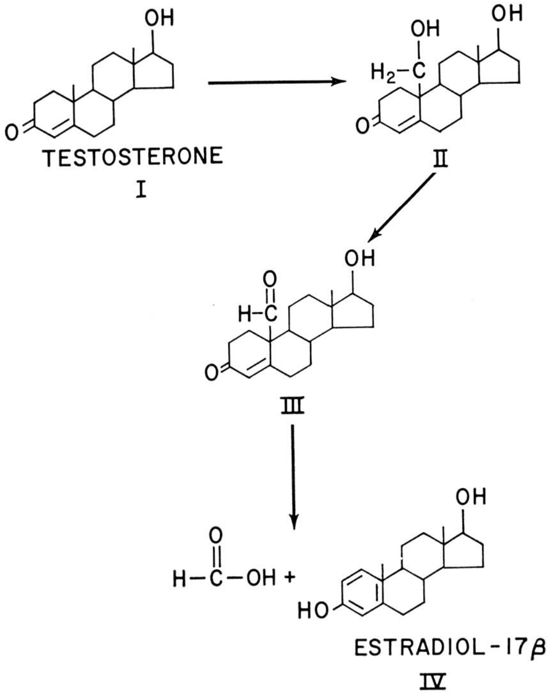

FIGURE 2-13. Biosynthesis of estrogens through 19-oxo-C_{19} steroids.
II. 19-hydroxytestosterone   III. 19-oxotestosterone

Thus far, biosynthesis of steroid hormones has been considered from the viewpoint of substrates, intermediates, and pathways. Another consideration is the manner of control of cycles with the related changes in the rate of hormone production. The action of hypothalamic-anterior pituitary controlling factors will be considered in detail by Doctors Savard, Mahesh, and Forleo.

Another possible means of control of ovarian steroid hormone biosynthesis will be presented here. These involve the control of steroid hormone biosynthesis by steroid hormonal substrates, intermediates and products at the level of the ovary. Incidentally, this control mechanism is not limited to the ovary. We have evidence that this is true for testicular and adrenal steroid hormone biosynthesis as well. Some examples of these mechanisms will be presented.

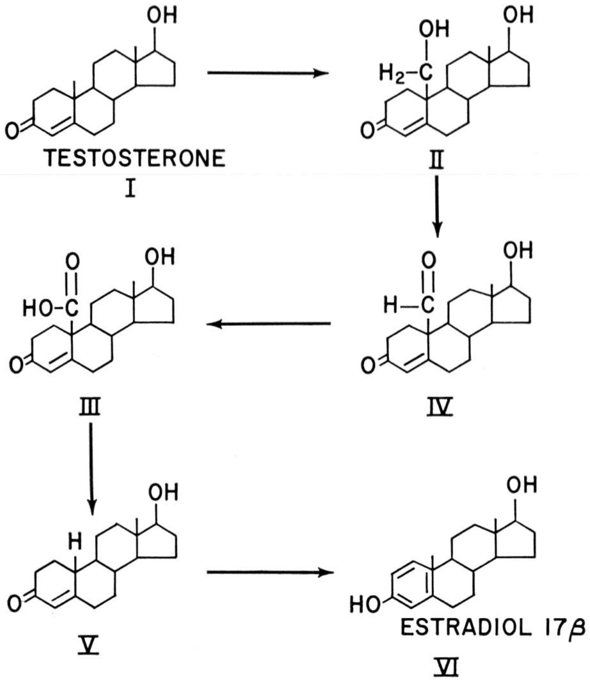

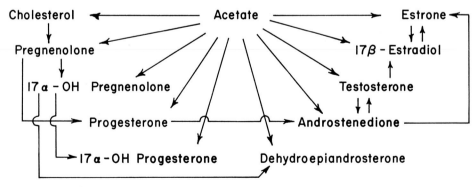

FIGURE 2-14. Biosynthesis of estrogens through 19-carboxy-C_{19} steroids.

    II. 19-hydroxytestosterone   IV. 19-oxotestosterone

    III. 19-carboxytestosterone   V. 19-nortestosterone

Ovarian Biosynthesis

FIGURE 2-15. Biosynthesis of ovarian steroids. Summary of results of actual *in vitro* studies.

TABLE 2-I
INHIBITION OF CHOLESTEROL SIDECHAIN CLEAVAGE
BY VARIOUS ADDED STEROIDS

Steroid Added (μg)	Isocaproic acid liberated (cpm)	Per cent Inhibition
Pregnenolone		
0	28000	—
10	10200	60.1
30	7140	74.5
100	3780	86.5
Progesterone		
10	18600	33.6
30	14100	49.5
100	9700	65.3
17α-hydroxyprogesterone		
0	22600	—
10	18600	17.3
30	20500	9.1
Testosterone		
10	22000	2.6
30	17600	22.1
Dehydroepiandrosterone		
10	18500	18.2
30	14100	37.4
Estradiol-17β		
0	29200	—
10	31900	0
30	31900	0
Cortisol		
10	27900	4.4
30	24400	16.3

Each incubation flask contained 33 mg acetone powder (2-25) suspended in 2.0 ml 0.066 M phosphate buffer, 500 μg TPNH in 0.1 ml 0. 066 M phosphate buffer 0.1 ml of 0.1 M MgCl₂, 2 x 10⁵ cpm 26-¹⁴C-cholesterol and the indicated steroid. Incubation 30 min. 37°C in air.

Table 2-I deals with the formation of pregnenolone from cholesterol using an acetone powder of corpus luteum tissue. The addition of pregnenolone at concentrations of 10, 30, and 100 μg produced the highly significant inhibitions of 60.7, 74.5, and 86.5 per cent, respectively, and progesterone was equally effective. Estradiol-17β, cortisol, testosterone, and 17α-hydroxyprogesterone were essentially inactive but dehydroepiandrosterone showed some reasonably inhibitory effect. This study clearly indicates that biosynthetic products of the corpus luteum can influence the early basic reaction of providing pregnenolone for the inclusive biosynthetic sequences to progesterone, androgens, and estrogens.

Figures 2-16 and 2-17 demonstrate that the reaction pregnenolone to progesterone may be accomplished by an enzyme system contained in a bovine corpus luteum acetone powder and is significantly restrained by minute concentrations of dehydroepiandrosterone and androst-4-ene-3, 17-

dione. Figure 2-18 illustrates this type of control of steroid hormone biosynthesis at various points in the biosynthetic scheme.

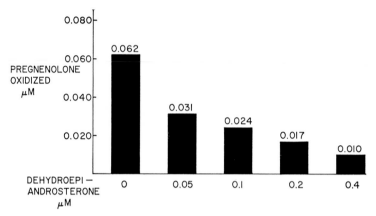

FIGURE 2-16. Inhibition of reaction pregnenolone to progesterone by addition of dehydroepiandrosterone to an incubate containing a bovine corpus luteum enzyme system.

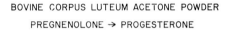

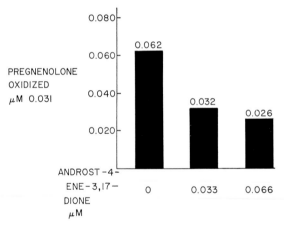

FIGURE 2-17. Inhibition of reaction pregnenolone to progesterone by addition of androst-
4-ene-3, 17-dione to an incubate containing a bovine corpus luteum enzyme system.

SUMMARY

The ovary, in common with other steroid hormone-producing glands,
converts acetate to cholesterol, the important if not obligatory precursor
of all steroid hormones. Cholesterol through a pathway involving 20α-hy-
droxycholesterol (or 22R-hydroxycholesterol)→20α, 22R-dihydroxycholes-

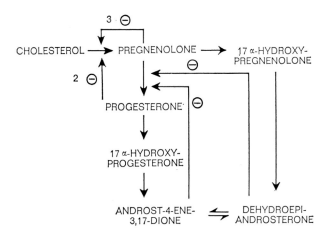

FIGURE 2-18. Inhibition of biosynthetic reactions *in vitro* using cell-free bovine corpus luteum preparations. The designations ⊖, 2.⊖, 3.⊖ indicate apparent degrees of inhibition. An order is indicated but no quantitative relationship is intended.

terol yields pregnenolone plus isocaproic aldehyde. The overall formation of progesterone, androgens, and estrogens is probably exclusively dependent on this pathway.

Pregnenolone and progesterone are proper substrates for androgen formation. The principal steroid hormone in this series is testosterone, which is biologically the most potent, followed in order of decreasing activity by androst-4-ene-3, 17-dione and dehydroepiandrosterone. Yet to be explored is the possibility of the presence in the ovary and in body fluids of other highly active androgens such as androst-5-ene-3β, 17β-diol, 17β-hydroxy-5α-androstan-3-one, androst-4-ene-3β, 17β-diol, androst-4-ene-3α, 17β-diol and 5α-androstane-3α, 17β-diol.

Estrogens are formed from androgens, and no other mechanism is known at this time. The process is essentially a removal of carbon 19 with the simultaneous or sequential aromatization of ring A of the steroid.

Control of ovarian steroid hormone biosynthesis is probably exercised by at least two major mechanisms. One, recognized for many years, involves the hypothalamic-anterior pituitary-ovary system. This mechanism is dependent on the gonadotrophic hormone which stimulates the formation of pregnenolone from cholesterol, perhaps at the reaction involving the 20α-hydroxylation of cholesterol.

A second means for the control of steroid hormone biosynthesis probably involves the direct inhibition of hormone formation at the ovarian cellular level by biosynthetic substrates, intermediates, and/or products.

Chapter 3

STEROID ANALYSIS IN THE STUDY OF OVARIAN FUNCTION

IAN F. SOMMERVILLE

Despite spectacular advances in knowledge of the nature and metabolism of the steroid hormones, the application of steroid analyses to the study of ovarian function and of endocrine factors in reproductive physiology and pathology is still at an early stage. Thus, although more than a quarter of a million steroids have been isolated or prepared by partial synthesis and it is already known that several hundred compounds are secreted or formed as metabolic products in the human body, many laboratories confine their analyses to the determination in urine of two groups of steroids (neutral 17-ketosteroids and 17-hydroxysteroids) and a small number of individual compounds (oestradiol-17β, oestrone, oestriol, and pregnanediol). Furthermore, the information gained from urinary analysis presents difficulties in interpretation since one urinary steroid may be derived from several precursors and the same precursor may be secreted by more than one endocrine gland. In addition, so many steps intervene between the moment of secretion of a hormone and the excretion of one or more of its urinary products that it can by no means be assumed that a simple relationship exists between endogenous secretion and urinary excretion. To this situation must be added the fact that many of the methods currently employed for the quantitative determination of urinary steroids are imperfect and that so many different techniques are employed that it is rarely possible to collate information from various centres. In view of these considerations, it is somewhat surprising that urinary steroid analyses do provide useful information about ovarian function, provided that the limitations of this approach are fully appreciated. Conversely, it is not surprising that a considerable number of questions of academic interest or practical importance remain unanswered.

As an example, we may consider the problem of replacement therapy.

If replacement therapy is to be other than empirical the following questions must be answered:

1. Is there a deficiency of endogenous progestogen and/or oestrogen?
2. If so, is this an absolute deficiency due to a low rate of endogenous secretion, or a relative deficiency due to abnormal intermediary metabolism? Is there a defect in tissue responsivity?
3. If there is a metabolic defect, what is the nature of the defect and would it be

40

possible to correct such a defect rather than to administer exogenous hormone which may also be subjected to abnormal metabolism?

4. If not, which hormone should be administered (e.g. is progesterone the best progestogen; which of the four thousand oral progestogens should be selected) and in what form will it be most efficiently transported to and received by the tissues?

5. Finally, is it sufficient to administer a single hormone?

The answers to many of these questions and to the other problems in diagnosis and therapy, to a great extent, await elucidation of some of the following points:

1. Steroid biosynthesis in components of healthy and pathological ovarian tissue and factors affecting steroidogenesis.

2. The mechanism of ovarian hormone secretion — factors involved in the passage of hormones into the effluent blood.

3. Transport of steroids in blood — involving chemical conjugation and protein binding — and entry into the cell of the target tissue.

4. The biochemical transformation associated with the induction of biological activity and the transformation of one hormone to another, e.g. androgen to oestrogen.

5. The role of the liver, kidney, and other tissues in intermediary metabolism; enterohepatic circulation (possible effect of changes in intestinal flora).

6. The role of ovarian hormones in feedback mechanisms affecting the hypophysis; the mechanism of antagonisms (e.g. between a metabolite and its precursor) and synergisms.

7. Variations in renal clearance must be known (and may contribute to diurnal variation in urinary steroid excretion).

There is a profound lack of knowledge of many of these topics, but it is a matter of considerable encouragement that they are being studied so intensively at the present time.

With regard to the choice of technique it should be noted that biological assay of steroids may complement the results of chemical determination although bio-assay is laborious and may lack specificity. In the past, bio-assay had the advantage of higher sensitivity than spectrophotometric methods but a marked increase in the sensitivity of physicochemical techniques is resulting from the use of double isotope derivative formation and gas-liquid chromatography and these new techniques permit the quantitative determination of the biologically active hormone rather than groups of metabolic products. This is well illustrated in the case of the androgens, where there have been three phases—the use of bio-assay in the 1930's; the measurement of the urinary neutral 17-ketosteroids (a poor index of androgen secretion), and more recently, the quantitative determination of the principal androgen, testosterone, in peripheral blood or urine.

The choice of chemical method is influenced by various factors, thus it would be an oversimplification to state that the ideal method possesses an optimal degree of accuracy, precision, sensitivity, and specificity. The first two criteria are extremely important for academic work, but it would be wasteful in effort to determine urinary neutral 17-ketosteroid excretion to the nearest microgram when latitude in interpretation for clinical purposes ranges over several milligrams (e.g. to screen hirsute women for latent adrenocortical dysfunction). A high degree of sensitivity is essential for quantitative determination in peripheral venous blood and is always useful since, even if relatively large amounts of steroids are present in a biological sample, sensitivity permits microanalysis of a smaller aliquot of the specimen. Specificity is essential for most research purposes, but for clinical evaluation of ovarian function it may seem illogical to determine only one of the numerous metabolites of an ovarian hormone. Although it is very desirable to use simple and rapid techniques for routine clinical work, this should not be achieved by crude techniques in which there is no satisfactory purification but by resort to more convenient methods for chromatography—such as thin-layer chromatography; by semiautomatic methods and the use of smaller volumes of urine or blood. As a semiautomatic technique with unrivalled sensitivity, gas-liquid chromatography offers the possibility of relatively rapid techniques which, if carefully controlled, conform to the criteria of a valid microanalytical procedure. However, gas-liquid chromatography is in a phase of rapid development and erroneous results are readily obtained by workers who do not have adequate experience. It is probable, therefore, that for urinary steroid analysis conventional methods involving column chromatography should continue to be used for some time. In this connection, it is unfortunate that improvement of urinary methods has not kept pace with recent developments in the determination of plasma steroids, since the more sensitive and sophisticated methods which are now available were evolved with the specific purpose of determining the submicrogram amounts of steroids which are present in plasma samples of convenient volume. There is an urgent need for standardization of techniques and for comparison of methods. In most instances the results should be corrected in terms of the recovery of an isotopically labelled internal standard, and while it is impractical for every determination to be an isolation, it is advisable to supplement a routine method by tests which provide additional evidence of identity. This is especially important when a new technique is applied or when an established technique is used for some new indication.

It should be noted that a technique which yields valid results in the analysis of samples from healthy subjects may be liable to serious error when applied to samples from patients with unusual pathologies. For these reasons, a laboratory where steroid analyses are performed should have facilities for the careful investigation of specificity.

The following comments are not intended to be a review of the vast and frequently contradictory literature, but some practical points will be illustrated with an indication of current developments in this field. The traditional approach to the study of ovarian function by steroid analysis has been the determination in twenty-four-hour specimens of urine of one of the metabolites (pregnanediol) of progesterone and of three oestrogens (oestradiol-17β, oestrone, and oestriol). Pending further developments, the technique of Brown, Bulbrook, and Greenwood[5] is to be recommended for oestradiol-17β, oestrone, and oestriol and that of Klopper, Michie, and Brown[43] for urinary pregnanediol. With regard to the former, care should be taken to ensure that the colorimetric reaction is not affected by the administration of drugs (e.g. senna, cascara, phenolphthalein, tranquillizers). The technique includes a saponification step which prevents interference by administered cortisone but may not entirely correct for the effect of other compounds. Careful purification of solvents is important in the technique for pregnanediol due to the nonspecificity of the colour reaction, and the correction factor of Allen[1] should be used.

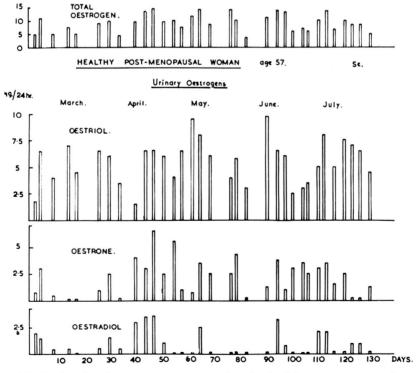

FIGURE 3-1. Study of urinary oestrogen excretion by healthy postmenopausal women.

Reference has already been made to the limitations of this approach and to the fact that these steroids have extraovarian precursors. Thus significant amounts are excreted by ovariectomized and postmenopausal women. The results which we obtained in a prolonged study of urinary oestrogen excretion by a healthy postmenopausal woman are shown in Figure 3-1 (the total oestrogens being plotted on a different scale at the top of the figure). The extent of the adrenocortical contribution to urinary pregnanediol (and pregnanetriol — which also has precursors of ovarian and adrenal origin) is illustrated in Figures 3-2 and 3-3 (from Pickett, Kyriakides, Stern, and Sommerville).[52] For this reason, it is more informative to determine these steroids in a dynamic test — by suppression of the adrenal cortex with dexamethasone and stimulation of the ovary by human pituitary gonadotropin, than to measure the resting levels of excretion. Studies involving adrenocortical suppression and some form of ovarian stimulation have been informative in the investigation of patients with amenorrhoea and the Stein-Leventhal syndrome.[39,40,50] Indications for the determination of urinary oestrogens or pregnanediol in single twenty-four-hour specimens, without suppression or stimulation, are relatively rare — functioning ovarian tumours, precocious puberty, adrenocortical carcinoma, pseudohermaphro-

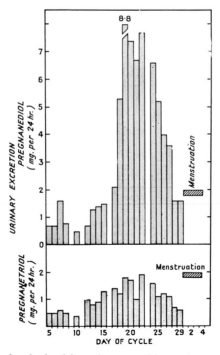

FIGURE 3-2. Study of a healthy volunteer with regular menstrual cycles.

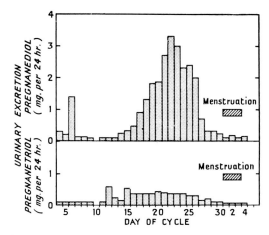

FIGURE 3-3. Study of a woman with regular menstrual cycles following bilateral total adrenalectomy.

ditism. On the other hand, it is possible that useful information could be obtained by the determination of other oestrogens in the urine. The three compounds which are usually measured probably account for less than twenty per cent of the oestrogen metabolites in urine — steroidal and non-steroidal — and the significance of these metabolites in relation to ovarian function is obscure. It should be possible to develop more convenient methods for their separation and determination than are available at present or to develop a comprehensive method for total urinary oestrogens. Outside the scope of this lecture is the application of oestrogen assays to the study of testicular function and the prognostic value of urinary oestriol assay in pregnancy.

The urinary excretion of several steroids throughout the menstrual cycle of a healthy woman is illustrated[53] in Figure 3-4. In menstrual disorders, the biphasic oestrogen excretion curve may be replaced — either by a plateau or monophasic curve at a high level as in cystic glandular hyperplasia or at a low level in anovular cycles[6]. The postovulatory rise in urinary pregnanediol is absent in anovular cycles and it is considered that the amount of this steroid (usually measured as a mixture of its C5 stereoisomers) reflects to some extent the functional activity of the corpus luteum — thus yielding more information about ovarian function than the mere indication that ovulation has occurred. It will be apparent that random samples are of no value for this purpose and that serial analyses throughout the cycle involve a formidable amount of technical work and inconvenience to the patient. Another limiting factor in the study of resting levels of urinary excretion is the variation in the amount excreted throughout the cycle by different

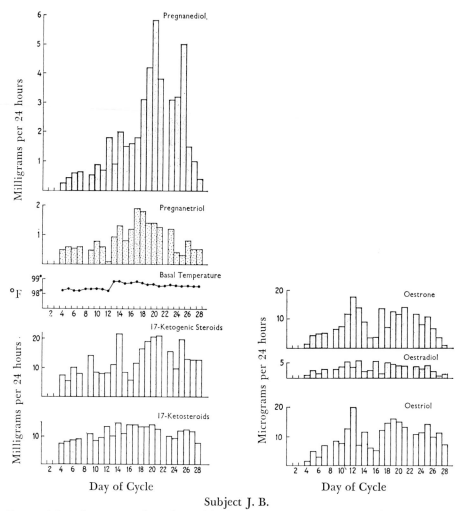

Subject J. B.

FIGURE 3-4. Urinary excretion of steroids throughout menstrual cycle of healthy woman.

individuals. An extreme example[53] is illustrated in Figure 3-5. This shows the results obtained in another healthy volunteer; the basal temperature record and cornification index indicated that ovulation occurred. Nonetheless, the urinary oestrogen excretion could be that of an ovariectomized woman; there is a rather indefinite rise of urinary pregnanediol and the cyclic excretion of pregnanetriol is not apparent. This individual was near the menarche, and it may be that ovarian steroidogenesis must be well established before the typical urinary-excretion values are obtained. This is the exception rather than the rule but the fact that such variations can occur, and the other problems mentioned above, discourages the use of daily assay of these steroids for the investigation of ovarian function.

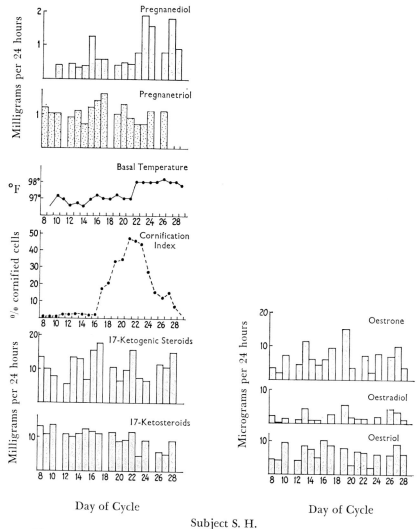

Subject S. H.

FIGURE 3-5. Extreme variations in urinary excretions obtained from a healthy volunteer.

Serial analysis of urinary pregnanediol and oestriol is of importance in assessing the effect of gonadotropin or clomiphene upon ovarian function in the treatment of infertility.[18,29,34] It is usual to confine the oestrogen assay to the determination of urinary oestriol but it may be helpful at this stage to measure urinary oestrone and oestradiol at the same time. Figure 3-6 shows the results which we obtained in urine specimens from a patient who received human pituitary gonadotropin followed by chorionic gonadotropin. This form of therapy will be discussed later in the symposium and I wish to make only one point: the rise in urinary oestriol may not be considered to constitute an excessive response; whereas the excretion of urinary oestradiol and, to a greater degree, of urinary oestrone is much higher than we have observed in other patients receiving similar amounts of gonadotropin. It will be appreciated that stimulation of ovarian steroidogenesis and the induction of ovulation are not synonymous, but since every precaution must be taken in the care of patients receiving these powerful preparations, this application of urinary assays is to be advocated.

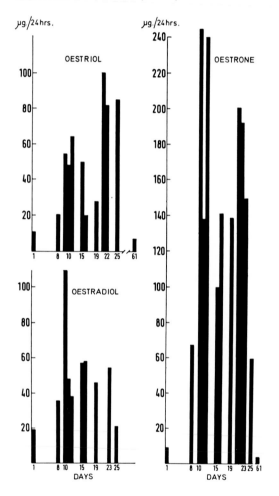

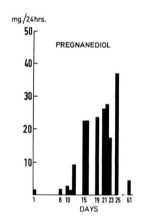

FIGURE 3-6. Oestrogenic steroids found in urine of a patient who received human pituitary gonadotropin followed by chorionic gonadotropin.

In addition to this indication for urinary steroid analysis, information has been obtained about the action of a variety of substances upon ovarian function. For example, this approach has been used to study the effect of 19-norsteroid derivatives.[49,59,60] In similar investigations, urinary gonadotropin of pituitary origin has been assayed and it is of interest to note that inhibition of ovulation by oral progestogens is not accompanied by a fall in urinary gonadotropin excretion — suggesting a direct action upon the ovaries, as reported by Brown, Fotherby, and Loraine, 1962. Reference has been made to the fact that urinary pregnanetriol (pregnane-3α, 17α, 20α-triol) has ovarian precursors;[8] the excretion of this steroid is suppressed by 19-norsteroid administration (e.g. 17α-ethynyl-19-nortestosterone; Norlutin®) and is lower in ovariectomized women. However, the lower values after ovariectomy are not further suppressed by the progestogen, and this has been interpreted as evidence for a selective action of this type of compound upon ovarian biosynthesis.[78] This inhibition of ovarian precursors of pregnanetriol has been used for the evaluation of ovarian function in patients with secondary amenorrhea in a proportion of whom, urinary pregnanetriol was not suppressed — indicating a possible defect in ovarian biosynthesis or in the release of gonadotropin.[23]

The determination of other urinary steroids is of value in the study of ovarian function. Thus pregnanetriol (pregn-5-ene-3α, 17β- 20α-triol) is excreted in increased amounts by patients with the Stein-Leventhal syndrome.[17] In a study performed in our department, Stern and Barwell[69] compared two groups of patients — one designated as Stein-Leventhal syndrome and the other having features of the syndrome, but not designated as such on clinical grounds. The excretion of this steroid was significantly high in the majority of the first group, and this assay may be regarded as a useful additional criterion in the diagnosis of the syndrome. Pregnanetriol-11-one (pregnane-3α, 17α, 20α-triol-11-one) is not present in detectable amounts in the urine of healthy women but is detectable in specimens from patients with the syndrome.[17]

The urinary excretion of neutral 17-ketosteroids in healthy men and women is in the range 7-22 mg per twenty-four hours. In this range also fall the values obtained in the majority of patients with idiopathic hirsutism, the Stein-Leventhal syndrome, and most ovarian tumours — for example, arrhenoblastoma — although the mean excretion in healthy women is lower than that of hirsute women or men. Accordingly, the determination of total neutral 17-ketosteroids in individual patients gives little information about ovarian androgen production although this simple test should be applied to specimens from all hirsute women in order to assess adrenocortical function. Fractionation of this group of steroids has been studied extensively and there are many reports of elevated urinary excretion of androsterone and aetiocholanolone — the principal urinary 17-ketosteroids in young adults — in hirsutism.[28] This may be discussed elsewhere in the symposium, but it can be stated that since these steroids are mainly derived from nonandrogenic or weakly androgenic precursors (notably dehydroepiandrosterone) a significant rise in the secretion rate of the principal androgen, testosterone, may not be reflected by a detectable increase in the urinary excretion of androsterone, aetiocholanolone, or total neutral 17-ketosteroids. For this reason, it is much more informative to determine testosterone in urine or, as will be discussed subsequently, in peripheral venous blood. Since the pioneer work of Dorfman and his group upon plasma concentrations,[22,24] the assay of testosterone has been the subject of numerous reports, but it should be noted that many aspects of this approach require further investigation. The specificity of some of the analytical techniques is doubtful, and reports in the literature do not always contain information about the clinical state of the patients. The relative merits of urinary and plasma assay are not yet fully established and it is certain that urinary testosterone (present as the glucuronide) is not a unique metabolite of the hormone. Conjugation of testosterone could occur before entry of the hormone into the plasma — for example, following synthesis in the liver — so that some of the excreted testosterone glucuronide might not be derived from plasma testosterone.[44] The 17α-epimer of testosterone, epitestosterone, is present in urine[45] but has not yet been detected in blood. The identification of logical precursors for this steroid and the study of its biological significance require further investigation.

When urinary testosterone and epitestosterone are measured together, significantly higher values are found in patients with hirsutism. This is illustrated in Figure 3-7 which summarizes results from various centres.

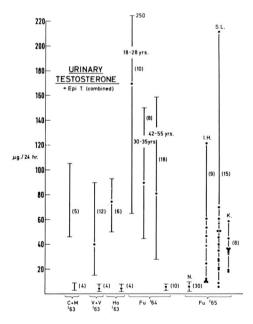

FIGURE 3-7. Higher values of urinary testosterone and epitestosterone found in patients with hirsutism.

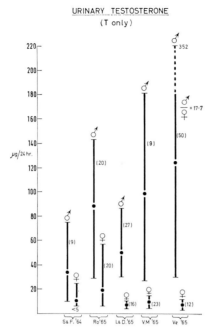

FIGURE 3-8. The results of techniques in which testosterone is determined after separation from the epimer.

The figure shows the range of values in healthy men (above) and women (below) obtained by Camacho and Migeon;[10] Vermeulen and Verplancke;[77] Horton *et al.*,[36] and Futterweit *et al.*[26] It will be seen that the values in healthy women are in a narrow range; whereas those for men vary considerably. On the right of the figure, elevated excretion is shown for nine women with idiopathic hirsutism and fifteen patients with the Stein-Leventhal syndrome (the eight values on the extreme right are from patients with Klinefelter's syndrome).[27] In Figure 3-8 the results of techniques in which testosterone is determined after separation from the epimer are shown. The overlap between the ranges of excretion which was observed by two groups[57,58] is not apparent in the remainder of these studies.[47,73,76] In healthy women, urinary testosterone excretion is in the range 2-14 μg per twenty-four hours; in men, 25-350 μg per twenty four hours. In Vermeulen's report the mean of the two groups yields a ratio of 17.7. This is very much greater than the difference between the mean excretion of neutral 17-ketosteroids by healthy men and women (with a ratio of approximately 1.7).

The importance of effecting adequate separation of epitestosterone is illustrated in Figure 3-9. This shows the work of Brooks;[3] Sparagana;[68] de Nicola, Dorfman, and Forchielli,[19] and unpublished data from Professor Ingiulla's department[66] — obtained by a gas chromatographic technique

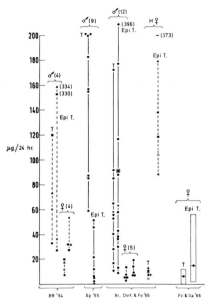

FIGURE 3-9. The importance of effecting adequate separation of epitestosterone.

developed in my department. It will be apparent that discrepancies occur between the results reported — for example, the finding of lower values for the epimer by Sparagana[68] — but, in general, there appear to be similar amounts of the two compounds in the urine of healthy women. This is also in accord with our own work upon this subject. Especial attention should be paid to the results in hirsute women in whom values for urinary testosterone were frequently in the normal range whereas markedly elevated excretion of epitestosterone was reported.[19] The method used in our work and by Forleo and Galli has not yet been published in detail,[67] but it effects an adequate separation of the epimers — either as the acetates or as the trimethylsilyl ethers. The gas chromatographic separation of the latter is shown in Figure 3-10. Although we have observed very high urinary excretion of epitestosterone in a patient with arrhenoblastoma, we have not as yet encountered hirsute patients with the marked difference observed by Dorfman and his co-workers. It should be emphasised that further work is indicated.

In recent years, the determination of steroids in human tissues and in body fluids other than urine has been facilitated by technical developments. However, it will be apparent from the following comments that despite remarkable advances problems remain in achieving satisfactory quantitative determination of certain important steroids which are present in low concentrations in peripheral venous blood. It will be seen that this applies especially to the determination of testosterone in plasma samples from healthy women and of oestradiol-17β and oestrone in samples collected throughout the menstrual cycle. Time does not permit a comprehensive review of this topic but it may be of interest to present some of our recent work in which plasma from peripheral venous blood has been analyzed on alternate days throughout the cycles of healthy women. These analyses were complemented by basal temperature records; the study of vaginal cytology and the determination of urinary oestradiol-17β, oestrone, oestriol, and pregnanediol.

A flow chart of the method for the simultaneous determination of progesterone, oestradiol-17β, and oestrone in human plasma is shown in Figure 3-11, as presented by Wyman and Sommerville, 1966. This involves the use

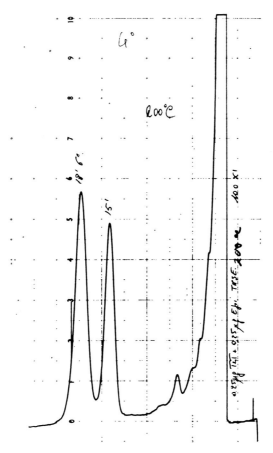

FIGURE 3-10. Separation of epitestosterone (15 mins.) and testosterone as trimethylsilyl ethers; 5 ft. col. of 3% XE 60 on Gas Chrom. Q (100/120 mesh) at 200°C; flame ionization detection.

of isotopically labelled internal standards; thin-layer chromatography with autoradiography of the plates; gas-liquid chromatography and liquid scintillation counting. A second internal standard is added prior to gas chromatography, and the calculation of the detector response depends upon the use of an automatic electronic digital integrator.[63] The technique of preliminary purification of the plasma extracts for the determination of progesterone is based upon that previously described by Collins and Sommerville in 1964.

PLASMA PROGESTERONE, OESTRADIOL-17β & OESTRONE

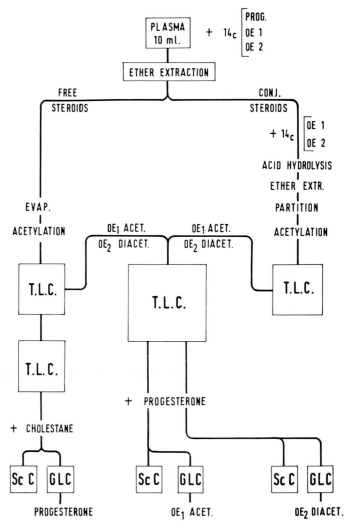

FIGURE 3-11. A flow-chart of the method for the simultaneous determination of progesterone, oestradiol-17β, and oestrone in human plasma.

Another type of technique for plasma steroid analysis utilizes the principle of double isotope derivative formation. This has been used for the determination of progesterone,[55] and although satisfactory, it has the disadvantage that the procedure is very time-consuming and great care is required in order to achieve a satisfactory "blank" value. The technique employed in the present work has the advantage that the analysis can be performed in one day; that 20α-hydroxy-pregn-4-en-3-one may be determined at the same time,[66] and that the two oestrogens are measured. On the other hand, measures to improve the sensitivity of the oestrogen determination are still under investigation. Figure 3-12 shows a comparison between plasma progesterone determinations by the new technique and that of Riondel *et al.*[65] It is very encouraging, in a field of research where contradictory results are so frequent, that the range of values is similar by two methods based upon different principles : 0.2 - 0.5 µg/100 ml plasma in the follicular phase and 0.5 − 2.5 µg/100 ml in the luteal phase. Similar values have been reported,[73] using gas chromatography with electron-capture detection.

PLASMA PROGESTERONE

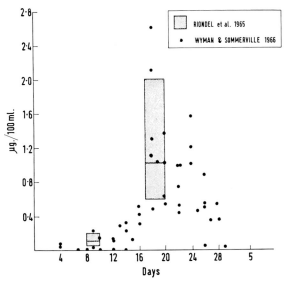

FIGURE 3-12. Comparison between plasma progesterone determinations by the new technique and that of Riondel *et al.*

To obviate the effect of diurnal, or circadian, variations the blood samples were all collected between 9:00 and 9:30 A.M. In addition, samples collected at four hourly intervals have been studied. Two examples are

shown in Figure 3-13. One value in the study of Subject E is significantly
low; further work is in progress to assess the incidence of circadian
variations.

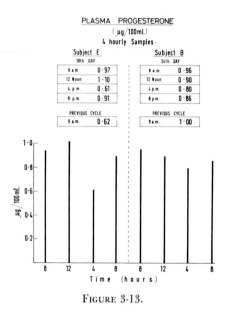

FIGURE 3-13.

Figure 3-14 shows the plasma progesterone concentrations in a healthy
woman (Subject B); the results of urinary steroid analysis are shown in
Figure 3-15. Basal temperature records and vaginal cytology indicated that

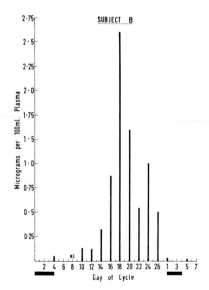

FIGURE 3-14. Plasma progesterone concentrations in a healthy woman.

ovulation occurred at about the sixteenth day of this cycle. It will be seen that the highest concentration of plasma progesterone was on the eighteenth day but that there was a significant preovulatory rise. The highest value for urinary pregnanediol was on the twentieth day; urinary oestriol was raised on the sixteenth day, preceded by some indication of a higher value for oestrone on the fourteenth day.

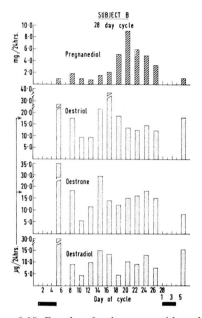

FIGURE 3-15. Results of urinary steroid analysis.

A similar study (Subject C) is shown in Figures 3-16 and 3-17 of another volunteer in whom ovulation occurred at approximately the thirteenth day of this cycle. It should be possible, by this approach, to carry out a detailed study involving more frequent assays at the time of ovulation.

In a preliminary study of random samples from a small group of healthy subjects, one individual had surprisingly high plasma progesterone concentration on the eleventh day of the cycle. This woman was selected for serial analyses in two subsequent cycles, and the results are shown in Figure 3-18. The first cycle was of twenty-seven-days duration and the second lasted for thirty days. The results are plotted with the approximate day of ovulation as a constant — the thirteenth day in the first cycle and the sixteenth day in the second. The results of urinary steroid analysis are shown in Figure 3-19. It will be seen that the occurrence of a high preovulatory level of circulating progesterone was confirmed in these cycles. These features of plasma progesterone concentration were not reflected in the urinary excretion of pregnanediol, which was similar to that of other women with ovulatory cycles. It will be noted that the urinary oestrogen excretion in this volunteer is less typical than the pregnanediol pattern and that the results — notably for oestradiol-17β in the luteal phase — are different in the two consecutive cycles. However, reference has already been made to variations in urinary oestrogen excretion from one cycle to another and a similarly low luteal

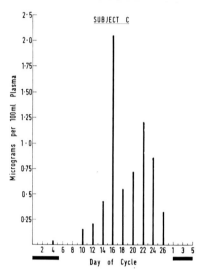

FIGURE 3-16. Study of a volunteer in whom ovulation occurred at approximately the thirteenth day of this cycle.

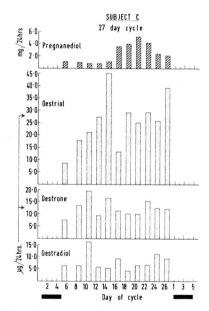

FIGURE 3-17. Further results of the study shown in Figure 3-16.

pattern for oestradiol-17β (Fig. 3-20) was associated with typical values for plasma progesterone.

Even if there was some abnormality of endocrine function in this apparently healthy woman, the discrepancy between circulating progesterone and urinary pregnanediol is of itself a finding of considerable interest. It is possible that this problem could be further elucidated by the simultane-

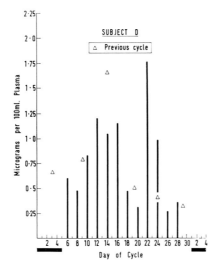

FIGURE 3-18. Results of analysis of healthy woman with high plasma progesterone concentration on the eleventh day of the cycle.

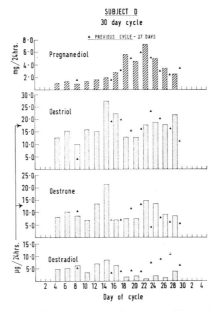

FIGURE 3-19. Results of urinary steroid analysis.

The Ovary

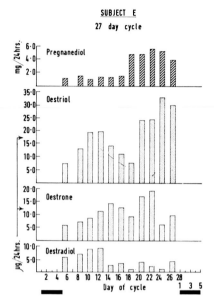

FIGURE 3-20. Typical values for plasma progesterone.

ous determination of plasma progesterone and pregnanediol throughout the menstrual cycle and a technique for this purpose has been the subject of a preliminary report.[67] Previously, plasma progesterone-pregnanediol ratios have been measured by a less sensitive method[20,65] in late pregnancy and during labour. An example of more recent work upon this problem is shown in Figure 3-21. It will be seen that there is a disproportionate rise in plasma pregnanediol excretion at a time when plasma progesterone concentration is unchanged, and there is again a discrepancy between plasma progesterone and urinary pregnanediol. We have not yet performed a similar study in nonpregnant women, but random samples of plasma collected from twenty-two healthy subjects contained 0.1 - 1.2 μg pregnanediol/ 100 ml in the follicular phase of the cycle and 0.5 - 4.5 μg/100 ml in the luteal phase (Sheerin and Sommerville, unpublished). These are preliminary results, but it is considered that this should be a useful approach to the study of progesterone secretion and metabolism in relation to menstrual disorders.

At the present time, it would be premature to speculate upon the possible contribution of plasma oestrogen determinations to the study of ovarian function, nor is it proposed to review the work which is in progress in attempts to evolve a satisfactory method. It should, however, be emphasized to clinical colleagues that despite these efforts, there is at present no thoroughly acceptable technique for the determination of the very low concentrations of oestrogen in the peripheral venous blood of nonpregnant women.

PLASMA PROGESTERONE ; PLASMA AND URINARY PREGNANEDIOL

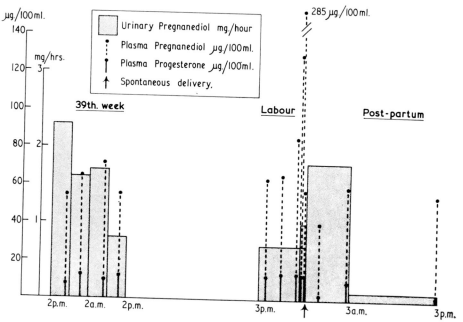

FIGURE 3-21. Ratios between plasma progesterone and pregnanediol during late pregnancy and during labour.

It has already been indicated that — despite certain theoretical considerations — urinary testosterone is a valuable index of androgen production. Some of these factors do not apply to the determination of plasma testosterone, and the following illustrations facilitate a comparison between results obtained in plasma and urine.

Figure 3-22 summarizes the plasma testosterone values obtained by nine groups of research workers.* It will be seen that the scatter of values for healthy women was more marked in the earlier studies and especial attention is drawn to the large series (forty-six women) reported by Van der Molen *et al.* As mentioned before, the concentrations in healthy women approach the limit of sensitivity of contemporary techniques and fourteen of the values were below this limit (0.02 μg/100 ml) . The mean value of the thirty-two measurable concentrations was 0.05 μg/100 ml, and the range was

---

*See references 9, 16, 24, 38, 42, 48, 56, 70, and 73.

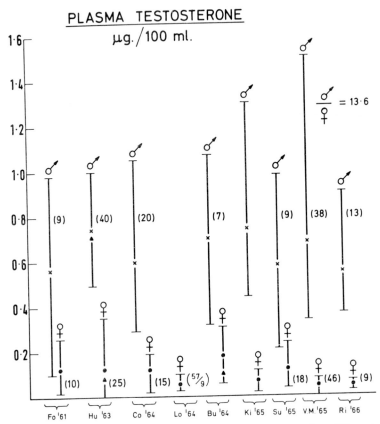

FIGURE 3-22. Summary of plasma testosterone values obtained by nine different groups of research workers.

from undetectable to 0.08 μg/100 ml. In healthy men, these workers found from 0.34 - 1.49 μg/100 ml plasma (mean 0.68 μg). The ratio of the means is 13.6 — comparable to the ratios for urinary testosterone. In a study,[48] fifty-seven assays were performed upon samples collected during seventeen ovulatory cycles of nine healthy women. The method of Riondel et al.[54] was used and the mean value for plasma testosterone was again found to be 0.05 μg/100 ml (although this technique is also working at its limit and these results are expressed without subtraction of a significant water blank of approximately 0.02 μg/100 ml). The values fell into a rather narrow range but there was some evidence for higher concentrations in postovulatory samples.

The values in Figure 3-22 are not corrected for the age of the patients, but, whereas urinary neutral 17-kestosteroids decline markedly with age, there is no significant fall in plasma testosterone in healthy men until the

ninth decade of life.[41] Although this point has not been studied systematically in women, it is unlikely to be significant in view of the narrow range
of values in healthy women of all ages.

The results obtained in women with hirsutism (H) and those in whom
this was associated with polycystic ovaries (HP) are shown in Figure 3-23.
The references are as for the previous figure with the addition of results
reported by Dignam *et al.*[21] On the left of the figure, there is a representative range and mean value for nonhirsute women. It is apparent that
elevated plasma testosterone occurs in these patients to a variable degree,
and there are contradictory results which may be largely related to the
selection of patients. This matter requires further investigation and other
workers have not observed markedly raised values in idiopathic hirsutism.[16,73] Figure 3-24 summarizes the results of Conti *et al.*[16] and shows the
lack of correlation between plasma testosterone and urinary 17-ketosteroid
excretion.

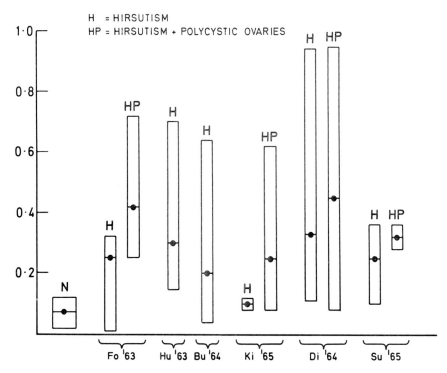

FIGURE 3-23. Results obtained in women with hirsutism and those in whom hirsutism
was associated with polycystic ovaries.

PLASMA TESTOSTERONE
CONTI et al 1964

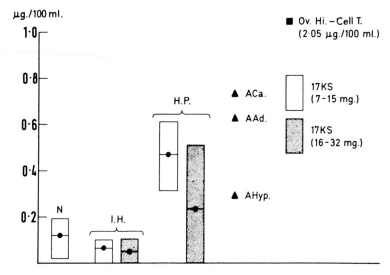

FIGURE 3-24. Results of a study by Conti *et al.* showing the lack of correlation between plasma testosterone and urinary 17-ketosteroid excretion.

In addition to assays in urine and peripheral venous blood, steroid analysis is being used in other ways in research upon ovarian function. Thus, information of considerable interest has been obtained by analysis of the fluid from cystic follicles and from follicle and corpus luteum cysts. These studies have revealed differences in the relative proportions of steroids in fluid from the ovaries of women with regular cycles; of patients with the Stein-Leventhal syndrome[30,61] and of women with functional uterine haemorrhage.[31] In recent work, Dr. Giorgi has compared the proportions of free and conjugated oestrogens in cyst fluid from women with regular cycles; under gonadotropin stimulation and with various gynaecological disorders. A difference in the ratio of free to conjugated was observed, with a relatively low concentration of conjugate in fluid from follicles and ratios approaching unity in corpus luteum cysts and cysts from patients with irregular bleeding. It would appear that conjugated oestrogens are synthesised by the ovary and that conjugation may play an important role in the mechanism and ovarian secretion.[32] Another valuable approach is the application of steroid analysis to ovarian venous blood[51] and ovarian tissue.[50] These topics will be discussed elsewhere in this symposium.

The study of secretion rates of ovarian hormones is a research application which yields vital information. Figure 3-25 is based upon recent work concerning the *in vivo* dynamics of testosterone and androstenedione.[37] The shaded circles represent the production rate of these two steroids (calculated from the metabolic clearance rates and mean plasma concentrations) and the contribution from one steroid to another is indicated. Accordingly, and with reservations which have been discussed in detail by Tait and Horton,[71] it would appear that the testosterone secretion of healthy women is of the order of 0.14 mg per day; whereas 7.8 mg per day is a representative value for healthy men.

ANDROGEN SECRETION RATES
mg. / day

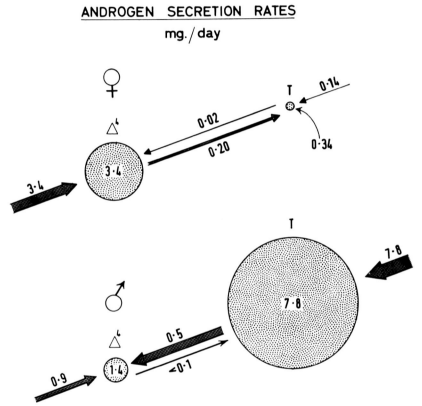

FIGURE 3-25. Secretion rates of ovarian hormones based upon recent work concerning the *in vivo* dynamics of testosterone and androstenedione. The shaded circles represent the production rate of these two steroids.

From these observations and the previous comments upon urinary 17-ketosteroids and the determination of testosterone in urine or plasma the progress which has been made in the study of androgen secretion will be apparent. If representative values are selected, the situation may be summarized as follows:

COMPARISON OF DIFFERENT INDICES OF ANDROGEN PRODUCTION
IN HEALTHY MEN AND WOMEN

	Men	Women	Ratio
Urinary 17-KS	14 mg/24 hr	8 mg/24 hr	1.7
Urinary testosterone	90 μg/24 hr	6 μg/24 hr	15.0
Plasma testosterone	0.7 μg/100 ml	0.05 μg/100 ml	14.0
Testosterone production rate (blood method)	7.8 mg/day	0.34 mg/day	22.9
Testosterone secretion rate	7.8 mg/day	0.14 mg/day	55.7

For the present, the determination of urinary testosterone (with careful separation of the epimer) or plasma testosterone affords the most convenient approach to the study of ovarian androgen. In addition, the scheme shown in Figure 3-25 emphasizes the need for further work upon the significance of the secretion of androstenedione (androst-4-ene-3, 17-dione) which appears to be the main androgen secreted by women and to be responsible for a major part of the circulating testosterone. With regard to the determination of the secretion rates of progesterone and oestrogen during the menstrual cycle, the situation is complicated by the interconversion of oestrone and oestradiol[35] and other considerations. The calculation from isotope-dilution techniques depends upon the existence of a steady state — as may apply to cortisol secretion under basal conditions[46] — and it will be apparent that this does not obtain during the menstrual cycle.[7,75] In a recent study, ^{14}C-oestradiol-17β and 3H-oestriol were injected simultaneously in women at different times of the cycle. There was evidence for an increased production of oestriol during the luteal phase which was not accountable to an increased rate of conversion of oestradiol to oestriol.[2] Although considerable information is accumulating relevant to these problems,[33,62,72] it must be concluded that this approach is not yet practicable for the systematic study of ovarian function.

Finally, there is the important use of steroid analysis for the study of ovarian biosynthesis *in vitro*. This subject will be discussed in detail by Dr. Savard and Dr. Dorfman in this symposium, but it may be of interest to illustrate some representative results obtained by the incubation of isotopically labelled ^{14}C-pregn-5-enolone with components of human gonadal tissue.[12,15] These are shown in Figures 3-26, 3-27, 3-28, and 3-29. It will be seen that the distribution of radiometabolites differs from one tissue component to another, yielding information about the sequence of enzymic transformations and the possible existence of biosynthetic defects in abnormal tissue. Further information can be gained by studies in which the transformations of labelled substrates by components of gonadal tissue are compared with respect to time.[11] This gives a dynamic record of the rate of

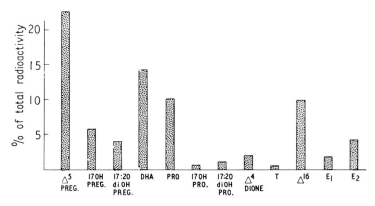

FIGURE 3-26. Incubation of human ovarian follicle with ^{14}C-pregn-5-enolone.

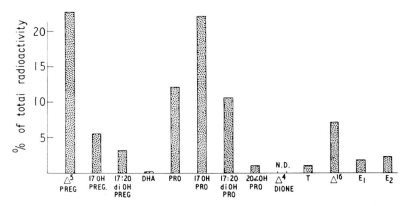

FIGURE 3-27. Incubation of human corpus luteum with ^{14}C-pregn-5-enolone.

transformation through various intermediaries. The *in vitro* approach has
its limitations but in our experience it fulfils a useful function, provided
that aliquots of tissue are incubated with a variety of intermediaries on the
biosynthetic pathways and that care is taken to effect definitive identification
of the products. The *in vitro* studies have proved helpful in pointing the
way to future work. Thus, the fact that the testis in the feminine type of
male pseudohermaphrodite has the capacity, under these experimental
conditions, to transform substrates to testosterone in large yields suggests
some aetiology other than excessive oestrogen secretion by the testes — such
as abnormal metabolism of the androgen. It should be emphasized, however,
that a large number of experiments must be performed before one can
assess representative patterns of transformation and further work upon
healthy gonadal tissue is indicated before it can be assumed that a biosynthetic defect is characteristic of any form of ovarian dysfunction.

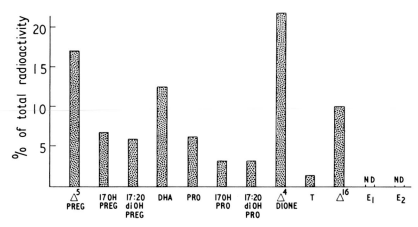

FIGURE 3-28. Incubation of tissue obtained at wedge resection from the ovary of a patient with the Stein-Leventhal syndrome.

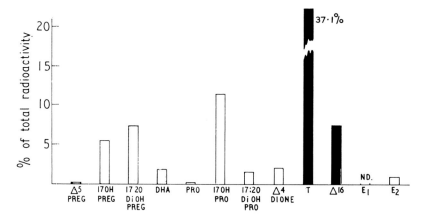

FIGURE 3-29. Incubation of testicular tissue from a patient with the feminine type of male pseudohermaphroditism.

In conclusion, there is no doubt that we are at the beginning of a new era in the study of human ovarian function when long-term studies can be initiated — using powerful analytical techniques. However, the sophisticated nature of these techniques brings new problems and future success must surely depend upon the skill of the biochemist; the rigorous standardization of laboratory technique, and the patience of clinical colleagues who fully appreciate the technical difficulties.

* * *

ACKNOWLEDGMENTS

It is a pleasure to thank Professor W. Ingiulla for the invitation to present this material, and to acknowledge the valuable assistance of Dr. W.

P. Collins, Miss Heather Wyman, Dr. M. I. Stern, Mr. B. M. Sheerin, and other members of the Unit; also past colleagues (notably Miss M. T. Pickett and Dr. E. P. Giorgi) and visiting fellows (Miss A. Marocchi, Dr. R. Forleo, and Dr. A. Galli) who contributed to this work. Clinical cooperation was provided by Professor S. G. Clayton, Dr. P. M. F. Bishop and Dr. J. R. Newton; the work was supported in part by a grant from the Medical Research Council.

REFERENCES

1. ALLEN, W. M.: *J Clin Endocr, 10:*71, 1950.
2. BARLOW, J. J., and LOGAN, C. M.: *Steroids, 7:*309, 1966.
3. BROOKS, R. V.: *Steroids, 4:*117, 1964.
4. BROOKS, R. V., and GIULIANI, G.: *Steroids, 4:*101, 1964.
5. BROWN, J. B.; BULBROOK, F. C., and GREENWOOD, F. C.: *J Endocr, 16:*41, 1957.
6. BROWN, J. B., and MATTHEW, G. D.: *Recent Progr Hormone Res, XVIII:*337, 1962.
7. BULBROOK, R. D.: In *Paulsen, C. A.* (Ed): *Estrogen Assays in Clinical Medicine.* 1965, p. 151.
8. BURGER, H. G., and SOMMERVILLE, I. F.: *Acta Endocr, 43:*95, 1963.
9. BURGER, H. G.; KENT, J. R., and KELLIE, A. E.: *J Clin Endocr, 24:*432, 1964.
10. CAMACHO, M., and MIGEON, C. J.: *J Clin Endocr, 23:*301, 1963.
11. COLLINS, W. P.: *Excepta Med Int Congr Ser, 111:*483, 1966.
12. COLLINS, W. P., and SOMMERVILLE, I. F.: *Nature, 203:*836, 1964.
13. COLLINS, W. P., and SOMMERVILLE, I. F.: *Excerpta Med Int Congr Ser, 83:*1303, 1964.
14. COLLINS, W. P., and SOMMERVILLE, I. F.: *Acta Endocr, Suppl 100:*84, 1965.
15. COLLINS, W. P.; FORLEO, R.; LEFEBVRE, Y., and SOMMERVILLE, I. F.: In *Androgens. Excerpta Med Int Congr Ser, 101:*120, 1965.
16. CONTI, C., et al.: *Research on Steroids, I:*77, 1964.
17. COX, R. I., and SHEARMAN, R. P.: *J Clin Endocr, 21:*586, 1961.
18. CROOKE, A. C., et al.: *J Obstet Gynaec Brit Comm, 70:*604, 1963.
19. DE NICOLA, A. F.; DORFMAN, R. I., and FORCHIELLI, E.: *Steroids, 7:*351, 1966.
20. DESHPANDE, N. G.; TURNER, A., and SOMMERVILLE, I. F.: *J Obstet Gynaec Brit Comm, LXVII:*954, 1960.
21. DIGNAM, W. J., et al.: *Acta Endocr (Kobenhavn), 45:*254, 1964.
22. FINKELSTEIN, M.; FORCHIELLI, E., and DORFMAN, R. I.: *J Clin Endocr, 21:*98, 1961.
23. FINKELSTEIN, M.; SERR, D., and WEIDENFELD, J.: *Research on Steroids, II:*399, 1966.
24. FORCHIELLI, E., et al.: *Anal Biochem, 5:*416, 1963.
25. FORLEO, R.; GALLI, A., and SEVERI, S.: *Excerpta Med Int Congr Ser, 111:*423, 1966.
26. FUTTERWEIT, W., et al.: *Steroids, 4:*137, 1964.
27. FUTTERWEIT, W., et al.: *J Clin Endocr, 25:*1451, 1965.
28. GALLAGHER, T. F., et al.: *J Clin Invest, 37:*794, 1958.
29. GEMZELL, C. A.; DICZFALUSY, E., and TILLINGER, K. G.: *J Clin Endocr, 18:*133, 1958.
30. GIORGI, E. P.: *J Endocr, 27:*225, 1963.
31. GIORGI. E. P.: *J Reprod Fertil, 10:*309, 1965.
32. GIORGI, E. P.: *J Reprod Fertil,* (in press).
33. GOERING, R. W.; MATSUDA, S., and HERRMAN, W. L.: *Amer J Obstet Gynec, 92:*441, 1965.

34. Greenblatt, R. B., *et al.: JAMA, 178:*101, 1961.
35. Gurpide, E., *et al.: J Clin Endocr, 23:*346, 1963.
36. Horton, R.; Rosner, J. M., and Forsham, P. H.: *Proc Soc Exp Biol Med, 114:*400, 1963.
37. Horton, R., and Tait, J. F.: In *Androgens. Excerpta Med Int Congr Ser, 101:*199, 1966.
38. Hudson, B., *et al.: Aust J Exp Biol Med Sci, 41:*235, 1965.
39. Jayle, M. F.: *Atti de Symp Internaz Ediz Scientif Salpietra (Firenze).* 1962, p. 120.
40. Jayle, M. F., *et al.: Clin Chim Acta, 7:*322, 1962.
41. Kent, J. R., and Acone, A. B.: In *Androgens. Excerpta Med Int Congr Ser, 101:*31, 1966.
42. Kirschner, M. A.; Lipsett, M. B., and Collins, D. R.: *J Chromatogr, 2:*360, 1964.
43. Klopper, A.; Michie, E. A., and Brown, J. B.: *Endocr, 12:*209, 1955.
44. Korenman, S. G., and Lipsett, M. B.: *J Clin Invest, 43:*2125, 1964.
45. Korenman, S. G.; Wilson, H., and Lipsett, M. B.: *J Biol Chem, 239:*1004, 1964.
46. Lazarus, L.: *J Clin Endocr, 22:*581, 1962.
47. Lim, M. Y., and Dingman, J.F.: *J Clin Endocr, 25:*563, 1965.
48. Lobotsky, J., *et al.: J Clin Endocr, 24:*1261, 1964.
49. Loraine, J. A., *et al.: Lancet, 2:*902, 1963.
50. Mahesh, V. B., and Greenblatt, R. B.: *Recent Prog Hormone Res, XX:*341, 1964.
51. Mikhail, G.; Zander, J., and Allen, W. M.: *J Clin Endocr, 23:*1267, 1963.
52. Pickett, M. T., *et al.: Lancet, 2:*829, 1959.
53. Pickett, M. T., and Sommerville, I. F.: *Acta Endocr, 41:*135, 1962.
54. Riondel, A., *et al.: J Clin Endocr, 23:*620, 1963.
55. Riondel, A., *et al.: J Clin Endocr, 25:*229, 1965.
56. Rivardla, M. A., and Migeon, C. J.: *Steroids, 7:*103, 1966.
57. Rosner, J. M., *et al.: J Clin Endocr, 25:*95, 1965.
58. Schubert, K., and Frankenberg, C.: *Hoppe Seyler Z Physiol Chem, 836:*91, 1964.
59. Serr, D. M., *et al.: Excerpta Med Congr Ser, 51:*174, 1962.
60. Shearman, R. P.: *Lancet, 1:*197, 1963.
61. Short, R. V., and London, D. R.: *Brit Med J, 1:*1724, 1961.
62. Siiteri, P. K.: *Steroids, 2:*6, 1963.
63. Sommerville, I. F.: In Lipsett, M. (Ed.): *Gas Chromatography of Steroids in Biological Fluids."* 1965, p. 53.
64. Sommerville, I. F.: *Research on Steroids, II:*147, 1966.
65. Sommerville, I. F., and Deshpande, N. G.: *J Clin Endocr, 18:*1223, 1958.
66. Sommerville, I. F., and Collins, W. P.: *Steroids, Suppl II:*223, 1965.
67. Sommerville, I. F., *et al.: Colloq on Endocr Functions of Ovary.* Paris, 1965 (in press).
68. Sparagana, M.: *Steroids, 5:*773, 1965.
69. Stern, M. I., and Barwell, J. O. H.: *J Endocr, 27:*87, 1963.
70. Surace, M., *et al.:* In *Androgens. Excerpta Med Int Congr Ser, 101:*16, 1966.
71. Tait, J. F., and Horton, R.: In Pincus, G., and Nakao, T., (Eds.): *Dynamics of Steroid Metabolism.* New York, Academic, 1965.
72. Thijssen, J. H. H., and Zander, J.: *Acta Endocr, 51:*563, 1966.
73. Van der Molen, H. J., and Groen, D.: In Lipsett, M. (Ed.): *Gas Chromatography of Steroids in Biological Fluids,* 1965, p. 153.

74. VAN DER MOLEN, H. J.; GROEN, D., and PETERSE, A.: In *Androgens. Excerpta Med Int Congr Ser, 101*:199, 1966.
75. VANDE WIELE, R. L.: In Paulsen, C. A. (Ed.) : *Estrogen Assays in Clinical Medicine.* 1965, p. 151.
76. VERMEULEN, A.: *Androgens. Excerpta Med Found,* p. 71, 1965.
77. VERMEULEN, A., and VERPLANCKE, J. C. M.: *Steroids, 2*:453, 1963.
78. WEIDENFELD, J.; SERR, D., and FINKELSTEIN, M.: *J Reprod Fertil, 12*:107, 1966.

Chapter 4

SECRETION OF ANDROGENS BY THE OVARY

VIRENDRA B. MAHESH

T HE EARLY developments in the understanding of the hormones secreted by the ovary were based primarily on the urinary excretion of various estrogens in pregnancy and their relationship with material isolated from hog ovaries.[1,8] Subsequently estrogens were isolated from the ovaries of animals from several species, horse testes, ox adrenals, and human placental tissues.[4,5,15,33] Based on the knowledge obtained by these studies on the production of estrogens, there developed an active interest in the estrogen precursors and pathways of ovarian steroidogenesis. The conversion of progesterone to $\triangle^4$-androstenedione via 17α-hydroxy progesterone was shown to occur in bovine ovaries and normal and pathologic human ovarian tissues by several investigators.[27,31,34,35] Aromatization of $\triangle^4$-androstenedione or testosterone to estrogens by the ovaries has also been amply demonstrated.[2,36] The *in vivo* conversion of cholesterol -4^{14}C to estrogens in the pregnant mare was reported by Heard *et al.*[11] This conversion has been shown to occur in the human ovary by Ryan and Smith.[26] Based on the results of these and several other investigations, it is now generally accepted that the major pathway of biosynthesis of estrogens in the ovary comprises the conversion of cholesterol to estrogens via $\triangle^5$-pregnenolone, progesterone, 17α-hydroxy progesterone, and $\triangle^4$-androstenedione (Fig. 4-1). Also present as a minor pathway is the conversion of cholesterol to estrogens via $\triangle^5$-pregnenolone, 17α-hydroxy-$\triangle^5$-pregnenolone, dehydroepiandrosterone, and $\triangle^4$-androstenedione (Fig. 4-1).

Although the pathways of biosynthesis of estrogens via $\triangle^4$-androstenedione and testosterone in the ovary were well worked out, it was of considerable interest to determine whether the androgens were merely intermediates in the biosynthesis of estrogens or actual secretory products of the ovary. The presence of androgens in ovarian tissue was suspected in 1925 when Champy and Kritch found androgenic activity in ovarian extracts.[6] The presence of androgens in the ovary was confirmed by the isolation of $\triangle^4$-androstenedione from pooled human ovarian tissue by Zander in 1958.[37] That the ovaries may actually secrete androgens was first suggested by the work of Dingemanse and Huis i'nt Veld[7] in 1951. These investigators observed a marked depression in urinary androsterone after castration in women. The secretion of androgen by the ovary in the Stein-Leventhal syndrome was suggested by the finding of marked reduction of urinary 17-ketosteroids after wedge resection by Greenblatt[10] in 1953. In order to study in a systematic manner the role of the ovary in the secretion of androgens the following studies were carried out by Mahesh *et al.*[18,23]: (1) fractionation and individual estimation of various steroids before and after adrenal suppression and stimulation of ovarian function with human pituitary

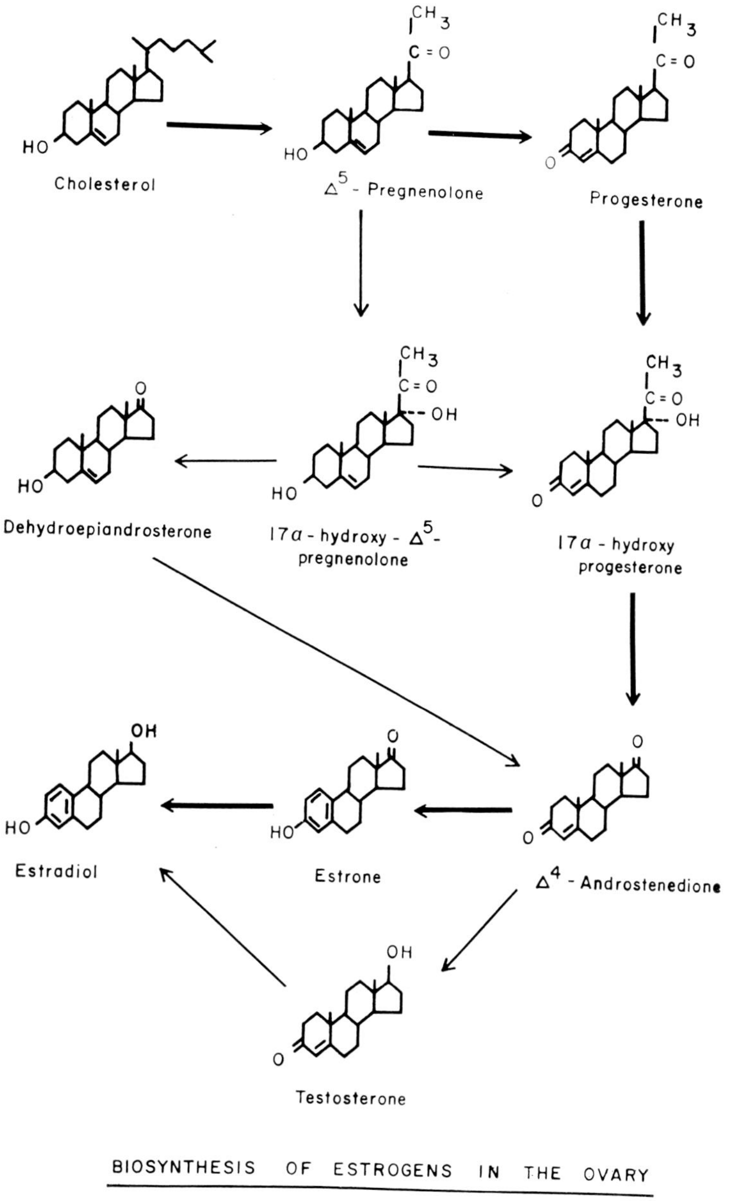

BIOSYNTHESIS   OF   ESTROGENS   IN   THE   OVARY

Figure 4-1.

follicle stimulating hormone (HP-FSH), (2) study of the steroid content of ovarian tissue, and (3) study of the steroid content of ovarian venous blood. These studies collectively have established that the normal ovary secretes small amounts of androgens, and the polycystic ovary as seen in the Stein-Leventhal syndrome, with some exceptions, secretes large amounts of androgens.

STUDY OF URINARY EXCRETION PATTERNS

Fractionation and individual estimation of various urinary steroids was carried out in normal and hirsute women before and after adrenal suppression by Mahesh *et al.*[19,20,22,23] In the group of hirsute women, thirty-one out of forty-five had an elevation in one or more 17-ketosteroid fractions. Urinary 11-oxygenated-17-ketosteroids, with very rare exceptions, are metabolites of steroids of adrenal origin such as cortisol and 11β-hydroxy-$\triangle^4$-androstenedione. For this reason whenever the elevation of urinary 11-deoxy-17-ketosteroids was accompanied by a similar elevation in 11-oxygenated-17-ketosteroids, the adrenals were considered to be partially or solely responsible for excessive androgen production. There were several hirsute patients who showed significant elevation (P <0.01) in the 11-deoxy-17-ketosteroid fraction as compared to values obtained from the urine of normal women. These steroids could arise from either adrenal or ovarian secretion. To differentiate between the adrenal or ovarian origin of androgens, adrenal suppression was attempted. With adrenal suppression by dexamethasone administration, the 11-deoxy-17-ketosteroids in five hirsute women showed good depression (Group 3a, mean value 1.2 mg per twenty-four hours) as compared to normal women (mean value 1.0 mg/24 hrs). However, in ten other hirsute patients the suppression was poor (Group 3b, mean value 3.9 mg/24 hrs) (Fig. 4-2). The difference in Group 3b as compared to normal women and the hirsute women in Group 3a is highly significant (P values in Students' T test and Duncan's multirange analysis <0.01). As the 11-oxygenated-17-ketosteroids and tetrahydrocorticoids were well suppressed in Groups 3a and 3b after dexamethasone administration, indicating good adrenal suppression, the residual 11-deoxy-17-ketosteroids in these groups were in all probability of ovarian origin, Group 3b showing excessive ovarian androgens as compared to those present in normal women and hirsute women in Group 3a. That the excessive ketosteroid production in Group 3b was of ovarian origin, is supported by an almost complete reduction of these values when ovarian function was suppressed by the administration of stilbestrol (Fig. 4-2). Confirmation of the ovarian origin of excessive androgens in Group 3b was obtained by a significant fall of these steroids after wedge resection of the ovary (Fig. 4-2). Poor depression of

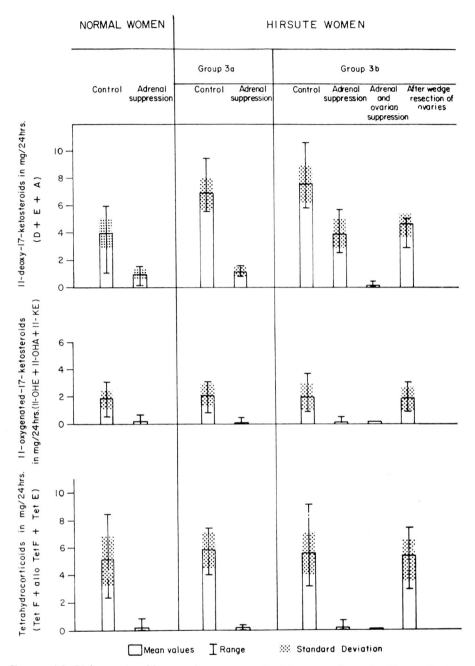

FIGURE 4-2. Urinary steroid excretion pattern in hirsute patients in Group 3 shows elevation in the 11-deoxy-17-ketosteroid fraction (P = .01). On dexamethasone administration, the depression of 11-deoxy-17-ketosteroids was poor in Group 3b as compared to normal women and hirsute women in Group 3a (P = .01). Administration of stilbestrol brought about a further decrease in this fraction in Group 3b. Wedge resection of the ovaries was carried out on five patients in Group 3b, and a significant fall in 11-deoxy-17-ketosteroids was noted three months after the operation. (Reproduced from Mahesh *et al.*: *J Clin Endocr, 24*:1283, 1964.)

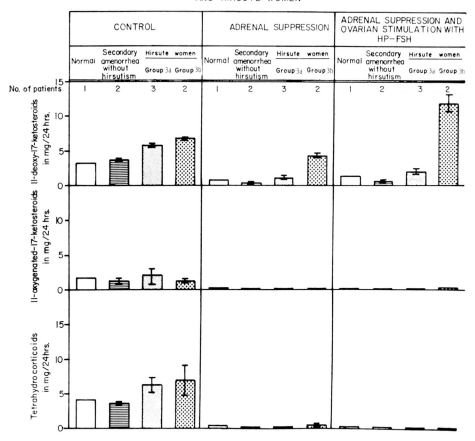

FIGURE 4-3. Note poor depression of 11-deoxy-17-ketosteroids on adrenal suppression and a marked increase in these steroids after ovarian stimulation with human pituitary FSH in Group 3b as compared to the normal and to patients in Group 3a. (Reproduced from Mahesh and Greenblatt; *J Clin Endocr, 24:*1293, 1964.)

17-ketosteroids after adrenal suppression in patients with hirsutism or the Stein-Leventhal syndrome has also been reported by other investigators.[3,12,14,16,25] Further confirmation of the ovarian secretion of androgens was obtained by stimulating with HP-FSH while on dexamethasone, one normally ovulating woman, two women with secondary amenorrhea without hirsutism, three patients from Group 3a, and two patients from Group 3b. There was a marked rise in the 11-deoxy-17-ketosteroids in Group 3b as compared to only small increases in the other groups studied (Fig. 4-3) thus confirming excessive ovarian androgen production by that group.

ANDROGEN CONTENT OF OVARIAN TISSUE

The androgen content of ovarian tissue removed during wedge resection of normal and polycystic ovaries had been studied by Mahesh *et al.*[18,20,22] The normal ovary contained only small quantities of $\triangle^4$-androstenedione (Fig. 4-4, Specimens 1-4); these results are in agreement with those of Zander,[37] Simmer,[30] and Short.[29] Large quantities of 17α-hydroxy progesterone and $\triangle^4$-androstenedione were isolated from the one normal ovary after *in vivo* stimulation with HP-FSH (Fig. 4-5, Specimen 10). The ovaries of patients with the polycystic ovary syndrome contained large quantities of either $\triangle^4$-androstenedione and 17α-hydroxy progesterone (Fig. 4-4, Specimens 5-8) and/or dehydroepiandrosterone (Fig. 4-4, Specimens 5, 8, and 9). Furthermore, when such patients were treated with human pituitary FSH, larger quantities of these steroids were isolated. The isolation of dehydroepiandrosterone from polycystic ovaries — which was originally reported by Mahesh and Greenblatt — has now been confirmed by Starka *et al.*[32] and Baulieu *et al.*[3] Large quantities of $\triangle^4$-androstenedione have been isolated from ovarian cystic fluid of patients with the Stein-Leventhal syndrome by Short[29] and Mahajan *et al.*[17]

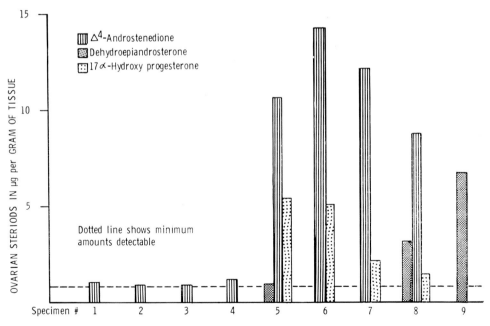

FIGURE 4-4. Steroid content of untreated normal and polycystic ovaries. Specimens 1-4; normal ovaries; Specimens 5-6: small polycystic ovaries; Specimens 7-9: typical large, pale, polycystic ovaries. (Reproduced from Mahesh and Greenblatt; (*Recent Progr Hormone Res, 20:*341, 1964.)

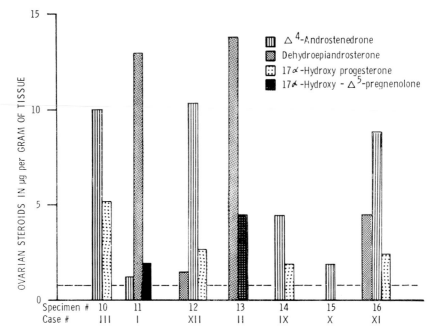

FIGURE 4-5. Steroid content of gonadotropin-stimulated normal and polycystic ovaries. Specimen 10: normal ovary, patient stimulated with HP-FSH; Specimens 11 and 12: polycystic ovaries, patients stimulated with HP-FSH; Specimens 13-16: polycystic ovaries, patients stimulated with HP-FSH followed by HCG. (Reproduced from Mahesh and Greenblatt; *Recent Progr Hormone Res, 20*:341, 1964.)

ANDROGEN CONTENT OF OVARIAN VENOUS BLOOD

The isolation of androgens from ovarian tissue or cystic or follicular fluid does not necessarily imply their secretion by the ovary. Their presence may merely be due to the fact that they are intermediates in the biosynthesis of estrogens as demonstrated by several *in vitro* studies. Studies of urinary excretion of various 11-deoxy-17-ketosteroids before and after adrenal suppression and after stimulation of ovarian function with human pituitary FSH are highly suggestive of small amounts of androgen secretion by the normal ovary and large amounts by some polycystic ovaries.[19,20,22,23] To establish beyond doubt that ovaries are capable of producing androgens, a study of the androgen content of ovarian venous blood was carried out by Mahesh *et al.*[20,22] Ovarian venous blood was collected from normally ovulating women who underwent surgery for various reasons around the time of ovulation and several patients with the Stein-Leventhal syndrome (Table 4-I). The normal ovarian venous blood contains only very small amounts of Δ^4-androstenedione. When treated with HP-FSH, the Δ^4androstenedione content was considerably greater. On the other hand, polycystic ovaries were

TABLE 4-I
ANDROGEN CONTENT OF OVARIAN PLASMA

Source	Treatment	Steroids (μg/100 ml of ovarian)* Venous Plasma		
		Testosterone	*Δ⁴-androstenedione*	*Dehydroepiandrosterone*
Normal ovary	None	<0.4	<0.4	<0.4
,,	,,	<0.4	<0.4	<0.4
,,	,,	<0.2	<0.2	<0.2
,,	,,	<0.3	<0.3	<0.3
,,	,,	<0.1	0.94	<0.1
,,	,,	<0.1	0.18	0.15
,,	,,	<0.1	0.74	0.11
,,	,,	<0.1	0.27	<0.1
Normal ovary	HP-FSH treated	<0.7	1.1	<0.7
Polycystic ovary	None	<0.3	20.9	<0.3
,,	,,	<0.5	13.1	<0.5
,,	,,	<0.45	<0.45	9.4
,,	,,	<0.1	14.2	2.4
,,	,,	0.12	23.1	0.9
,,	,,	<0.1	3.8	2.8
,,	,,	<0.1	7.4	4.7
Polycystic ovary	HP-FSH treated	<0.5	<0.5	15.4
,,	,,	<0.4	2.1	<0.4
,,	,,	<0.5	8.5	3.8

*Minimum amounts detectable were dependent on the volume of ovarian venous plasma available and the method used.

capable of secreting large quantities of Δ^4-androstenedione and/or dehydro-epiandrosterone. The presence of androgens in ovarian venous blood from normal women has been confirmed by Gandy et al.,[9] Horton et al.,[13] and Mikhail et al.[24] Seeman and Saracino[28] found elevated levels of 17-keto-steroids in ovarian venous blood as compared to peripheral blood in patients with polycystic ovaries. These investigators, however, did not identify the androgens secreted by the ovary.

CONCLUSIONS

The studies carried out by several groups of investigators have established that androgens are secretory products of the ovary. The normal ovary secretes only small quantities of androgens, principally Δ^4-androstenedione. Polycystic ovaries may secrete large quantities of Δ^4-androstenedione and/or dehydroepiandrosterone. However, this is not universally true for all polycystic ovaries.

REFERENCES

1. ALLEN, E., and DOISY, E. A.: An ovarian hormone: Preliminary report on its localization, extraction, partial purification and action in test animals. *JAMA, 81:*819, 1923.

2. BAGGET, B., et al.: The conversion of testosterone $-^{14}C$ to estradiol $-^{14}C$ by human ovarian tissue. *J Biol Chem, 221:*931, 1956.

3. BAULIEU, E. E.; MAUVAIS-JARVIS, P., and CORPECHOT, C.: Steroid studies in a case of Stein-Leventhal syndrome with hirsutism. *J Clin Endocr, 23:*374, 1963.

4. BEALL, D.: The isolation of α-estradiol and estrone from horse testis. *Biochem J, 34:* 1293, 1940.

5. BEALL, D.: The isolation of estrone from ox adrenals. *J Endocr, 2:*104, 1940.

6. CHAMPY, C., and KRITCH, N.: *C R Soc Biol (Paris), 92:*683, 1925.

7. DINGEMANSE, E., and HIUS I'NT VELD, L. G.: Origin of androsterone in the urine of women. *Acta Endocr (Kobenhavn), 7:*71, 1951.

8. DOISY, E. A.; VELLER, C. D., and THAYER, S.: Folliculin from urine of pregnant women. *Amer J Physiol, 90:*329, 1929.

9. GANDY, H. M.; MOODY, C. B., and PETERSON, R. E.: Androgen levels in ovarian and adrenal venous plasma. Proceeding of the 6th Pan American Congress of Endocrinology, *Excerpta Med Int Congr Ser, 112:*223, 1965.

10. GREENBLATT, R. B.: Cortisone in the treatment of hirsute women. *Amer J Obstet Gynec, 66:*700, 1953.

11. HEARD, R. D. H., et al.: Biogenesis of sterols and steroid hormones. *Recent Progr Hormone Res, 12:*45, 1956.

12. HERRMANN, W.; BUCHNER, F., and MORRIS, J. McL.: The problem of mild adrenal hyperplasia. *Fertil Steril, 11:*74, 1960.

13. HORTON, R.; ROMANOFF, E., and WALKER, J.: Androstenedione and testosterone in ovarian venous and peripheral plasma during ovariectomy for breast cancer. *J Clin Endocr, 26:*1267, 1966.

14. JAYLE, M. F., et al.: Excretion des steroides chez des femmes presentant un virilisme pilaire associe à des troubles du cycle menstruel. *Acta Endocr (Kobenhavn), 36:* 375, 1961.

15. MacCorquodale, D. W.; Thayer, S. A., and Doisy, E. A.: The crystalline ovarian follicular hormone. *Proc Soc Exp Biol Med, 32*:1182, 1934.

16. MacDonald, P. C.; VandeWiele, R., and Lieberman, S.: Precursors of urinary 11-desoxy-17-ketosteroids of ovarian origin. *Amer J Obstet Gynec, 1*:86, 1963.

17. Mahajan, D. K.; Shah, P. N., and Eik-Nes, K. B.: Steroids in cyst fluid obtained from polycystic ovaries of hirsute women. *J Obstet Gynaec Brit Comm, 70*:8, 1963.

18. Mahesh, V. B., and Greenblatt, R. B.: Isolation of dehydroepiandrosterone and 17α-hydroxy-△⁵-pregnenolone from the polycystic ovaries of Stein-Leventhal syndrome. *J Clin Endocr, 22*:441, 1962.

19. Mahesh, V. B., and Greenblatt, R. B.: Physiology and pathogenesis of the Stein-Leventhal syndrome. *Nature, 191*:888, 1961.

20. Mahesh, V. B., and Greenblatt, R. B.: Steroid secretions of the normal and polycystic ovary. *Recent Progr Hormone Res, 20*:341, 1964.

21. Mahesh, V. B., and Greenblatt, R. B.: Urinary steroid excretion patterns in hirsutism II. *J Clin Endocr, 24*:1293, 1964.

22. Mahesh, V. B., *et al.:* Secretion of androgens by the polycystic ovary and its significance. *Fertil Steril, 13*:513, 1962.

23. Mahesh, V. B., *et al.:* Urinary steroid excretion patterns in hirsutism I. *J Clin Endocr, 24*:1283, 1964.

24. Mikhail, G.; Zander, J., and Allen, W. M.: Steriods in human ovarian vein blood. *J Clin Endocr, 23*:1267, 1963.

25. Pesonen, S.; Timonen, S., and Mikkonen, R.: Symptoms and etiology of the Stein-Leventhal syndrome. *Acta Endocr (Kobenhavn), 30*:405, 1959.

26. Ryan, K. J., and Smith, O. W.: Biogenesis of estrogens by the human ovary III: Conversion of cholesterol −4¹⁴C to estrone. *J Biol Chem, 236*:2204, 1961.

27. Savard, K., *et al.:* Formation of androgens by human arrhenoblastoma tissue. *J Clin Endocr, 21*:165, 1961.

28. Seeman, A., and Saracino, R. T.: Contribution à l'étude de la formation d'androgenes par l'ovarie. *Acta Endocr (Kobenhavn), 37*:31, 1961.

29. Short, R. V.: Further observations on the defective synthesis of ovarian steroids in the Stein-Leventhal syndrome. *J Endocr, 24*:359, 1962.

30. Simmer, H. H.: Androgene polyzystiche ovarien and hirsutism. *Deutsch Med Wschr, 88*:1661, 1963.

31. Solomon, S. S.; VandeWiele, R., and Lieberman, S.: The *in vitro* synthesis of 17α-hydroxy progesterone and △⁴-androstenedione from progesterone by bovine tissue. *J Amer Chem Soc, 78*:5453, 1956.

32. Starka, L.; Matys, Z., and Janata, J.: Der nachiveis von dehydroepiandrosterone in menschlichen sklerocystischen ovarien. *Clin Chim Acta, 7*:776, 1962.

33. Veller, C. D.; Thayer, S., and Doisy, E. A.: The preparation of crystalline follicular ovarian hormone. *J Biol Chem, 87*:357, 1930.

34. Warren, J. C., and Salhanick, H. A.: Steroid biosynthesis in the human ovary. *J Clin Endocr, 21*:1218, 1961.

35. Wiest, W. C.; Zander, J., and Holmstrom, E. G.: Metabolism of progesterone −4 ¹⁴C by an arrhenoblastoma. *J Clin Endocr, 19*:297, 1959.

36. Wotiz, H. H., *et al.:* Studies in steroid metabolism: The conversion of testosterone-¹⁴C to estrogens by human ovarian tissue. *J Biol Chem, 222*:487, 1956.

37. Zander, J.: Steroids in the human ovary. *J Biol Chem, 232*:117, 1958.

Chapter 5

STUDIES ON STEROID METABOLISM OF HUMAN OVARIAN TISSUE

W. INGIULLA AND R. FORLEO

IN RECENT YEARS, STUDIES based upon the incubation of ovarian components with isotopically labelled substrates have contributed a great deal of
information to the biosynthesis of ovarian hormones.[6,17,33,34] This type of
study offers an understanding of the probable biosynthetic processes which
lead to the formation of steroids within the ovary, the significance and interrelationships between steroid intermediaries and ovarian morphology, and
the possible existence of syndromes involving abnormal steroid metabolism.

The present report concerns macrodissection of human ovaries into
follicular tissue, corpora lutea, postmenopausal stroma tissue, and tissue
resected from micropolycystic ovaries, and contains examples of three experimental approaches. In the first instance, separate portions of single
ovarian components were incubated with a variety of labelled steroids, i.e.
pregnenolone (3β-hydroxypregn-5-ene-20-one), progesterone (pregn-4-ene-
3,20-dione), 17-OH progesterone (17α-hydroxypregn-4-ene-3,20-dione),
dehydroepiandrosterone (3β-hydroxyandrosten-5-ene-17-one), androstenedione (androst-4-ene-3, 17-dione) and testosterone (17β-hydroxyandrost-4-ene-
3-one) for a constant period of time (5 hours). This approach was adopted
in order to obtain information regarding the relative enzyme activities
within the same tissue component, and eventually to interpret a comprehensive series of results obtained under comparable experimental conditions, so as to compare steroid transformations between components of
healthy and pathological tissue. More recently, separate portions of the
same component have been incubated with the same substrate for progressive periods of time. This approach is illustrated by incubation of two corpora lutea with progesterone, 17-OH progesterone, and dehydroepiandrosterone for twenty minutes to five hours, and is used to provide further
evidence on the sequence of steroid transformations and the possible existence of rate-limiting steps. Thirdly, single ovarian components have been
subdivided and incubated with the same substrate for a constant time but
with the addition of possible stimulatory or inhibitory substances to the
flask. This procedure is illustrated by the addition of human menopausal
gonadotropin (HMG), medroxyprogesterone acetate (MAP) and ethinyl
oestradiol (EE) to separate flasks containing labelled pregnenolone and
ovarian tissue resected from micropolycystic ovaries.

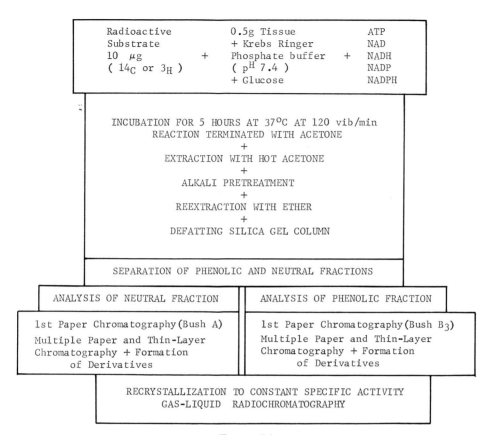

| Radioactive
Substrate
10 μg
(^{14}C or ^{3}H) | + | 0.5g Tissue
+ Krebs Ringer
Phosphate buffer
(p^{H} 7.4)
+ Glucose | + | ATP
NAD
NADH
NADP
NADPH |

INCUBATION FOR 5 HOURS AT 37°C AT 120 vib/min
REACTION TERMINATED WITH ACETONE
+
EXTRACTION WITH HOT ACETONE
+
ALKALI PRETREATMENT
+
REEXTRACTION WITH ETHER
+
DEFATTING SILICA GEL COLUMN

SEPARATION OF PHENOLIC AND NEUTRAL FRACTIONS

ANALYSIS OF NEUTRAL FRACTION	ANALYSIS OF PHENOLIC FRACTION
1st Paper Chromatography(Bush A) Multiple Paper and Thin-Layer Chromatography + Formation of Derivatives	1st Paper Chromatography(Bush B$_3$) Multiple Paper and Thin-Layer Chromatography + Formation of Derivatives

RECRYSTALLIZATION TO CONSTANT SPECIFIC ACTIVITY
GAS-LIQUID RADIOCHROMATOGRAPHY

FIGURE 5-1.

CONDITIONS FOR INCUBATION

The incubation techniques were as described by Forleo and Collins,[9] but the method for the isolation and identification of the radiometabolites has been modified (Fig. 5-1) notably by the additional use of thin-layer chromatography (TLC) and the recrystallization of every metabolite to constant specific activity.[10]

Fresh tissue was used in all studies—the incubation beginning ten to twenty minutes after surgery. The radioactive substrates were added to the flasks before preparing the tissue and taken to dryness under a stream of nitrogen. As the major enzymes involved in steroid transformations are oxidases, reductases, desmolases, and isomerases, the coenzymes essential for these transformations, i.e. nicotinamide-adenine dinucleotide (NAD) and its reduced form (NADH), nicotinamide-adenine dinucleotide phosphate (NADP) and its reduced form (NADPH) were added to the buffer (Krebs Ringer phosphate; pH 7.4 + 200 mg% glucose) to give a constant ratio to the weight of tissue (1.0 gm tissue; 5.0 ml of buffer containing 0.004 M of each cofactor) .

SUBSTRATES

The following substrates were obtained from The Radiochemical Centre, Amersham, England:

Pregnenolone-4-^{14}C	s.a.	19.8 mc/mM
Pregnenolone-7α-T	s.a.	103 mc/mM
Progesterone-4-^{14}C	s.a.	21.7 or 26.1 mc/mM
17α-OH progesterone-4-^{14}C	s.a.	37.0 mc/mM
Dehydroepiandrosterone-4-^{14}C	s.a.	33.7 mc/mM
Androstenedione-4-^{14}C	s.a.	34.8 mc/mM
Androstenedione-7α-T	s.a.	888 mc/mM
Testosterone-4-^{14}C	s.a.	21.5 or 29.2 mc/mM

The incubations were performed in 25-ml Erlenmeyer flasks which were placed in a water bath at 37°C and shaken mechanically (120 vib/-min) . At the end of the incubation time, the reactions were terminated by the addition of 20 ml acetone to each flask which was then stored in a refrigerator (4°C) overnight.

METHOD FOR ANALYSIS OF RADIOMETABOLITES

The contents of each flask were extracted with hot acetone, followed by mild hydrolysis of the dried extract with sodium hydroxide. The steroids were then reextracted with ether which was washed and dried. The crude extracts were then purified on a column of silica gel as described by Forleo and Collins.[9] After separation of the neutral and phenolic steroids by solvent partition, the two fractions were initially separated by paper chromatography and subsequently by paper and TLC after acetylation. The final products were crystallized to constant specific activity. The procedures for analysis of the neutral extract are summarized in Figure 5-2 and described in detail by Forleo *et al.*[10]

Throughout the procedure the total number of counts was determined at each successive step in the isolation of the products, and corrected for quenching and counting efficiency. The recovery of steroid at each step was then corrected to 100 per cent in terms of loss of total counts and the radio activity in each recrystallized metabolite was expressed as the percentage conversion of substrate.

CORPORA LUTEA

Huang and Pearlman[15] demonstrated that the human corpus luteum could synthesize progesterone and 20α-dihydroprogesterone (20α-hydroxy-pregn-4-en-3-one) from labelled acetate. Further studies[14] with this substrate showed that in addition 17-OH progesterone, androstenedione, oes-

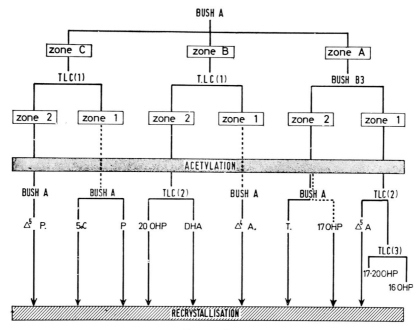

FIGURE 5-2.

tradiol-17β, oestrone and pregnenolone were also formed by corpora lutea. Furthermore, tracer studies with labelled steroids suggested that in this tissue the principal steroid transformations followed the sequence pregnenolone-progesterone-17-OH progesterone-androstenedione-oestrone and oestradiol-17β.[9,15,28,36,37] The endogenous concentration of dehydroepiandrosterone has been shown to be comparatively low,[35] and the labelled steroid has not been identified by recrystallization data from incubations with acetate or pregnenolone.[14,17,28] However, Ingiulla *et al.*[17] and Flickinger *et al.*[7] have demonstrated a very active transformation of dehydroepiandrosterone added to corpora lutea with an associated high yield of oestrone and oestradiol.

In the present study one incubation with each substrate (which appeared to be representative) has been selected for presentation until sufficient data has been accumulated for statistical analysis. The number of incubations which have been performed with corporea lutea are as follows:

1. Constant time experiments
    Pregnenolone (7)
    Progesterone (5)
    17-OH progesterone (2)
    Androstenedione (3)

Testosterone (3)
Dehydroepiandrosterone (1)
2. Kinetic experiments
Progesterone (1)
17-OH progesterone (1)
Dehydroepiandrosterone (2)

CORPORA LUTEA

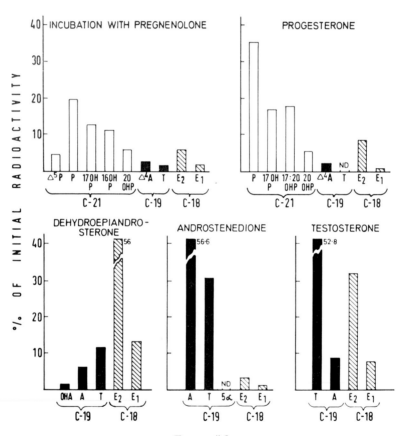

FIGURE 5-3.

Representative results with pregnenolone, progesterone, dehydroepiandrosterone, androstenedione, and testosterone are shown in Figure 5-3. In each instance, the first column represents unmetabolized substrate and each subsequent column indicates the percentage of radioactivity in the purified steroid. Sample figures for the recrystallization of products have been reported.[11]

The results suggest that 3β-hydroxydehydrogenase activity is especially high in copora lutea, but the high level of C-21 △⁴-3-ketosteroids from both pregnenolone and progesterone together with the low yields of androstenedione suggest low desmolase activity. Dehydroepiandrosterone was not detected in any of the seven incubations with pregnenolone, but the incubation of this substrate with one corpus luteum resulted in a high transformation of substrate with large accumulation of oestradiol-17β and oestrone Incubations with androstenedione and testosterone showed a good transformation to oestradiol-17β and oestrone, and demonstrate that the 17β ketosteroid reductase activity favoured the formation of androstenedione.

These general observations were investigated further by subdivision of a corpus luteum removed on day twenty-four after the last menstrual period. The tissue was minced and divided into eleven portions each weighing 100 mg. Three were incubated with 2 μg of progesterone for thirty minutes, one hour, and five hours respectively. The results obtained from this experiment are illustrated in Figure 5-4.

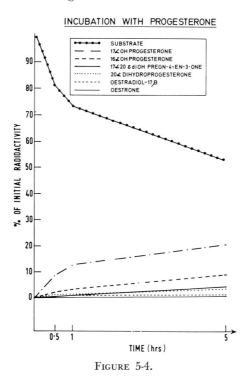

FIGURE 5-4.

Another four portions were incubated with 17-OH progesterone and the reactions terminated after thirty minutes, one, two hours, and five hours. The results are presented in Figure 5-5. The remaining four portions of tissue were incubated with dehydroepiandrosterone over the same period of time and the results are shown in Figure 5-6. Figures for the crystallization of each product in this series of experiments have been reported elsewhere.[10]

The results from these dynamic studies support and extend the previous constant time experiments. Thus, when progesterone was used as substrate there was good progressive 17-hydroxylation, but with both progesterone and 17-OH progesterone there was only a small accumulation of androstenedione supplying further evidence of low desmolase activity. These findings may be explained by a high endogenous level of progesterone as

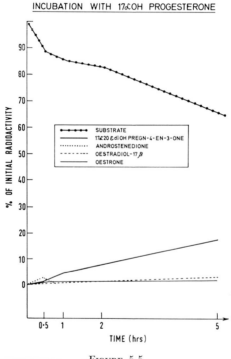

FIGURE 5-5.

suggested by Mahajan and Samuels[24] from their work on the effect of progesterone upon steroid transformations in rat testis.

The studies with dehydroepiandrosterone for progressive periods of time showed a rapid conversion to androstenedione, followed by the formation of oestrone and oestradiol-17β in high yield. The 17 reduction product of dehydroepiandrosterone, androst-5-ene-3β, 17β-diol was not isolated from any of the incubations and there was only a small yield of testosterone, suggesting low 17-ketosteroid reductase activity. In this connection it is also interesting that Mahajan and Samuels found that progesterone appeared to inhibit 17-ketosteroid reductase activity in the rat testis.

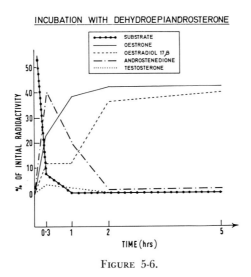

INCUBATION WITH DEHYDROEPIANDROSTERONE

FIGURE 5-6.

FOLLICULAR TISSUE

In a comprehensive series of experiments Ryan and Smith[29-32] investigated the enzymatic capacity of follicular cyst lining dissected from ovaries stimulated by the administration of ovine FSH to patients before surgery. The following steroids (in order of decreasing radioactivity) were isolated from the incubation of 25 gm of tissue with 200 μg acetate-1-C[14]-oestradiol-17β, oestrone, androstenedione, dehydroepiandrosterone, 17-OH progesterone, 17-OH pregnenolone (3β, 17α-dihydroxypregn-5-ene-20-one), progesterone, pregnenolone.

Oestradiol-17β and oestrone were isolated from a similar experiment with cholesterol, while 17-OH progesterone, androstenedione, and testosterone together with oestrone and oestradiol-17β were isolated as metabolites from labelled progesterone. A further incubation in the same series with androstenedione gave a high yield of oestrone together with oestradiol-17β and testosterone.

Other studies with nonstimulated ovarian tissue and pregnenolone,[1] followed by dual labelled studies[20] with progesterone-7-^{3}H and pregnenolone-4-^{14}C, suggested that pregnenolone was a better substrate than progesterone for the production of C-19 steroids throughout the menstrual cycle in tissue excluding corpora lutea. In addition, studies with labelled dehydroepiandrosterone have shown the conversion of this substrate to oestrogens.[38]

Further studies have been reported on the transformation of labelled steroids by separate aliquots of tissue mince from the lining of a large follicular cyst removed from a patient with juvenile metropathia.[4] In this instance, analysis of the transformation products from pregnenolone, progesterone, dehydroepiandrosterone, and androstenedione suggested that although there was a large accumulation of oestradiol-17β and oestrone from all substrates, the series of transformations tended to favour retention of the $\triangle^5$-3β-hydroxy group. Other studies[9] upon the incubation of macrodissected follicles with progesterone generally showed a decreased 20α-hydrogenase activity and a larger accumulation of androstenedione than in corpora lutea.

In the present study, three follicles have been incubated with progesterone, two with dehydroepiandrosterone, one with 17-OH progesterone, two with androstenedione, and three with testosterone. Representative results have been selected and illustrated in Figure 5-7.

Analysis of the results shows a similar transformation of testosterone and androstendione to that obtained in corpora lutea. Also there was a high transformation of dehydroepiandrosterone to androstenedione, although androst-5-ene-3β, 17β-diol was isolated in small yield from this tissue. When progesterone was substrate, there was low 20α-hydrogenase activity associated with an increased accumulation of androstenedione.

Pregnenolone has not been used as substrate in this series with follicular tissue but the experiments of Ryan[29] and Kumari and Goldzieher[20] strongly suggest that $\triangle^5$-3β-hydroxysteroid intermediaries may be more important in this tissue than in corpora lutea.

MICROPOLYCYSTIC OVARIAN TISSUE

Although there is limited knowledge on biosynthetic pathways in isolated human follicular tissue as compared with corpora lutea, there have been numerous studies on the biochemical aspects of micropolycystic ovaries. It has now been firmly established that tissue obtained from these ovaries by wedge resection has the ability to produce large amounts of androstenedione from various precursors *in vitro.** However, the extent of oestrogen production by this type of tissue is less clearly established. Impaired aromatization when compared to incubations of normal tissue minces under identical conditions has been reported.[1,13,16,37] On the other hand, O'Donnell and McCaig,[27] using sliced tissue stimulated with human menopausal gonadotrophins, reported the isolation of oestrone and oestradiol-17β from ^{14}C-acetate, and with similar tissue, Chapdelaine *et al.*[3] reported that the production of oestradiol-17β from dehydroepiandrosterone, androstenedione, and testosterone was practically the same as in normal tissue.

---

*See references 1, 3, 5, 16, 19, 21, 22.

FOLLICULAR TISSUE

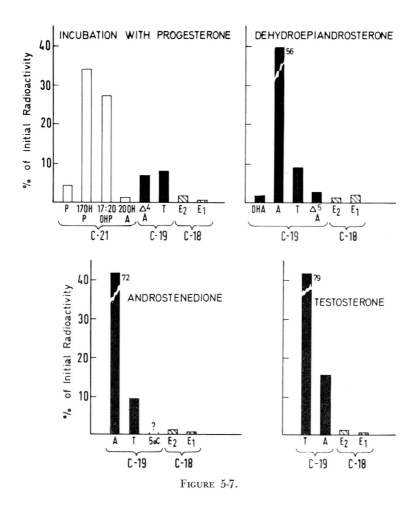

FIGURE 5-7.

In the present series of experiments two aliquots of micropolycystic tissue have been incubated with pregnenolone, six with progesterone, five with dehydroepiandrosterone, two with 17-OH progesterone, nine with androstenedione, and eight with testosterone. Representative results from this study are illustrated in Figure 5-8; the recrystallization data have been previously presented.[2,12]

The distribution of radioactivity from all substrates is strikingly different to that seen in normal follicular tissue and corpora lutea. There is a lack of aromatization, which is associated with a high accumulation of androstenedione. The tissue appears to be very active in 17-hydroxlyase and

MICROCYSTIC TISSUES

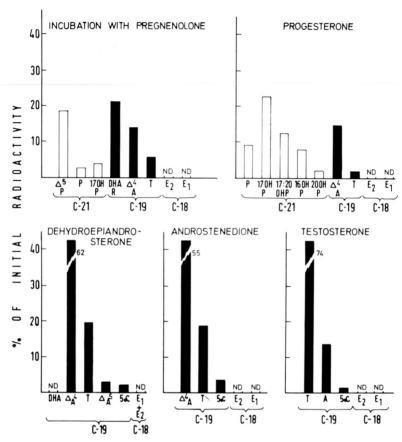

FIGURE 5-8.

3β-ol dehydrogenase activity as indicated by the low recoveries of pregnenolone, progesterone, and dehydroepiandrosterone when these steroids were added as substrates. However, in the incubation with pregnenolone there was a good recovery of dehydroepiandrosterone, suggesting that pathways involving retention of the $\triangle^5$-3β-hydroxy group may be important in this tissue, as first suggested by the studies of Mahesh and Greenblatt.[25] The consistently high yield of androstenedione is not only interesting with regard to the infertility and hirsutism associated with this syndrome, but also in the light of the recent report by MacDonald and Siiteri[26]. The secretion-rate studies performed by these workers indicate that the oestrogens present in patients with micropolycystic ovaries are mainly attributable to the peripheral transformation of androstenedione to oestrogens and not to direct secretion by the ovary.

Of additional interest, and probably associated with the large accumulation of androstenedione, is the isolation of 5α-androstane-3, 17-dione from incubations with micropolycystic ovarian tissue.[17]

More recently, we have attempted either to stimulate micropolycystic tissue *in vitro* with HMG (Pergonal 500) or to block some enzymatic reactions in the production of androstenedione by medroxyprogesterone acetate (MAP) or ethinyl oestradiol (EE). The results from a study with pregnenolone-4-^{14}C as substrate are shown in Figure 5-9. The recrystallization figures for each radiometabolite have been reported.[12] Again neither oes-

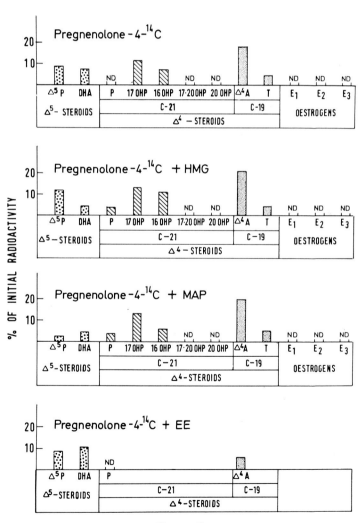

FIGURE 9.

trone nor oestradiol-17β was produced in sufficient quantity to permit definitive identification, and in all incubations androstenedione was the predominant metabolite. Other studies upon incubation of the same tissue with progesterone, 17-OH progesterone and dehydroepiandrosterone showed a good conversion of all substrates to androstenedione. The addition of HMG to the medium did not appear to modify the distribution of radioactivity from pregnenolone, neither did the addition of MAP, although EE did appear to inhibit 3β-hydroxysteroid dehydrogenase activity.

POSTMENOPAUSAL STROMA TISSUE

The contribution of the ovary to the oestrogens found in urine after the menopause has been the subject of much discussion and speculation. Very few *in vitro* studies with postmenopausal tissue and labelled steroid substrates have been reported. However, in 1956, Wotiz *et al.*,[39] reported that ovarian tissue (removed twenty years after the menopause and showing marked cortical stromal hyperplasia) was able to convert testosterone to oestrone and oestradiol-17β. Subsequently, Lemon *et al.*[23] found small quantities of oestrogens after incubating three postmenopausal ovaries with acetate-1-[14]C. Preliminary studies upon the conversion of neutral intermediaries were reported by Warren and Salhanick,[37] who incubated a post menopausal ovary with labelled progesterone and were only able to find 20α-dihydroprogesterone, whereas Forleo and Collins,[9] Forleo,[8] and Ingiulla *et al.*[18] incubated postmenopausal tissue with progesterone, androstenedione, and testosterone, and were able to demonstrate mainly 20α-hydrogenase and 17-β reductase activity, other enzymes being about or slightly active.

In the present series five incubations with pregnenolone have been undertaken, eleven with progesterone, one with 17-OH progesterone, five with dehydroepiandrosterone, eleven with androsterone, eleven with androstenedione, and eight with testosterone.

Representative results are illustrated in Figure 5-10, the full details have been reported elsewhere. The additional use of pregnenolone and dehydroepiandrosterone as substrates demonstrates very low $\triangle^5$-3β-ol dehydrogenase activity. In addition the presence of 20α-hydrogenase, and 17-ketosteroid reductase activity seems well established. However, there does appear to be a distinct lack of 17α-hydroxylation of C-21 steroids and desmolase activity.

GENERAL DISCUSSION

One of the most difficult problems in this type of study is the homogeneity of the tissue used for incubation. It is apparent that the ovary is a complex of different types of tissue with different steroidogenic potentials,

POSTMENOPAUSAL STROMA TISSUE

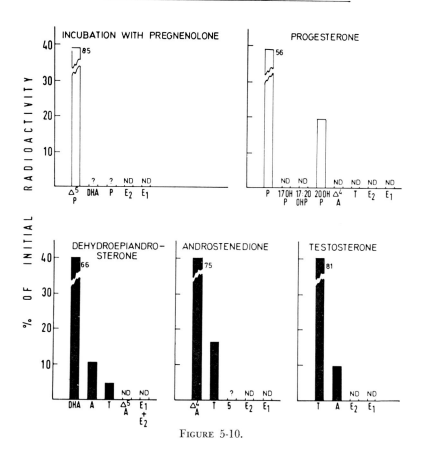

FIGURE 5-10.

and if this is not taken into account little information is gained. Certain problems arise for example with regard to evaluation of the ovarian stroma in ovaries from premenopausal women. In fact it is very difficult to separate the stromal cells of the cortex from the residue of thecal and follicular atresia or the medullary stroma from nests of hilar cells. In an attempt to assess the structures used in the present study, a complimentary part of each component was fixed for histological investigation. The tissue mince consists of fragments 0.1 to 1 mm size and this maintains to a certain extent the integrity of the cells. In theory the result might be influenced by the extent to which the cell membranes are damaged, but when a series of experiments are carried out on aliquots of the same tissue and with the same substrate, there is considerable reproducibility.

One of the more important factors which we have taken into consideration[16] is the ratio of substrate to the weight of tissue. It is obviously undesirable to overload the system by the introduction of an excess of steroid, and it would be desirable to use quantities of steroids which are similar to the tissue content under physiological conditions; although at the present time definite evidence is lacking on this point. Accordingly, it is our practice to add the minimum quantity of substrate which will permit adequate identification of the principal metabolites while keeping constant the ratio 1:50,-000 of radioactive substrate to tissue. For comparative studies it is important that this ratio be constant despite differences in the specific activity of the added substrate. It has been noted that, in the past, a tissue has been incubated with two radioactive steroids in quantities which differ by as much as 1:20. It is obviously impossible to speak of a greater metabolism of one substrate with respect to another or to interpret the results in terms of preferential metabolism when the quantities of starting material are so different.

Another important point is the possible influence of the endogenous concentration of steroid in the tissue which may affect the capacity for metabolism of the added substrate. Kowal *et al.* (1964) have shown a possible inhibition exercised by various steroids on several enzymatic processes. It is possible that an excess of endogenous steroid—for example, progesterone in the corpus luteum—may influence the metabolism of the radioactive substrate. It is for this reason that we have attempted analysis by gas-liquid radiochromatography in order to ascertain at the beginning and at the end of the incubation the mass of endogenous steroid which is present in relation to the quantity of added substrate. It would appear that this determination of initial and final specific activity could be applicable to a number of technical problems. For the present, the impossibility of determining the quantity of all endogenous steroids must be considered as a limitation in the interpretation of results. However, from the limited information available it does not appear likely that the endogenous levels would grossly interfere with the general conclusions deduced from the *in vitro* studies.

REFERENCES

1. AXELROD, L. R., and GOLDZIEHER, J. W.: *J Clin Endocr 22:431*, 1962.
2. BRUNI, V.; CATTANEO, A., and FORLEO, R.: *Riv Ostet Ginec, 22:29*, 1967.
3. CHAPDELAINE, A.; SANDOR, T., and LANTHIER, A.: *Canad J Biochem, 41:635*, 1963.
4. COLLINS, W. P., and SOMMERVILLE, I. F.: *Proceedings of the Second International Congress of Endocrinology, Part 2.* 1964, p. 1303.
5. CONTI, C., *et al.: Eur J Steroids, 2:45*, 1967.
6. DORFMAN, R. I., and UNGAR, F.: *Metabolism of Steroid Hormones.* New York, Academic, 1965.

*This work was supported by a grant from the Consiglio Nazionale delle Ricerche. The authors are indebted to Dr. C. Sbiroli, Dr. V. Bruni, and Mrs. Carniani, for skilled assistance and to Dr. William P. Collins and Dr. Ian F. Sommerville for advice

7. FLICKINGER, G. L.; CHUNG-HSIU WU, and TOUCHSTONE, J. C.: *Acta Endocr (Kobenhvn)*, *54:*30, 1967.

8. FORLEO, R.: *Research on Steroids, 1:*319, 1964.

9. FORLEO, R., and COLLINS, W. P.: *Acta Endocr (Kobenhvn), 46:*265, 1964.

10. FORLEO, A., et al.: *Steroids, 6:*617, 1967.

11. FORLEO, R.; BRUNI, V., and SBIROLI, C.: *Riv Ostet Ginec, 22:*1, 1967.

12. FORLEO, R.; BRUNI, V., and SBIROLI, C.: *Monogr Ostet Ginec Endocr Metab, 38:*1, 1967.

13. GANDAR, R.: *Bull Fed Gynec Obstet Franc, 15:*304, 1963.

14. HAMMERSTEIN, J.; RICE, B. F., and SAVARD, K.: *J Clin Endocr, 24:*597, 1964.

15. HUANG, W. Y., and PEARLMAN, W. H.: *J Biol Chem, 238:*1308, 1963.

16. INGIULLA, W.; FORLEO, R., and BRUNI, V.: In *Androgens in normal and pathological conditions Excerpta Medica Foundation Int Congr Series, 101:*58, 1966.

17. INGIULLA, W.; FORLEO, R., and BRUNI, V.: *Proceedings of the Second International Congress on Hormonal Steroids. Int Congr Series, 132:*411, 1967.

18. INGIULLA, W., and GASPARI, F.: La sindrome menopause. *L'ovaria Umana Durante il Climaterio.* Torino, 1965, pp. 57-134.

19. KASE, N.; KOWAL, J., and SOFFER, L. J.: *Acta Endocr (Kobenhvn), 39:*411, 1963.

20. KUMARI, L., and GOLDZIEHER, J. W.: *Acta Endocr (Kobenhvn), 52:*455, 1966.

21. LANTHIER, A., and SANDOR, T.: *Metabolism, 9:*861, 1960.

22. LANTHIER, A., and SANDOR, T.: *Acta Endocr (Kobenhvn), 39:*145, 1962.

23. LEMON, H. M., et al.: *International Symposium on Mammary Cancer, 1958.*

24. MAHAJAN, D. K., and SAMUELS, L. T.: *Fed Proc, 21:*209, 1962.

25. MAHESH, V. B., and GREENBLATT, R. B.: *Recent Progr Hormone Res, 20:*341, 1964.

26. McDONALD, P. C., and SIITERI, P. K.: *Abstracts Second International Congress of Hormonal Steroids, Milan. Excerpta Med Int Congr Ser, 111:*151, 1966.

27. O'DONNELL, V. C., and McCAIG, J. G.: *Biochem J, 71:*9, 1959.

28. RYAN, K. J.: *Acta Endocr (Kobenhvn), 44:*81, 1963.

29. RYAN, K. J., and SMITH, O. W.: *J Biol Chem, 236:*705, 1961.

30. RYAN, K. J., and SMITH, O. W.: *J Biol Chem, 236:*710, 1961.

31. RYAN, K. J., and SMITH, O. W.: *J Biol Chem, 236:*2204, 1961.

32. RYAN, K. J., and SMITH, O. W.: *J Biol Chem, 236:*2207, 1961.

33. RYAN, K. J., and SMITH, O. W.: *Recent Progr Hormone Res, 21:*367, 1965.

34. SAVARD, K.; MARSH, J. M., and RICE, B. F.: *Recent Progr Hormone Res, 21:*285, 1965.

35. SIMMER, H., and VOSS, H. E.: *Klin Wschr, 38:*819, 1960.

36. SWEAT, M., et al.: *Biochim Biophys Acta, 40:*289, 1960.

37. WARREN, J. C., and SALHANICK, H. A.: *J Clin Endocr, 21:*1218, 1961.

38. WEST, C. D., and NAVILLE, A. H.: *Biochemistry, 1:*645, 1962.

39. WOTIZ, H. H., et al.: *J Biol Chem, 222:*487, 1956.

Chapter 6

HIRSUTISM AND THE STEIN-LEVENTHAL SYNDROME

ROBERT B. GREENBLATT AND ROBERT F. CONIFF

T HE SYMBOLIC significance of unusual piliary growth has always intrigued man. Samson of biblical fame, when shorn of his hair, lost his strength. In our own day, the long-haired, bearded Bohemian, like sheep in wolf's clothing, betrays his masculinity. The clinical phenomenon of a bearded woman suckling her newborn infant at her swollen breast was recorded on canvas in 1631 by Ribera. It is said that the Duke of Alcala wished to preserve for posterity this unusual event. The reluctant artist completed the commission much against his esthetic and artistic sense (Fig. 6-1). Woman forever fears the onset of unusual and excessive hairiness. Subconsciously she is haunted by the historic memory that man, in his phylogenetic development, emerged not only erect but void of much of the thick pelage which covers the bodies of all primates to which he belongs.

The marked interest in ovarian physiology and chemistry noted in the past several years stems from several observations that the ovary may be a source of androgens and a factor in hirsutism. Our knowledge of steroidogenesis has advanced to the degree that answers may now be attempted to some of the questions concerning ovarian chemistry in hirsutism.

Many women, with increased hair growth on the face, and/or chest, abdomen, and extremities have no other stigmata of endocrine disturbance. This type of hypertrichosis frequently is a familial or racial trait. The Mongolian, Negroid, and American Indian races are noticeably less hairy than Caucasians. Furthermore, Caucasians of peri-Mediterranean origin are frequently more hairy than their more northern cousins. All this would indicate marked hereditary variability in either "end organ" sensitivity to androgens or an inborn predisposition for hair growth.

Genetic hirsutism most often appears in late childhood or at the time of pubescence after which it gradually increases until stabilizing in the third decade of life. A sudden onset and rapid progression of hair growth, particularly when associated with menstrual disturbances or evidence of virilism, is more suggestive of an underlying endocrine disturbance. Hypertrichosis is also seen in anorexia nervosa and other emotional stressful states, in juvenile myxedema, and as a rare atavistic manifestation (Fig. 6-2).

A simplified etiological classification of hirsutism might include the following:

1. Genetic — atavistic; racial, and individual predisposition
2. Adrenal origin
   Cushing's syndrome
   Virilizing adrenal tumors
   Congenital adrenal hyperplasia
   Adrenal dysfunction
3. Ovarian origin
   Stein-Leventhal syndrome
   Virilizing ovarian tumors
4. Abnormalities in sexual development
   Male pseudohermaphroditism

FIGURE 6-1. Appearance of Magdalena Ventura.

Gonadal dysgenesis with androgenic manifestations
Gonadal dysgenesis with contralateral testis
5. Miscellaneous
    Iatrogenic — hormonal
    Psychogenic (stress)
    Drugs
    Porphyria

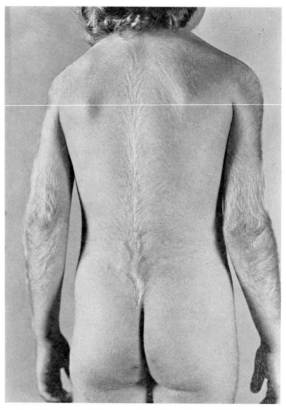

FIGURE 6-2. Hypertrichosis as atavistic manifestation in a child. (Reproduced from *The Hirsute Female*, Greenblatt, R. B. (Ed.), Springfield, Ill., Thomas 1963.)

ENDOCRINE ASPECTS OF HIRSUTISM

That sexual hair growth is initiated and maintained by androgens has been established by numerous observations of patients with either hypofunctional or hyperfunctional disorders of the adrenals or gonads. In men, the gonadal secretion of testosterone, the only true androgen, induces the usual secondary sexual characteristics, including the typical male sexual hair pattern. Although the ovaries normally secrete small amounts of androgens, the major stimulus of sexual hair growth in women comes from adrenal androgens. The latter are considerably less potent than testosterone and cause masculinization only when secreted in excessive amounts. An understandable consequence of all this has been an emphasis on the study of androgen secretion in hirsute women, in particular the study of the urinary metabolites of androgens, the 17-ketosteroids.

Urinary Steroid Excretion Studies in Hirsutism

It is well recognized that single estimations of routine 17-ketosteroids in hirsutism are of little diagnostic value except in cases of adrenal tumors or hyperplasia where markedly elevated values (above 30 mg/24 hrs) are found. There is a significant overlap between the values of routine 17-ketosteroids in normal women and those with simple hirsutism due to the relatively crude methods employed in routine determinations. In addition, increases in the secretion of testosterone may be of sufficient magnitude to cause hirsutism and yet contribute little or nothing to the total daily urinary 17-ketosteroid pool.

Androgen secretion can be more reliably evaluated by chromatographic separation and purification of the 17-ketosteroids followed by the estimation of individual steroids. However, even this procedure has its failings, since certain adrenal and ovarian androgens are identical and give rise to identical urinary metabolites. Nonetheless, the estimation of the various steroid fractions before and after adrenal suppression with dexamethasone may frequently offer a rough measure of ovarian and adrenal androgen secretion. Enough information is usually supplied by such a test; although more extensive studies would include ovarian suppression with stilbestrol and ovarian stimulation with FSH (Table 6-I). However, such testing requires prolonged hospitalization and expense. Such refined procedures are not generally available and remain impractical for routine clinical use.

THE STEIN-LEVENTHAL SYNDROME

A considerable number of women present with hirsutism accompanied by menstrual disturbances and infertility. In 1935, Stein and Leventhal[35] reported on such a group of women in whom bilaterally enlarged polycystic ovaries were demonstrable. Hirsutism was common but not an invariable finding. When diagnostic wedge resections of the ovaries were performed, many of these patients responded with regular menses and subsequent pregnancy. These observations established this combination of clinical features as a distinct syndrome. Since then a plethora of literature has accumulated on the subject, particularly that dealing with disturbed adrenal and ovarian steroidogenesis in this disorder. A result of this has been considerable confusion as to what exactly constitutes the Stein-Leven-

TABLE 6-I
URINARY STEROIDS AND CREATININE IN MG. PER 24 HRS. IN CONTROL PERIOD AND DURING ADRENAL AND OVARIAN SUPPRESSION AND STIMULATION TESTS

Treatment	Day of urinary determination	Total neutral 17-ketosteroids	Total 17-ketogenic steroids	Fractionation 11 oxy-17-ketosteroids	Fractionation 11-deoxy-17-ketosteroids	Tetrahydro-corticoids	Creatinine	Allen Test (Qual.)
Control	Day 1	21.3	4.9	1.4	10.5	2.8	1195	negative
Control	Day 2	13.2	5.5	1.2	8.9	1.9	759	—
ACTH, 25 U. I. V.	Day 3	30.1	18.7	1.6	11.2	9.7	1337	negative
ACTH, 25 U. I. V.	Day 4	26.8	39.7	3.7	14.5	16.5	1228	negative
Dexamethasone, 2 mg q 6 h from day 5 to 8	Day 7	10.3	3.4	0.3	3.8	undetectable	1337	—
	Day 8	7.5	3.1	0.25	2.9	undetectable	1119	—
Dexamethasone, 2 mg q 6 h plus stilbestrol 2.5 mg b-i-d from day 9 to 11	Day 10	5.6	3.9	—	—	—	1153	—
	Day 11	6.9	3.7	undetectable	0.5	undetectable	1356	—
Dexamethasone and stilbestrol in above dosage plus HP-FSH, 4 mg b-i-d from day 12 to 14	Day 13	6.5	1.6	undetectable	0.9	undetectable	1281	—
	Day 14	7.6	3.5	undetectable	2.1	undetectable	1179	—

thal syndrome, and what the pathogenesis of the disorder might be. Some observers deny the existence of such an entity.

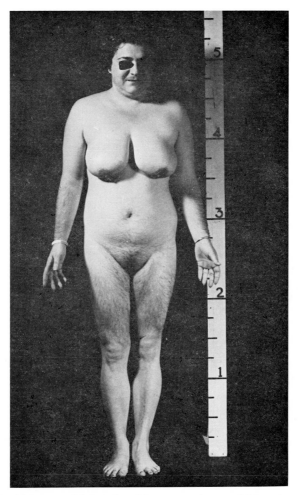

FIGURE 6-3. E. C. thirty-year-old female with amenorrhea and hirsutism and other signs of virilization (change of voice, clitoral enlargement) who responded remarkably to bilateral wedge resection of polycystic ovaries. (Reproduced from Greenblatt, *et al.:* Gynecologie Pratique, No 1, 1967.)

CLINICAL FEATURES

Clinically, the vast majority of patients classified as having Stein-Leventhal syndrome do not exhibit any masculinization other than hirsutism (Fig. 6-3 and 6-4). Clitoral enlargement, alopecia, and deepening of the voice are but rare accompaniments. These patients are basically feminine, with good breast development and normal female contours. Cytological study of their vaginal smears generally reveals fair to good estrogen effect, with atrophic smears only occasionally encountered. Endometrial biopsies often show a persistent proliferative effect but may vary from an atrophic endometrium to adenomatous hyperplasia. The latter is clinically expressed in bouts of profuse bleeding followed by prolonged periods of amenorrhea. Basal body temperatures are monophasic (anovulatory) in type. Ovulatory failure and infertility are the hallmarks of the syndrome, with hirsutism being more variable in frequency and degree or *completely absent*.

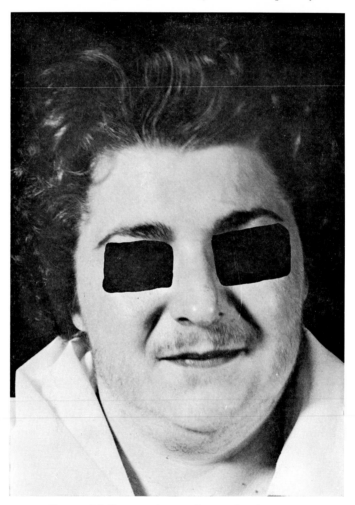

FIGURE 6-4. Same patient as the one in Figure 6-3.

HISTOPATHOLOGY

The ovarian morphology in this disorder, in its most classical form, consists of a myriad of microfollicular cysts with hyperplasia and luteinization

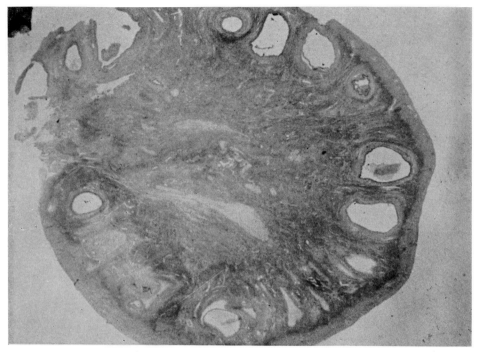

FIGURE 6-5. Photomicrograph of cross section of polycystic ovary. Note the thickened capsule and the numerous microcysts occupying the cortex. (Reproduced from *The Hirsute Female*.)

of the theca interna, fibrotic thickening of the ovarian cortex and tunica, and varying degrees of stromal luteinization (Fig. 6-5). The absence of corpora lutea and albicantia is striking and confirms the anovulation. Ovaries with these changes are enlarged, pale and glistening — and have been described as "oyster," "pearly," or "porcelain" in appearance (Fig. 6-6).

Stromal luteinization is occasionally quite prominent and may take the form of collections or nests of luteinized cells.[4,25] This latter finding is usually associated with increased clinical evidence of masculinization (clitoral enlargement, temporal hair recession, increased muscle mass). Moreover, hyperthecosis of the ovaries in virilized women has been considered as a distinct entity by some clinicians.[17,37] These luteinized stromal cells are thought to be a possible source of androgens.[32]

PATHOGENESIS OF THE SYNDROME

The Ovary as a Source of Androgens

Androgen secretion by both normal and polycystic ovaries has now been well established. In 1958, Zander[39] and in 1962, Mahesh and Greenblatt[20]

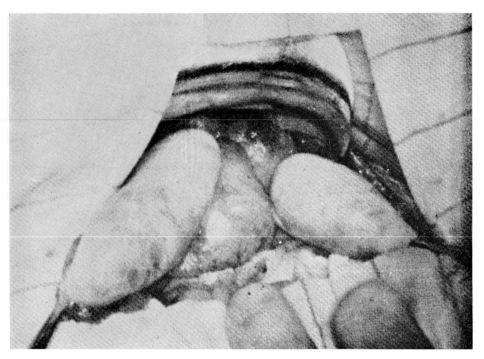

FIGURE 6-6: Typical appearance of polycystic ovaries at laparotomy. Note the enlargement and elongation with a smooth, pearly white glistening surface. (Reproduced from *The Hirsute Female*.)

isolated small quantities of $\triangle^4$-androstenedione from normal human ovaries. Furthermore, significantly increased amounts of $\triangle^4$-androstenedione and dehydroepiandrosterone have been isolated from wedges of polycytic ovaries. Testosterone has not been isolated from normal or Stein-Leventhal ovaries, but may be recovered after incubation of ovarian tissue slices with labelled acetate.[21] The peripheral conversion of $\triangle^4$-androstenedione and dehydro-epiandrosterone to testosterone is also well documented.[3,22] In any event, androgens appear as a necessary intermediate of estrogen synthesis in the ovary of normal females but in increased amounts in the Stein-Leventhal syndrome. These findings have culminated in the concept of an ovarian enzymatic disorder, characterized by a relative inadequacy of either the $\triangle^5$-3β-ol-dehydrogenase or the aromatizing systems.[23,33] The increased secretion of weak androgens by Stein-Leventhal ovaries and their subsequent conversion to testosterone would certainly explain the presence of hirsutism, as well as the increased plasma testosterone noted by Dorfman.[7] It must be stressed, however, that these ovaries also secrete estrogens, as is clinically apparent.

Some recent reports on ovarian steroidogenesis are of interest. Ryan and Petro[30] studied steroid biosynthesis after separating granulosa and thecal cells. Their results would indicate the conversion of pregnenolone to progesterone was considerably greater in the granulosa cells, while an alternate pathway via $\triangle^5$ compounds (17α-hydroxypregnenolone, dehydroepiandrosterone) was more apparent with thecal cells. Furthermore, Rice and Savard[27] report that their studies on the stromal compartment of the human ovary indicate that the stroma forms androgens (dehydroepiandrosterone, $\triangle^4$-androstenedione, and testosterone) *in vitro* as its principal steroidal products and noted a greatly augmented formation of androgens by the stroma of polycystic ovaries.

The Role of the Ovary

Another concept of pathogenesis is that of primary hyperovarianism caused perhaps by an inherent increased responsiveness of the ovaries to endogenous gonadotropins.[11] Such hypersensitivity to gonadotropins has been observed in Stein-Leventhal patients treated with exogenous human gonadotropins or with clomiphene, causing occasionally acute and massive ovarian enlargement that seems to be dose related. It might be conjectured that, in the Stein-Leventhal ovaries, too many follicles respond to endogenous FSH, rather than a few; eventually producing a myriad of follicular cysts and ovarian enlargement. The endogenous LH is insufficient to induce ovulation because of "dilution" by the increased ovarian mass and because of inadequate maturation of any one follicle. When exogenous FSH is given, some follicles are further matured so that when LH (HCG) is added, ovulation and corpus luteum formation occur. The finding of multiple corpora lutea and reported multiple pregnancies after gonadotropin therapy would substantiate this concept.[9,11] Similarly, both the reduction of ovarian mass by wedge resection, and the induction of increased endogenous gonadotropin release by clomiphene tend to increase the amount of gonadotropin per unit of ovarian mass, and so lead to ovulation. Again, whether the altered steroid biosynthesis in these ovaries results in, or is a result of, the altered pituitary-ovarian axis remains speculative.

The Role of Gonadotropins

The exact etiology of the above described changes remains controversial. Some evidence exists for a primary hypothalamic-pituitary disorder in the findings of a continuous secretion of LH, without the characteristic ovulatory peak.[15,36] The relationship of the thecal and stromal luteinization to excessive or more likely to continuous LH excretion is also suggestive. This is analogous to the secretion pattern of ICSH in the male. Thus some investigators propose "masculinization of the hypothalamus" as being a possible etiologic mechanism, resulting in failure of cyclic ovulatory LH release and disturbance in the hypothalamic-pituitary-ovarian feedback mechanism (Fig. 6-7). Barraclough's experimental work with the rat in this regard is provocative.[1,2] The success of induction of ovulation by human gonadotropins and by clomiphene tends to lend support to a concept of a disturbed hypothalamic-pituitary system. Whether this is a primary or a secondary factor in the Stein-Leventhal syndrome remains to be established. Suffice it to say that testosterone administered to five-day-old rats results in persistent estrus. It is doubtful if the persistent estrus seen in women with the Stein-Leventhal syndrome is analogous since an ovulatory response does not occur in rats following clomiphene.[29]

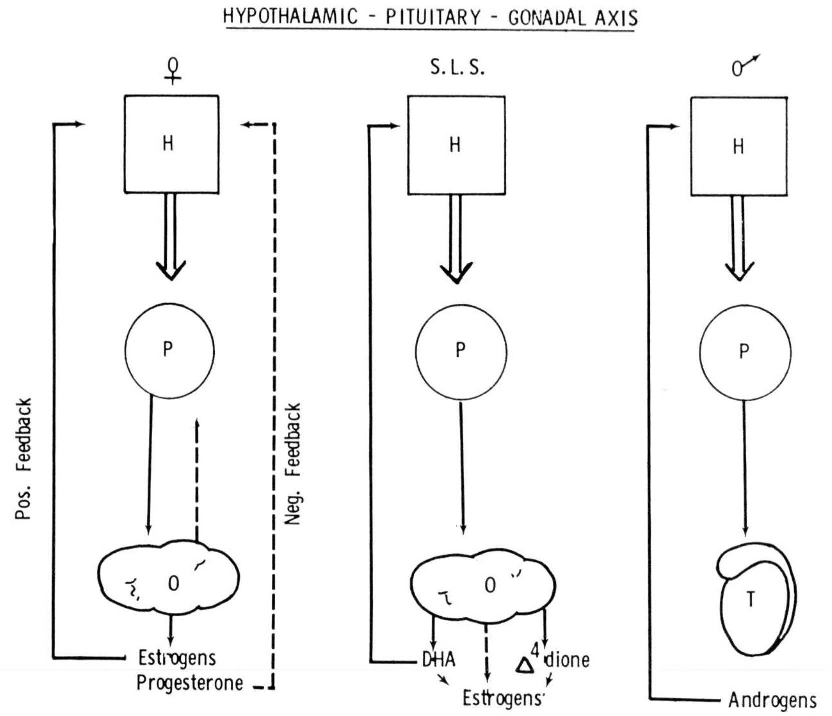

FIGURE 6-7. Rhythmic versus tonic secretion of gonadotropins. H-hypothalamus, P-pituitary, O-ovary, T-testis. (Reproduced from Greenblatt et al.: Gynecologie Pratique.)

The Role of the Adrenal

Finally, the role of the adrenals in the Stein-Leventhal syndrome must be considered. There undoubtedly is a group of women who clinically resemble the Stein-Leventhal syndrome, but in whom biochemical studies point to adrenal dysfunction rather than to primary ovarian dysfunction.

Mahesh, Greenblatt, *et al.*,[24] employing adrenal suppression with dexamethasone, ovarian suppression with stilbestrol, and ovarian stimulation with gonadotropins (FSH), were able in a large series so studied to delineate those cases where the adrenals seemed to be the primary contributor of excessive androgens. Similar work has been done by Netter *et al.*,[26] who coined the term "dynamic tests." Such tests are quite helpful in distinguishing adrenal from ovarian disorders, but are not available to the vast majority of physicians.

The finding of increased amounts of pregnanetriolone in the urine of patients with Stein-Leventhal syndrome by Shearman, Cox, and Gannon[17] in 1961 increased speculation as to the role of the adrenals in the disorder, since this compound usually is only identifiable in cases of congenital adrenal hyperplasia. The ovary does not have the 11-hydroxylase enzyme system necessary for the production of this compound (11-ketopregnanetriol). Leventhal[18] postulates that the abnormal urinary excretion of DHA, pregnanetriolone, and Δ^5-pregnenetriol in patients with Stein-Leventhal syndrome results from secondary adrenal involvement. This, he believed, leads to a modest build-up of androgens and other cortisol precursors like that seen in congenital adrenal hyperplasia, and might explain the occasional response of patients to corticosteroid therapy.

Thus, in summary, the clinical, histopathologic and biochemical evidence strongly implicates the ovary as the site of primary derangement in the Stein-Leventhal syndrome. The role of the adrenal would seem to be secondary; whereas the role of hypothalamic-pituitary dysfunction in the induction of the syndrome remains to be clarified. There seems to be little doubt that hirsutism, when present, reflects the increased secretion of physiologically active androgens by the ovaries and/or adrenals.

DIAGNOSIS

The diagnosis of the disorder is best accomplished by a combination of the clinical findings, urinary 17-ketosteroid assays before and after dexamethasone suppression, and gonadal visualization. The urinary 17-ketosteroids are determined on two control twenty-four-hour specimens following which dexamethasone, in a dosage of 2 mg every six hours, is given for the subsequent four days. Twenty-four hour urine collections are again obtained for 17-ketosteroid determinations on the last two days. In most instances of Stein-Leventhal syndrome, the 17-ketosteroids will assay in the normal to mildly elevated range (10-20 mg/24 hrs). With adrenal suppression, the values may fall to the 5-10 mg range, indicating relatively poor ovarian suppression and pointing to a gonadal origin of the androgens. When 17-ketosteroids are markedly suppressed by dexamethasone to levels of 2-3 mg per twenty-four hours then a primary adrenal disorder may be suspected. A more sophisticated assay method is the fractionation of the urinary 17-keto-steroids into 11-oxygenated and 11-deoxy-17-ketosteroids. The 11-oxygen-ated-17-ketosteroids are of adrenal origin. The 11-deoxy-17-ketosteroids are of both adrenal and ovarian origin. Failure to suppress 11-deoxy-17-keto-steroids suggests an ovarian origin (Table 6-II).

TABLE 6-II
STEIN-LEVENTHAL SYNDROME
E.C. 30, - AMEN., HIRSUTISM, INFERTILITY (8 YRS.)

	11 deoxy-17ks	*11 oxy-17ks*	*Tetra OHCS*
Controls	10.7 mg	2.7 mg	7.1 mg
ACTH	14.2 ”	5.1 ”	26.2 ”
Dexamethasone	5.2 ”	—	—
Dex. + FSH + HCG	7.9 ”	—	—

TABLE II. E. C. thirty years old. Note complete suppression of 11-oxy-17-ketosteroids and tetra OHCS by dexamethasone, while 11-deoxy-17-ketosteroids remain elevated. (Reproduced from Greenblatt et al.: Gynecologie Pratique.)

When bilateral ovarian enlargement cannot be readily determined by palpation, gonadal visualization may be employed. Gynecography, utilizing the pneumoperitoneum technique, has been used by many clinicians with success as an indirect method of visualizing the ovaries (Fig. 6-8). It gives a rough approximation of ovarian size and configuration. Culdoscopy or culdotomy provide direct methods of visualization, but are more compli-cated to perform. Their advantage lies not so much in discerning the size of the ovaries as in their appearance. All of these methods will, in addition, help to rule out the presence of ovarian neoplasms.

MANAGEMENT

The treatment of the Stein-Leventhal syndrome may be divided into those methods aimed at the control of hirsutism and those aimed at the correction of the ovulatory failure. In young, unmarried girls and women, with little or no hirsutism, clomiphene may be used to regulate menses.[13] In the progressively hirsute patient, it is our considered opinion that a healthy wedge resection should be undertaken as early as possible in the hope of modifying or arresting the further progress of the hypertrichosis.

Glucocorticoids have been employed with some success in inducing menses and ovulation in amenorrheic hirsute females suspected of having the Stein-Leventhal syndrome.[12,16] However, it is probably most effective in those patients with a suspected adrenal component as demonstrated by good 17-ketosteroid suppressability. The hazards of long-range therapy with glucocorticoids are numerous, and hirsutism is rarely modified. Indeed, in

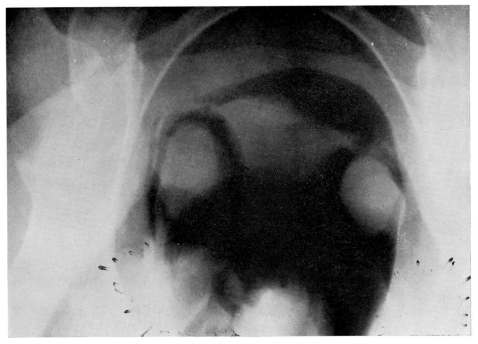

FIGURE 6-8. Gynecography. Note bilaterally enlarged and elongated ovaries, comparatively to normal-size uterus.

some instances it may aggravate the hairiness. Therefore, cortisone, prednisone, and related steroids would seem to be indicated primarily for short-term use in inducing ovulation. Occasionally, one sees a patient where a combination of wedge resection and corticoids (Fig. 6-9) is successful in the induction of ovulation, the use of either one alone having met with failure.

Gonadotropins have also been successfully used in the Stein-Leventhal syndrome to induce ovulation. Pregnant mares' serum (PMS) and/or HCG have not been generally successful. However, Crooke in England and Gemzell, *et al.* in Sweden, using purified human pituitary follicle stimulating hormone (HP-FSH) followed by HCG (LH-like), were able to report successful induction of ovulation and pregnancy.[6,10] More recently, human urinary menopausal gonadotropins (Pergonal) followed by HCG have been used with success in anovulatory states.[19,28] The Stein-Leventhal ovaries are extremely sensitive to these agents; acute cystic ovarian enlargement with ascites or rupture have been reported (Fig. 6-10), and some fatalities have occurred.[38] Multiple pregnancies and increased fetal loss are common.

Although the preceding measures hold promise in the medical management of the syndrome, at the present time bilateral wedge resection offers

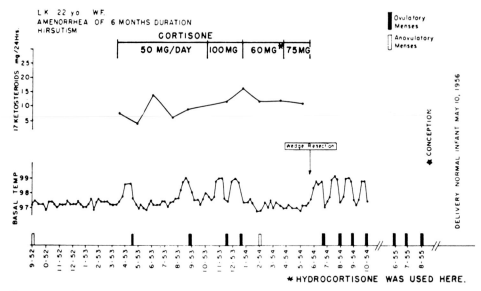

FIGURE 6-9. L. K. twenty-two years old. Note sporadic ovulations on cortisone and the establishment of regular, ovulatory menses following wedge resection. (Reproduced from *The Hirsute Female.*

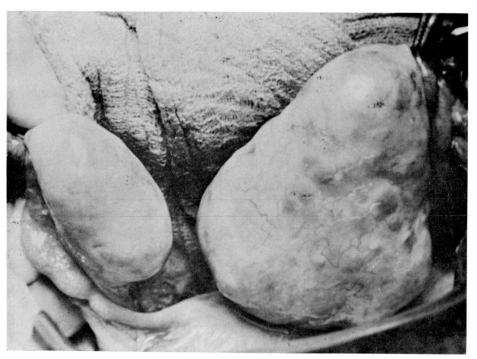

FIGURE 6-10. The polycystic ovary may respond to exogenous human FSH by a four to five fold increase in size. Note increased vascularity of the capsule.

the best chance of correcting the menstrual disturbance and infertility. The great majority (60 to 80 per cent) of operated patients will resume regular ovulatory menses, and most of these will conceive.[34] Since the highest incidence of conceptions occurs in the first several years following wedge resection, and since the syndrome can recur after surgery, wedging is probably best reserved until such time when the patient is desirous of pregnancy.[5] As mentioned previously, the larger ovaries show a much better response to surgery than do small polycystic ovaries. It must be emphasized that wedge resection results in considerable regression of hair growth in a few; in most, hair growth is simply held in abeyance, halting its further progression.

TABLE 6-III
EFFECT OF 17α-METHYL-B-NORTESTOSTERENE ON ACNE AND HIRSUTISM

No. of patients	Treated for	Dose	Duration	Results
12	Acne	50-400 mg	3-10 months	Improvement in 11
16	Hirsutism	50-400 mg	3-10 months	Improvement in 12

Mild hirsutism per se is probably best managed by purely cosmetic means (bleaches, dipilatories, electrolysis) and reassurance. Sequential estrogen-progestogen preparations employed in contraceptive regimens may be used to advantage in adolescent girls with mild hirsutism. The effect of cyclic estrogenic agents in adequate doses is the inhibition of gonadotropin and the resultant suppression of ovarian function, with a possible lessening of androgen production and hence modifying the hirsutism. We have also had some success in retarding hair growth by the administration of SKF 7690, 17α-methyl-B-nortestosterone, an experimental antiandrogen[14] (Table 6-III), which, it is believed, competes with endogenous androgens at the target organ level (pilosebaceous apparatus). This and future similar drugs offer new hope for the medical management of hirsutism.

SUMMARY

Hirsutism may be genetic, idiopathic, or endocrine in etiology. "Simple" hirsutism is most often nonendocrine in nature but may be the initial manifestation of a virilizing syndrome or other endocrine disorder. When additional clinical features of virilism are present, major adrenal and gonadal disorders must be suspected.

A large number of women are seen with hirsutism, menstrual disorders, and infertility. Many of these are found to have large microcystic ovaries and, when present, are categorized as Stein-Leventhal syndrome. The latter syndrome, however, is clinically quite variable and considerable confusion surrounds its pathogenesis. However, the fact that typical Stein-Leventhal ovaries secrete increased amounts of androgens seems to be established beyond reasonable doubt and would explain the hirsutism. A variant of the syndrome is believed to be caused by increased adrenal androgens and may explain failure of wedge resection in what appeared to be typical cases. Much remains to be explained about this interesting syndrome.

In conclusion, it is the consensus of the authors that the microcystic disease of enlarged ovaries represents a disturbance in ovarian steroidogenesis. The ovulatory disorder may be favorably modified by improving the ratio of gonadotropins available per unit of ovarian mass. This may be accomplished by ovarian wedge resection, clomiphene, or gonadotropin administration.

REFERENCES

1. BARRACLOUGH, C. A.: Production of anovulatory, sterile rats by single injections of testosterone propionate. *Endocrinology, 68:*62, 1961.

2. BARRACLOUGH, C. A., and GORSHI, R. A.: Evidence that the hypothalamus is responsible for androgen-induced sterility in the female rate. *Endocrinology, 68:*68, 1961.

3. BAULIEU, E., and ROBEL, P.: Androst-5-ene-3β-, 17β-diol- 17α-^{3}H to testosterone 17α-^{3}H and 5α and 5β-androstane-3α, 17β-diol-17α^3H *in vivo. Steroids, 2:*111, 1963.

4. BENEDICT, P. H., *et al.:* Ovarian and adrenal morphology in cases of hirsutism or virilism and Stein-Leventhal syndrome. *Fertil Steril, 13:*380, 1962.

5. BUXTON, C. L., and VANDE WIELE, R. L.: Wedge resection for polycystic ovaries: Critical analysis of forty operations. *New Eng J Med, 251:*293, 1954.

6. CROOKE, A. C., *et al.:* Effect of human pituitary follicle stimulating hormone and chorionic gonadotropin in Stein-Leventhal syndrome. *Brit Med J, 1:*1119, 1963.

7. DORFMAN, R. I.: Steroid hormones in gynecology. *Obstet Gynec Survey, 18:*65, 1963.

8. GEIST, S. H., and GAINES, T. A.: Diffuse luteinization of the ovaries and associated with the masculinization syndrome. *Amer J Obstet Gynec, 43:*975, 1942.

9. GEMZELL, C. A.: *Colloquia on Endocrinology, Ciba Fdt., XIII.* London, J&A Churchill, Ltd., 1960, p. 191.

10. GEMZELL, C. A.; DICZFALUSY, E., and TILLINGER, C.: Clinical effect of human pituitary follicle-stimulating hormone (FSH). *J Clin Endocr, 18:*1333, 1958.

11. GREENBLATT, R. B.: *The Hirsute Female,* Springfield, Ill., Thomas, 1963, pp. 149-176.

12. GREENBLATT, R. B.: Cortisone in treatment of hirsute woman. *Amer J Obstet Gynec, 66:*700, 1953.

13. (a) GREENBLATT, R. B., *et al.:* Induction of ovulation with MRL/41. *JAMA, 178:*101, 1961.

    (b) GREENBLATT, R. B.: Induction of ovulation with clomiphene. In Greenblatt, R. B. (Ed.): *Ovulation.* Philadelphia, Lippincott, 1966, pp. 134-149.

14. GREENBLATT, R. B.; ZARATE, A., and MAHESH, V. B.: The clinical use of 17α-methyl-B-nortestosterone as an antiandrogen. In *Proceedings of the Sixth Pan American Congress of Endocrinology. Excerpta Med Int Congr Ser, 99:*176, 1965.

15. INGERSOLL, F. M., and MCARTHUR, T. W.: Longitudinal studies of gonadotropin excretion in Stein-Leventhal syndrome. *Amer J Obstet Gynec, 77:*795, 1959.

16. JEFFERIES, W. McK.: Glucocorticoids and ovulation. In Greenblatt, R. B. (Ed.): *Ovulation*. Philadelphia, Lippincott, 1966, pp. 62-74.

17. Koss, L. G.; PIERCE, V., and BRUNSCHWIG, A.: Pseudothecomas of the ovaries. *Cancer, 17:*76, 1964.

18. LEVENTHAL, M. L., and SCOMMEGNA, A.: Multiglandular aspects of the Stein-Leventhal syndrome. *Amer J Obstet Gynec, 87:*445, 1963.

19. LUNENFELD, B.; MANZI, A., and VOLET, B.: *First International Congress Endocrinology (Copenhaven), Abstract #295,* 1960, p. 587.

20. MAHESH, V. B., and GREENBLATT, R. B.: Isolation of dehydroepiandrosterone and 17-hydroxy-$\triangle^5$-pregnenolone from the polycystic ovaries of the Stein-Leventhal syndrome. *J Clin Endocr, 22:*441, 1962.

21. MAHESH, V. B., and GREENBLATT, R. B.: Steroid secretions of normal and polycystic ovary. *Recent Prog Hormone Res, 20:*321, 1964.

22. MAHESH, V. B., and GREENBLATT, R. B.: The *in vivo* conversion of dehydroepiandrosterone and androstenedione to testosterone in the human. *Acta Endocr (Kobenhavn), 41:*400, 1962.

23. MAHESH, V. B., *et al.:* Secretion of androgens by the polycystic ovary and its significance. *Fertil Steril, 13:*513, 1962.

24. MAHESH, V. B., *et al.:* Urinary steroid excretion patterns in hirsutism. I. Use of adrenal and ovarian suppression tests in study of hirsutism. II. Effect of ovarian stimulation with human pituitary FSH on urinary 17-ketosteroids. *J Clin Endocr, 24:*1283, 1964.

25. MORRIS, J. M., and SCULLY, R. E.: *Endocrine Pathology of the Ovary*. St. Louis, Mosby, 1958, pp. 46-50.

26. NETTER, A., *et al.:* Les épreuves dynamiques dans le syndrome de Stein-Leventhal. *Ann Endocr (Paris), 21:*590, 1960.

27. RICE, B. F., and SAVARD, K.: Steroid hormone formation in the human ovary: IV. Ovarian stromal compartment; formation of radioactive steroids from acetate-1-14C and action of gonadotropins. *J Clin Endocr, 26:*593, 1966.

28. ROSEMBERG, E., and ARIAS, A.: *Forty-sixth Meeting of the Endocrine Society.* 1964, p. 138.

29. ROY, S.; GREENBLATT, R. B., and MAHESH, V. B.: Effects of clomiphene and intrasplenic ovarian autotransplantation on the anovulatory cystic ovaries of rats having androgen-induced persistent estrus. *Fertil Steril, 15:*310, 1964.

30. RYAN, K. J., and PETRO, Z.: Steroid biosynthesis by human ovarian granulosa and thecal cells. *J Clin Endocr, 26:*46, 1966.

31. SHEARMAN, R. P.; COX, R. I., and GANNON, A.: Urinary pregnanetriolone in the diagnosis of the Stein-Leventhal syndrome. *Lancet, 1:*260, 1961.

32. SHIPPEL, S.: The ovarian theca cell. Part IV. The hyperthecosis syndrome. *J Obstet Gynaec Brit Emp, 62:*321, 1955.

33. SHORT, R. V., and LONDON, D. R.: Defective biosynthesis of ovarian steroids in Stein-Leventhal syndrome. *Brit Med J, 1:*1724, 1961.

34. STEIN, I. F.: The management of bilateral polycystic ovaries. *Fertil Steril, 6:*189, 1955.

35. STEIN, I. F., and LEVENTHAL, M. L.: Amenorrhea associated with bilateral polycystic ovaries. *Amer J Obstet Gynec, 29:*181, 1935.

36. TAYMOR, M. L., and BARNARD, R.: LH excretion in polycystic ovary syndrome. *Fertil Steril, 13:*501, 1962.

The Ovary

37. Travis, R.; Aaron, T. B., and Stone, B.: Ovarian hyperthecosis and virilization: Report of a case. *Obstet Gynec, 25:*797, 1965.
38. Vande Wiele, R. L., and Turksoy, R. N.: Treatment of amenorrhea and of anovulation with human menopausal and chorionic gonadotropins. *J Clin Endocr, 25:* 370, 1965.
39. Zander, T.: Steroids in the human ovary. *J Biol Chem, 232:*117, 1958.

Chapter 7

OVARIAN PHYSIOCHEMISTRY

(Panel Discussion)

PROFESSOR INGIULLA, Moderator

Dr Ingiulla: Dr. Dorfman, do you think that some functional ovarian tumors lose some of the active enzymatic systems in normal steroid biosynthesis?

Dr. Dorfman: On the contrary, some tumors appear to possess more extensive properties, particularly 11 and 21 hydroxylases, which form compounds closer to the adrenocortical type.

Dr. Ingiulla: Dr. Sommerville, what do you consider to be the usefulness and the significance of the measurement of pregnanetriol?

Dr. Sommerville: Because of the variations which occur between urinary pregnanetriol-excretion levels in women with regular menstrual cycles and the fact that this steroid has adrenocortical as well as ovarian precursors, the study of resting levels is unlikely to yield useful information about ovarian function. On the other hand, it may be of interest to determine urinary pregnanetriol in stimulation-suppression test. Urinary pregn-5-enetriol determination is of value in the investigation of hirsutism and perhaps I should expand my previous comments upon Dr. Stern's work in our Unit. Urinary pregn-5-enetriol has been assayed in specimens from eighty-six women — twenty-four of whom had been designated as Stein-Leventhal on clinical grounds; sixty-two had some of the features of the syndrome but were not designated as such. In 67 per cent of the Stein-Leventhal group the excretion was then 0.2 mg per twenty-four hours; whereas in the other group the excretion was less than 0.1 mg per twenty-four hours in 77 per cent. We believe that this assay constitutes a useful additional criterion in the diagnosis of the syndrome.

Dr. Ingiulla: What method do you suggest for routine measurement of the urinary oestrogens from the practical point of view for application in the clinic?

Dr. Sommerville: As I have indicated, improvement of urinary methods is overdue, and in addition, the answer to this question depends to some extent upon the type of routine or research application. However, I should still recommend the modified method of Brown[1] or a short version if only one of the oestrogens is to be determined.

DR. INGIULLA: What is the importance of separate measurement of the three principal oestrogens and what is the significance, from a clinical standpoint, of a change in their relationship?

DR. SOMMERVILLE: This is a difficult question and it is probable that we must determine the oestrogens separately in long-term studies in order to obtain a clear answer. There is evidence that the three classical oestrogens are secreted per se, and I should have thought that it would be advisable to measure them separately at the present stage of knowledge. On the other hand, a case can be made for a total oestrogen determination, when by total we mean the whole spectrum of oestrogen products in human urine.

DR. INGIULLA: Which do you think more useful, the measurement of progesterone in the blood or of urinary pregnanediol?

DR. SOMMERVILLE: Despite the logical criticisms of urinary-pregnanediol assay as an index of endogenous progesterone secretion, serial analyses are of definite value for the study of ovarian stimulation or suppression. However, I have indicated that plasma progesterone determination — possibly supplemented by plasma pregnanediol — may be more informative, especially with regard to progesterone metabolism, for the study of acute changes (e.g., for detailed investigation at the time of ovulation) and essential for valid calculation of secretion rate.

DR. INGIULLA: Dr. Sommerville is reminded that many of the participants are hospital chiefs, who may wonder which endocrinological tests he believes to be indispensable for a hospital department. I think that my colleagues would appreciate his view.

DR. SOMMERVILLE: Urinary testosterone and epitestosterone or plasma testosterone as indices of androgen production; urinary neutral 17-ketosteroids and 17-hydroxycorticoids to assess adrenocortical function; urinary oestradiol-17β, oestrone, and oestriol for the limited application outlined in my chapter and especially as a control upon the degree of ovarian stimulation induced by various agents; and similar indications for the determination of urinary pregnanediol are indispensable.

DR. INGIULLA: The curve of plasma concentration of progesterone is maximal at the eighteenth to twentieth day; whereas that of urinary pregnanediol is at the twenty-second to twenty-third day. Do you think that this time interval may represent a test of the speed of peripheral metabolism of progesterone?

DR. SOMMERVILLE: This is an interesting suggestion and emphasizes the number of unknown factors. It would appear from the work of Zander and others that progesterone may pass into fat deposits and then undergo reabsorption and further metabolism. It is possible that progesterone is quantitatively reduced to pregnanediol and that the small proportion of the hormone excreted as this metabolite depends upon further metabolism of the pregnanediol and, in addition, upon the rate of formation of the water soluble sodium pregnanediol glucuronidate.

DR. INGIULLA: Dr. Siiteri, from the clinical point of view, can the test for secretion rate be used now or is it in the experimental phase?

DR. SIITERI: Very expensive equipment for measuring radioactivity, as well as other instruments are necessary to perform secretion-rate studies. Also, the extensive purification of tracers and urinary metabolites requires a minimum of five days time for even the simplest determination. Therefore, it would appear at this time that this approach is not practical as a clinical method. Such studies must be performed in a research laboratory or large medical center which has the necessary equipment and personnel.

DR. INGIULLA: In a series of *in vitro* incubation studies of Stein-Leventhal ovaries, we have constantly found a blockage of aromatizing enzymes with higher production of androstenedione, although in some of these cases urinary estrogens were at quite normal levels. Where do these estrogens come from? Dr. Siiteri, could you answer this question, through a "panoramic" view on "secretion rate" studies?

DR. SIITERI: *In vivo* secretion rate studies have thrown new light on many difficult problems. A few examples of the kind of information one can obtain with these techniques are in order. The first *in vivo* measurement of hormone secretion was performed by Dr. Pearlman, who measured the secretion rate of estrogen in pregnant women.[2] The procedure he and others have used is known as the urinary method and involves the intravenous injection of a tracer dose of isotopically labelled hormone, for example estradiol containing stable tritium in the molecule. Urine is then collected until all of the radioactivity which will ultimately be excreted in a specific metabolite is in fact excreted. This period varies from one to five days depending on the hormone under study. One or more radiometabolites are then isolated from the urine collection in pure form and their specific activity, i.e. the amount of radioactivity per unit weight, is determined. The essence of this method derives from the dilution principle which we have all utilized at one time or another when diluting acid or some other chemical solution. The simple dilution law gives rise to all of the formulae which are used; although they may look very much more complicated. From this type of experiment one obtains an estimate of the amount of endogenous hormone that is produced during a certain time period, usually expressed as milligrams or micrograms per day, from the following expression:

$$\text{secretion rate} = \frac{R}{\text{Specific activity metabolite } t}, \text{ where } R = \text{the amount of}$$

radioactivity injected and t = the time of urine collection. There are several conditions which must be met for this method to be valid, the most critical of which is that the urinary metabolite which is selected must be derived only from the hormone whose secretion is to be measured. In the case of estradiol secretion in the nonpregnant woman one can make this measurement from any of the three estrogens shown at the top of the first slide. However, as is now well known, there is a great deal more of estriol produced during pregnancy, since it can be formed by a second pathway as shown at the right of Figure 7-1. Since dilution of estriol occurs by the two pathways shown, it is no longer a unique metabolite of estradiol and cannot be used for measuring estradiol production during pregnancy. Similar problems of multiple precursors arise when attempting to measure the secretion rates of the androgens and of progesterone by this simple urinary method. Solutions to many of these problems have been provided by the many elegant experiments carried out in Dr. Seymour Lieberman's laboratory at Columbia University over the past ten years.

Another *in vivo* use of isotopes has been to study quantitatively the operation of a particular biosynthetic or metabolic pathway *in vivo*. By utilizing an experimental design which employs two radioactive tracers,

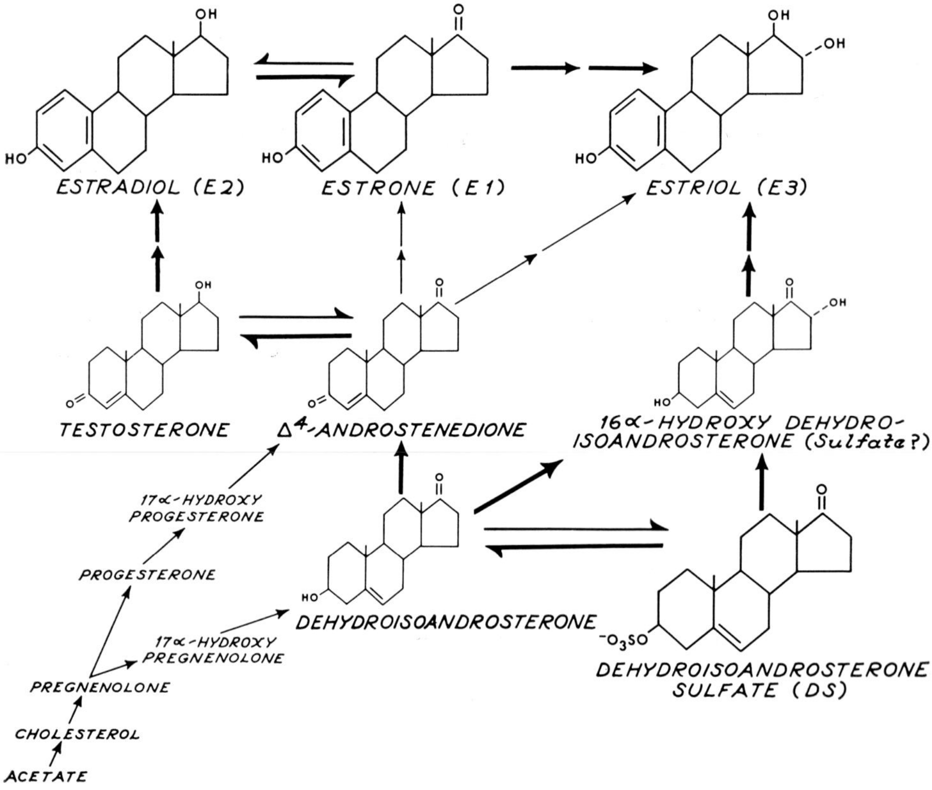

FIGURE 7-1.

Dr. Paul MacDonald and I have shown that dehydroisoandrosterone sulfate, derived from the adrenal gland, is an important precursor for placental estradiol production during pregnancy. That is, we have been able to demonstrate with this *in vivo* isotope method that the placenta does not produce estrogens by *de novo* pathways, but rather abstracts dehydroiso-androsterone sulfate from its blood supply and converts it to estradiol via the reactions shown in Figure 7-1. Thus we have been able to quantitate simultaneously (1) the extent of conversion of maternal dehydroisoandro-sterone sulfate to estradiol, (2) the total production rate into the maternal circulation of both hormones, and (3) the fraction of the total amount of the latter formed from the former. The results of these studies have recently been summarized.[3]

As mentioned earlier, measurement of the secretion rates of androgens, such as $\triangle^4$-androstenedione and testosterone, by the urinary method is subject to error due to lack of a unique urinary radiometabolite of the hormone. Another approach to this problem involves the measurement of the blood production rate as described by Tait[4] and others. The term "blood production rate" is defined as the total amount of hormone which enters the circulation regardless of whether it arises from glandular secretion or by peripheral conversion of some other precursor to the hormone. The method involves the measurement of the metabolic clearance rate (MCR) of the hormone by a constant infusion of the labelled hormone until equilibrium is attained; that is, until a constant blood level of radioactivity as the hormone is achieved. The metabolic clearance rate is then calculated by dividing the infusion rate by the blood concentration of radioactive hormone at equilibrium. If we make the assumption that a steady state exists during the experiment then the production rate of the hormone into blood must be equal to its removal rate (MCR). Therefore we can indirectly estimate the production rate by multiplying the metabolic clearance rate by the blood concentration of endogenous hormone. These then are the two basic types of methods for measuring *in vivo* hormone production: the urinary method and the blood production rate method.

Since we are speaking of hirsutism and the Stein-Leventhal syndrome, I should like to present an experimental design which utilizes all of the above methods and a few results that we have obtained which bear on the mechanism of formation of estrogens in these women. The experimental design is shown in Figure 7-2. Estrone bearing tritium (3×10^6 cpm) and $\triangle^4$-androstenedione containing carbon - 14 (30×10^6 cpm) are infused in a ratio of 1:10. Blood samples are collected at intervals near the end of the infusion when equilibrium has been reached. Urine is also collected following the infusion for three days. From urine collection we isolate estrone, estradiol, and estriol and determine both the tritium/carbon-14 ratios and the specific activities of each metabolite.

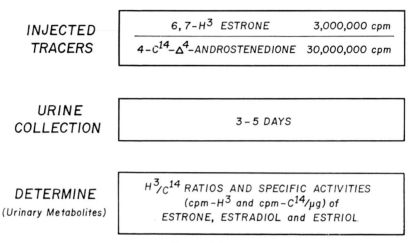

FIGURE 7-2.

Figure 7-3 illustrates how the extent of conversion of circulating $\triangle^4$-androstenedione to estrone is measured by examining the isotope ratios of the urinary metabolites. The example indicates a 1 per cent conversion of injected $\triangle^4$-androstenedione to estrone which would yield 3×10^5 cpm of carbon-14 labelled estrone. If this estrone is metabolized in an identical fashion to the injected tritium-labelled estrone then the isotope ratio of urinary metabolites of estrone will be $\dfrac{3 \times 10^6 \text{ cpm tritium}}{3 \times 10^5 \text{ cpm carbon-14}}$, or 10. It can be seen that if one divides the injected tritium to carbon-14 ratio by the urinary ratio, $\dfrac{0.1}{10} \times 100$, one obtains the conversion value which was 1 per cent. That is the first thing that we can measure with this design.

Figure 7-4 indicates how the blood production rate of $\triangle^4$-androstenedione is measured. First, the metabolic clearance rate is obtained from the infusion rate and the plasma concentration of radioactive $\triangle^4$-androstenedione at equilibrium. Secondly, the plasma concentration of endogenous $\triangle^4$-androstenedione is measured by chemical techniques. If then the metabolic clearance rate is multiplied by its plasma concentration, one obtains the production rate of $\triangle^4$-androstenedione into plasma expressed as mg per day.

Finally, Figure 7-5 indicates how estrogen production is analyzed. The amount of estrone which is derived from circulating $\triangle^4$-androstenedione

$(PR_{\triangle^4}^{EI})$ can be calculated very simply by multiplying the blood production rate of $\triangle^4$-androstenedione (Fig 7-4) by the fraction of carbon-14 $\triangle^4$-androstenedione which is converted to estrone (Fig. 7-3). It is important to remember that this production rate does not measure estrogen which was formed in the ovary. By using the urinary method the total production of estrone (PR^{EI}) is obtained by dividing the total amount of tritium infused as estrone radioactivity by the specific activity of urinary estrone with respect to tritium multiplied by the days of collection. The amount of estrone derived from circulating $\triangle^4$-androstenedione is expressed as a percentage of the total estrone production as is shown at the bottom of the figure.

CALCULATION OF THE EXTENT OF CONVERSION OF C^{14}-ANDROSTENEDIONE TO C^{14}-ESTRONE

CONVERSION TO ESTRONE

INJECTED TRACERS

H^3-ESTRONE $(3 \times 10^6$ cpm) —— 100% $\longrightarrow$ 3×10^6 cpm $E1$-H^3

C^{14}-ANDROSTENEDIONE $(30 \times 10^6$ cpm) —— 1% $\longrightarrow$ 3×10^5 cpm $E1$-C^{14}

H^3/C^{14} RATIO   0.1   10

FRACTION OF C^{14}-ANDROSTENEDIONE $\longrightarrow C^{14}$-ESTRONE $= \dfrac{H^3/C^{14} \text{ Ratio of Injected Tracers}}{H^3/C^{14} \text{ Ratio of Urinary Estrone}}$

$$= \frac{0.1}{10} = 0.01 = 1\%$$

FIGURE 7-3.

When we did this kind of experiment in normal women and in anovulatory hirsute women, we obtained the results shown in Figure 7-6. The plasma production rate of $\triangle^4$-androstenedione in two normal subjects was 3.0 and 3.8 mg per day. The conversion of $\triangle^4$-androstenedione to estrone was 0.8 per cent in each subject, that is, around 1 per cent of circulating $\triangle^4$-androstenedione was converted to estrone. This yielded in one subject $24\mu g$, and in the second subject $26\mu g$ of estrone per day. The total production of estrone by the first subject was seventy-two, while the total estrone production by the second subject, who was near ovulation, was $289\mu g$ per day. Expressed as percentages, the fraction of total estrone production derived from circulating $\triangle^4$-androstenedione in the two subjects was 33 per cent and nine per cent, respectively.

DETERMINATION OF BLOOD PRODUCTION RATE
OF ANDROSTENEDIONE

1. METABOLIC CLEARANCE RATE $(MCR_{\Delta^4\text{-}A}) = \dfrac{INFUSION\ RATE\ (cpm\ C^{14}/24\ hrs.)}{cpm\ C^{14}\text{-}ANDROSTENEDIONE/L\ plasma}$
[Liters of plasma/day]

2. PLASMA CONCENTRATION OF ANDROSTENEDIONE $(c\ \Delta^4\text{-}A)$
[μg/Liter plasma]

PRODUCTION RATE ANDROSTENEDIONE INTO PLASMA $= (MCR_{\Delta^4\text{-}A})(c\ \Delta^4\text{-}A)$
$(PR_b^{\Delta^4\text{-}A})$

FIGURE 7-4.

PRODUCTION OF ESTRONE FROM CIRCULATING
Δ^4-ANDROSTENEDIONE

$$PR_{\Delta^4\text{-}A}^{E1} = (PR_b^{\Delta^4\text{-}A})\,(fraction\ of\ C^{14}\text{-}\Delta^4\text{-}A \rightarrow C^{14}\text{-}E1)$$

TOTAL PRODUCTION OF ESTRONE

$$PRE1 = \frac{R^{E1^{H3}}}{sa\ E1^{H3} \cdot t}$$

$\dfrac{PR_{\Delta^4\text{-}A}^{E1}}{PRE1}$ X 100 = Percent of total Estrone derived
from circulating Δ^4-Androstenedione

FIGURE 7-5.

When we came to the study of three anovulatory subjects with Stein-Leventhal disease, we found that because the blood levels of Δ^4-androstenedione were very much higher, their production rates were correspondingly higher: 14.1 mg, 13.4 mg, 8.4 mg per day. In other words, the production rate of Δ^4-androstenedione in these subjects is about four to five times higher than normal. The conversion rate of circulating Δ^4-androstenedione to estrone was the same as in the normal subjects, or about 1 per cent.

However, the amount of estrone derived from $\triangle^4$-androstenedione, 113, 134, and 61μg per day was nearly the same as the total estrone production in each subject, 141, 181 and 95μg, respectively. Therefore, about 70 to 80 per cent of the total estrogen which these anovulatory, hirsute women were producing was derived from circulating $\triangle^4$-androstenedione. It would appear that this was not produced in the ovary, since we have made similar measurements in castrated women and the conversion rate of $\triangle^4$-androstenedione to estrone has been normal.

PRODUCTION OF ESTRONE FROM CIRCULATING $\triangle^4$-ANDROSTENEDIONE IN FEMALE SUBJECTS

Subject	Plasma Production $\triangle^4$-Androstenedione (mg/24 hrs.)	% Conversion $\triangle^4$-A-C^{14} $\longrightarrow$ El-C^{14}	Production Rate (μg/24 hrs.)		El$_T$ Derived from Circulating Androstenedione
			El$_{\triangle^4\text{-A}}$	El$_T$	
Normal-31-25	3.0	0.8	24	72	33%
Normal-37-12	3.8	0.8	26	289	9%
Anovulatory-21	14.1	0.8	113	141	80%
Anovulatory-25	13.4	1.0	134	181	74%
Anovulatory-19	8.4	0.7	61	95	64%
Arrhenoblastoma-17	12.0	0.8	96	120	80%

FIGURE 7-6.

As we have heard, Dr. Mahesh, Dr. Sommerville, Professor Forleo in Professor Ingiulla's laboratory, and others have found greatly elevated $\triangle^4$-androstenedione but little estrogen production by polycystic ovaries by *in vitro* techniques, by measuring glandular content, and by measuring ovarian vein levels. We have observed a similar picture by this *in vivo* method. Furthermore, these studies help to explain the findings of others who have previously shown — in fact, Dr. Mahesh earlier presented data which indicated this — that the *in vivo* secretion rate of estrogens in these women was in the normal range. The paradox presented by the contradictory *in vitro* and *in vivo* evidence for estrogen production by the polycystic ovary can be explained by the extraovarian formation of large amounts of estrone from circulating $\triangle^4$-androstenedione. Finally, with regard to the mechanism of anovulation in this condition which Dr. Greenblatt spoke of, while the origin of the problem may lie in the hypothalamus, a ready explanation is suggested by these results. If these women produce a *constant* high level of extraglandular estrogen, as seems likely, they in effect have a built-in contraceptive factory with could easily suppress ovulation.

DR. INGIULLA: Dr. Dorfman, what do you think of secretion rates, and how do you consider it from a metabolic point of view? What clarification can you offer?

DR. DORFMAN: The data presented clearly show that the peripheral source of estrogens is an important aspect in the Stein-Leventhal syndrome. A few years back, we showed that the plasma estrone and estradiol values of a limited number of Stein-Leventhal patients were about equal to that found in the plasma of normal individuals. This would fit rather well with the fact that the appearance of this type of patient is not one of hyperovarianism from the point of view of estrogenicity. The data of Dr. Mahesh and others do not completely agree with some studies published some years back showing that the estrone and estradiol content of ovarian tissue in this syndrome was indeed equal to, if not slightly greater. I agree however, that the studies were not quite as elegant as those of Dr. Siiteri, and it may be that on repetition these values may change.

However, I would like to add one point here. It is entirely possible — I should like to pass this question on to Dr. Greenblatt for his discussion — that there may well be individuals in whom there is a peculiarity in the amount of estrogens produced. We have studied only one such patient, who did not show hirsutism or virilism. As a matter of fact, this patient with polycystic ovaries had a menstrual disorder with a significant increase in the amount of estrone and estradiol but not of testosterone in her plasma. But in direct response, I should say that these studies take advantage of some of the most modern and elegant techniques, and advance our understanding of estrogen biosynthesis in the Stein-Leventhal syndrome.

DR. GREENBLATT: I think that Dr. Dorfman's case is a legitimate one. All of us who have seen many patients with the Stein-Leventhal syndrome are struck by the fact that the occasional patient has a marked adenomatous hyperplasia of the endometrium — so atypical and so hyperplastic that the endometrial histology in not infrequently mistaken for carcinoma *in situ,* or endometrial carcinoma. The few cases that I have seen with marked atypia, or severe adenomatous hyperplasia, may indeed reflect unusual amounts of estrogens produced by the particular patient. I think that there are all kinds of variants to the syndrome. It may well be that estrogens in increased amounts are produced in some of these patients; while in others, increased amounts of androstenedione or dehydroepiandrosterone are converted peripherally to estrogens.

DR. INGIULLA: The possibility of differentiating between hirsutism of adrenocortical or ovarian origin is of great concern. From the practical point of view it is important to attempt to distinguish between idiopathic hirsutism and hirsutism associated with excessive androgen production and then to attempt to define whether the latter is mainly associated with the adrenal cortex or the ovary. I should like to say a few words about our own experience in the determination of urinary testosterone and epitestosterone.

Whereas technical difficulties are still encountered in the determination of plasma testosterone in the peripheral venous blood of women, the determination of urinary testosterone and epitestosterone is readily performed by modern techniques involving thin-layer and gas-liquid chromatography. The importance and usefulness of this type of urinary steroid determination for diagnostic purposes is evident when one compares the excretion of urinary neutral 17-ketosteroids, testosterone, and epitestosterone in various clinical conditions (Table 7-I). It will be seen that urinary testosterone and epitestosterone constitute more significant indices than the excretion of urinary 17KS. Thus the difference in the ranges of excretion of testosterone and its epimer as between men and woman is much more evident, and significant changes in testosterone excretion in hirsute women may not be reflected in 17KS values.

TABLE 7-I
MEAN VALUES (AND LIMITS) FOR THE URINARY EXCRETION OF
TESTOSTERONE AND EPITESTOSTERONE (AFTER ENZYME
HYDROLYSIS) (185 DETERMINATIONS).

Subjects	No.	Testosterone μg/24 hrs		Epitestosterone μg/24 hrs		17-ketosteroids mg/24 hrs	
Normal women (20-40 yrs)	12	5.5	(<1-11,9)	6.9	(2-17,8)	7	(1,6-11,1)
Hirsute women	26	13.9	(2-30)	16.9	(1,3-81,5)	9.9	(2,8-17,3)
Postmenopausal women	6	3.7	(3,1-4,4)	1.4	(<1-2,2)	6	(3,7-8,9)
Ovariectomized women	6	3.5	(<1-7,4)	2.3	(<1-4,8)	5.1	(4,4-6,7)
Healthy men (20-30 yrs)	5	78	(44-140)	49	(9-118)	13.2	(12,3-14,2)

With regard to serial analyses in normal menstrual cycles, I do not believe that a systematic investigation has as yet been reported, and I should add that our investigations indicate that urinary epitestosterone excretion is significantly raised in the luteal phase of the normal menstrual cycle. The rise in epitestosterone appears to precede the main peak of pregnanediol excretion. This not only indicates a certain independence of the two hormones but emphasizes that we should not base our interpretation upon the determination of a few urinary steroids (Fig. 7-7).

A raised excretion of urinary testosterone is not a constant finding in hirsute women, and this may be a useful guide to aetiology which can be further investigated by such dynamic tests as suppression of the adrenal cortex by dexamethasone. By concurrent determination of testosterone, epitestosterone, and 17KS before and after dexamethasone suppression, we have found three combinations of results in hirsutism (see Table 7-II) :

1. The excretion of all three may be suppressed.
2. Low levels of excretion of testosterone and 17KS may be associated with a lack of suppression of epitestosterone.

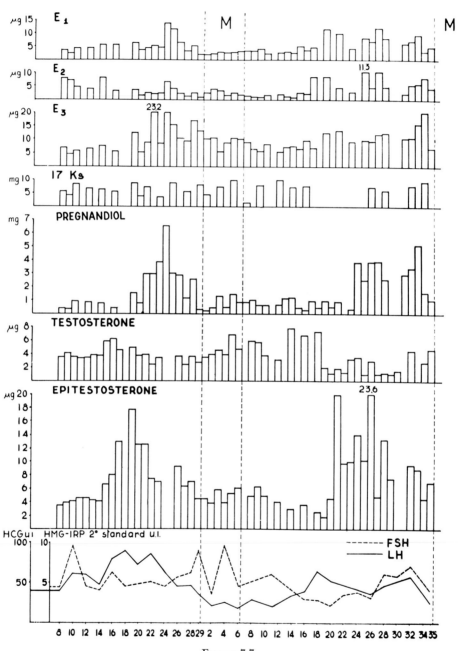

FIGURE 7-7.

3. The excretion of urinary 17KS may be suppressed without suppression of the excretion of testosterone or epitestosterone.

The fact that dexamethasone may not suppress testosterone excretion in certain patients with hirsutism may indicate an ovarian source of androgen. Furthermore, 17KS excretion is almost invariably increased following the administration of ACTH; whereas there may or may not be an effect upon testosterone excretion.

Testosterone assay has yielded some interesting results in the study of individual patients. Thus, in a patient with the Stein-Leventhal syndrome in whom there was an increase in the urinary excretion of 17KS and pregnanediol and a low excretion of oestrogens, there was a high excretion of testosterone and epitestosterone. When the ovarian function was stimulated with HMG during adrenocortical suppression with dexamethasone, there was a fall in urinary pregnanediol excretion (presumably of adrenal origin), an increase of oestrogen excretion, a decrease of 17KS, and no significant change in the urinary excretion of testosterone and epitestosterone (Fig. 7-8).

The lack of effect of dexamethasone upon testosterone excretion suggested that the androgen was predominantly of ovarian origin and this was confirmed by wedge resection which was followed by a marked fall in testosterone excretion; whereas 17KS values showed little change.

In another patient with Stein-Leventhal syndrome and marked hirsutism there was a low level of excretion of oestrogens, pregnanediol, 17KS, testosterone, and epitestosterone. Following the administration of 500 mg clomiphene there was an ovulation followed by a menstrual period. The urinary excretion of oestrogens and pregnanediol increased as in a normal cycle and, with the return of ovarian activity, there was an increase in testosterone and epitestosterone excretion which was not accompanied by any increase of 17KS excretion. These results suggest a latent deficiency in the biosynthesis of ovarian steroids which was revealed by clomiphene stimulation and the ovarian origin of the androgen was suggested by the lack of a simultaneous change in the urinary excretion of 17KS.

Further information was obtained by the study of a third patient with the Stein-Leventhal syndrome in whom dexamethasone suppression and ACTH stimulation affected 17KS excretion but had no effect upon the excretion of testosterone and epitestosterone. On the contrary, inhibition of ovarian function by the administration of an antiovulatory preparation, induced a fall in testosterone and epitestosterone excretion with no change in 17KS. This provides us with a counterproof of the ovarian origin of testosterone and of its epimer. Finally, this observation of the effect of such

TABLE 7-II
TEST OF ADRENOCORTICAL SUPPRESSION BY DEXAMETHASONE

			Testosterone µg/24 hrs		Epitestosterone µg/24 hrs		17-ketosteroids mg/24 hrs	
			before	after	before	after	before	after
Group a). Diminution of urinary excretion of testosterone, epitestosterone and neutral 17-Ks	P.P.	19 yrs	12.3	5.6	12.2	5.8	4.9	1.9
	C.N.	16 yrs	18.1	4	13.5	6.2	7.8	4.2
	P.M.	20 yrs	27.4	3.3	14.6	10.2	13	3.6
	R.A.	26 yrs	30	9.1	24	18.3	10.7	3.4
	T.M.	27 yrs	8.1	2.6	7.5	4.6	—	7.3
Group b). Diminution of urinary excretion of testosterone and 17-Ks, but not of epitestosterone	B.R.	18 yrs	24.4	9.8	6.8	15.8	13.2	3.7
	B.M.	31 yrs	6	2.4	4.6	16.2	5.6	3.1
	V.V.	22 yrs	11.3	5.3	5.1	10.5	8.9	1.4
	E.M.	25 yrs	10.2	5.3	11.5	47.5	9.8	4.8
Group c). Diminution of urinary excretion of 17-Ks, but no effect upon testosterone and epitestosterone	G.F.	19 yrs	16.5	21	16.2	19.5	17.3	2.7
	S.A.	30 yrs	13	11.1	29.5	28.9	13.5	4.7
	V.M.	39 yrs	12.8	18.9	21	32	8.6	4.5

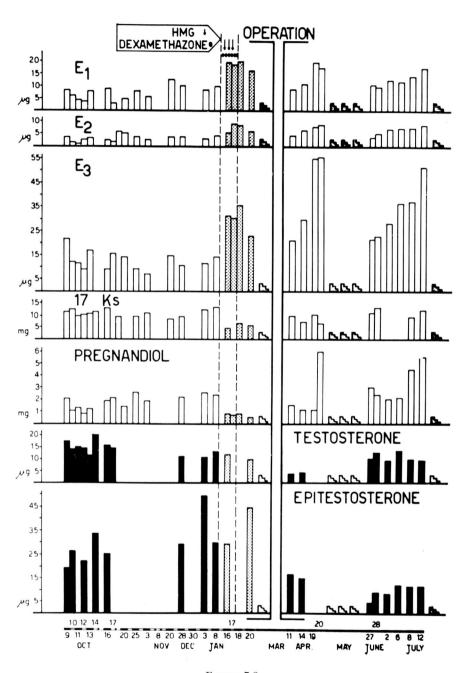

FIGURE 7-8.

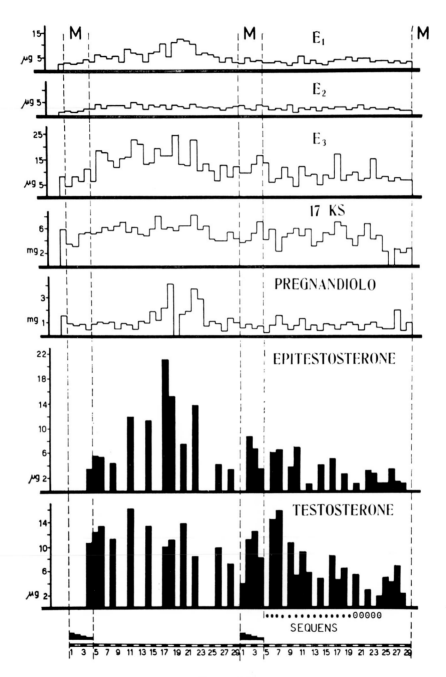

FIGURE 7-9.

a change on urinary steroid excretion is in accord with the efficacy of oestrogen-progesterone therapy in hirsutism of ovarian origin — a form of treatment which is ineffective when the etiology is associated with adreno-cortical dysfunction (Fig. 7-9). For the latter type of hirsutism, suppression with corticoids is the therapy of choice.

Perhaps Dr. Dorfman will give us his opinion upon the practical value of the determination of urinary testosterone and epitestosterone and may provide us with an explanation for the disassociated behaviour of testosterone and its 17-epimer and the concomitant rise which we have observed in the urinary excretion of epitestosterone and pregnanediol during the luteal phase of normal menstrual cycles.

DR. DORFMAN: Professor Ingiulla, you have presented me with a rather heavy dose of data. I am interested in cyclic variation of the epitestosterone during the menstrual cycle, which you have shown to be related to changes in pregnanediol. Unfortunately, I cannot give you any explanation.

DR. INGIULLA: Thank you, Dr. Dorfman. I should like to come back to the possibilities of distinguishing ovarian origin from adrenal origin of hirsutism. In answering this question will Dr. Greenblatt consider not only the diagnostic aspect, but also the clinical-therapeutic point of view, the practical level?

DR. GREENBLATT: We believe that we have a technique whereby frequently we can distinguish hirsutism of adrenal from that of ovarian origin. If on the dexamethasone the 11-oxygenated 17-ketosteroids are completely suppressed, and the 11-deoxy 17-ketosteroids are poorly suppressed, we believe the hirsutism to be of ovarian origin. If both are adequately suppressed, then we feel that the hirsutism is of adrenal origin. Treatment can be undertaken according to these findings. The administration of the sequential contraceptive pill containing 100 μg of ethinyl estradiol or its equivalent has been found useful in the management of hirsutism in the adolescent girl. If the androgens are of adrenal origin, we administer small amounts of dexamethasone (0.75 mg) or prednisone (5 mg) for considerable periods of time. Occasionally glucocorticoids may worsen the tendency to hypertrichosis. Where we feel that we cannot distinguish between hirsutism of ovarian or adrenal orgin, combined suppression of adrenal and ovary is undertaken. Electrolysis should be encouraged since regrowth of hair is minimal if an active regimen of hormonal therapy is undertaken. Hirsutism is most difficult to treat, and we have little to offer other than the program outlined. It is hoped that antiandrogens will sooner or later become available. We have had some promising results in several of our hirsute patients employing 17α-methyl-B nortestoterone. The following case study is revealing.

A markedly hirsute female of twenty-one years of age complained of primary amenorrhea and mild voice changes. Her breasts were poorly developed; the clitoris was slightly enlarged; facial hair was such that she was required to shave daily. Palpable enlarged ovaries were found on pelvic examination and wedge resection was performed of typically enlarged polycystic ovaries. Neither improvement in the hypertrichosis nor onset of menses occurred. The antiandrogen was then administered orally in doses of 300-400 mg per day for a period of about one year. Daily facial hair shavings (dry electric razor) were collected throughout the experiment. Not only was there marked reduction in hair growth as evidenced by the reduction in weight of hair shavings (Fig. 7-10), but sebum production was also greatly lessened. A satisfactory antiandrogen may prove the ideal way of treating the hirsute female.

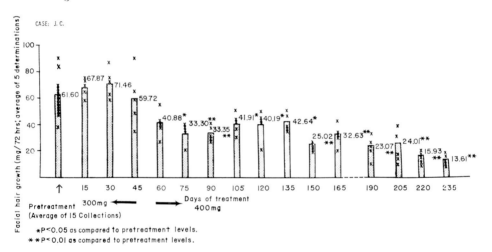

FIGURE 7-10. Facial hair weight in mg/24 hrs. in hirsute patient before and after administration of 17 α methyl-B nortestosterone. Pretreatment levels are an average of fifteen collections, while other values are grouped in units of five collections (five 72-hr. periods).

DR. INGIULLA: Dr. Dorfman, can I have your opinion?

DR. DORFMAN: I should like to make a short comment on the question of differential diagnosis, of trying to place the blame either on the adrenal or the ovary. Although I realize that Drs. Mahesh and Greenblatt and others have attained some useful and important information using a dexamethasone suppression test, I worry about this on a fundamental basis. Dr. Siiteri has mentioned, and we have demonstrated some time ago, and Dr. Mahesh has published the fact that there is the ability of one gland like the ovary to take out of the circulation a substance and refashion it to a more active androgen. In other words, dehydroepiandrosterone sulphate can be removed by the ovary through the action of a sulphatase, converted to the free compound and then oxidized and reduced properly to $\triangle^4$-androstenedione and testosterone in turn. So I think that when you suppress the adrenal you run the risk of decreasing this source of weak androgen which can be fabricated into strong androgens. I am wondering whether Dr. Greenblatt might consider, in his stimulation tests, a more direct and rather more rapid approach; that is, subjecting his patient to a stimulation with something like a luteinizing hormone preparation, maybe intravenous HCG (human chorionic gonadotropin), and a few hours later measure plasma testosterone to see if it is elevated. Such techniques have been used by Lippset and others and seem to be a dynamic way of expressing the functional capacity, and is analogous in many ways to the very successful adrenal reserve test, using ACTH and the change in cortisol concentrations in the plasma.

DR. GREENBLATT: We are quite aware that some of the French investigators have been employing human chorionic gonadotropin in a dynamic test of ovarian function, to see if urinary 17-ketosteroids are increased. We have not been able to reproduce their results. It may well be that Dr. Dorfman's suggestion of administering intravenous HCG and then measuring plasma testosterone will offer a great deal more. Thus far we have confined our studies to measuring urinary 17-ketosteroid fractions, estrogens, and tetrahydrocorticoids following dexamethasone suppression and stimulation with human pituitary gonadotropins.

DR. INGIULLA: We are evaluating urinary testosterone levels following dexamethasone suppression and HMG stimulation as a test in the study of the hirsute female. I have two questions for Dr. Mahesh: (1) In the case in which the polycystic ovary was not able to produce estrogens after stimulation with gonadotropins, what type of gonadotropins was used, FSH or HCG? and (2) Do you think that the dose was adequate?

DR. MAHESH: In answer to this question, first of all the studies that we showed here only pertained to the ovarian vein blood. Since the ovarian vein blood was taken after stimulation with human pituitary FSH (this is the gonadotropin that we have used), we do not know what the level was before giving human FSH. The second thing I should like to mention is that we have carried out a number of studies with human pituitary FSH after adrenal suppression. We find that in most of the cases the estrogenic response was poor. I should like to say one or two words about this. First of all, our initial experience was with human pituitary FSH which was comparatively pure — which had less than 10 per cent contaminant of LH. With this preparation we did not get an overwhelming estrogen response. On the other hand, in later experience with FSH from postmenopausal urine (Pergonal) containing a much higher ratio of LH — we did get a fairly good response in estrogen fractions. The quality of gonadotropin used and the ratio of FSH and LH seem to be important in the type of response. As to dosage, we used an equivalent of about 4 mg per day of the NIH FSH standard in terms of FSH activity. This dose seems to be adequate as far as ovulation is concerned. In view of the fact that excessive ovarian response may be obtained with an overdose of human FSH, care should be taken as to the size of the dose employed.

DR. INGIULLA: A last question from Professor Shockaert directed to Dr. Greenblatt: In a case of an early diagnosis of Stein-Leventhal in a young unmarried woman is it advisable to go ahead with the operation or wait for marriage or the period just preceding it? That is, can you choose the date for operation?

DR. GREENBLATT: The consenus currently in vogue in the USA is that the wedge resection should not be undertaken until the girl is married or ready for marriage. Ovarian suppression may be undertaken until the patient is ready for marriage. Many gynecologists feel that wedge resection should not be performed until after marriage since the results may prove to be only temporary. It is my considered opinion, however, that wedge resection should be undertaken in young unmarried women if the hirsutism is marked and progressive.

REFERENCES

1. BROWN, J. B., *et al.*: *J Endocrinol, 16*:49, 1957.
2. PEARLMAN, W. H.; PEARLMAN, M. R. J., and RAKOFF, A. E.; *J Biol Chem, 209*:803, 1954.
3. SIITERI, P. K., and MacDONALD, P. C.: *J Clin Endocr, 26*:751, 1966.
4. TAIT, J. F.: *J Clin Endocr, 23*:1285, 1963.

Chapter 8

THE "CLASSIC" PILL

G. I. M. SWYER

I T IS NOW SOME ELEVEN years since Dr. Gregory Pincus and his colleagues[37] introduced the combined estrogen-progestogen oral contraceptive, and so it may perhaps justifiably now be called the "classic" pill, since it does ante-date by quite some time the more recent developments which will be dis-cussed later.

It is accepted beyond dispute that oral contraceptives of the combined type are superior to all other methods of birth control for the prevention of pregnancy. They have an efficiency, when used according to the proper instructions, of virtually 100 per cent, and their use is becoming increas-ingly widespread. For example, the Food and Drug Administration of the United States has estimated that the number of users in that country has gone up from 400,000 in 1961 to 5,000,000 in 1965. In other countries it is estimated that some 2,000,000 women were taking these compounds in late 1965.[55] However, acting systemically instead of, as in the case of other contraceptive methods, locally, this widespread use has raised questions of harmlessness in the minds of clinicians and public alike. These ques-tions apply not merely to short-term use but also to the long-term, since continuous use for periods of many years could well become commonplace.

Compounds of this type have, of course, already been in therapeutic use for a considerable time. Thus, synthetic oestrogens have been so used since 1938, and the first orally active progestogen since 1940, although the 19-norsteroids and other, newer progestogens have been used clinically only since 1955. The employment of these compounds in gynecology has been extensive, but it could be argued that their continuous, even though cyclic use, over long periods of time, was uncommon before the advent of oral contraception. Nevertheless, studies on small numbers of women who have been so treated, in some cases for fifteen years and more, do not appear to have revealed harmful effects.

Concern about the possible harmfulness of oral contraceptives arises, for the most part, either from theoretical considerations of the effects of altering the hormonal balance (e.g. Dodds[10]) or from the reporting of the occurrence of diseases of various kinds in oral contraceptive users. There is, of course, a temptation, when disease becomes manifest in any person using drugs such as oral contraceptives, to invoke a cause-and-effect relationship. But such a relationship could only be accepted when it is shown that the incidence of the disease among users of these drugs is significantly greater than among nonusers, or when a biological mechanism has been demonstrated by experimental results. In the case of oral contraceptives, no such conditions have yet been completely fulfilled. Since throughout the world the number of women using oral contraceptives is now large, it is to be expected that most diseases, rare as well as common, will be encountered among these women.

The long-term administration of exogenous steroids, of the types used in oral contraceptives, can lead to a wide variety of effects on the body and its functions; it is proposed to review some of these, particularly from the point of view of possible adverse reactions.

Taking first the effects on the endocrine system and dealing with the pituitary and hypothalamus, it can be said in summary that experimental studies in humans have shown that oral contraceptives have little, if any, effect on the so-called "total gonadotrophin" output, but appear to suppress the release of luteinizing hormone which, in the untreated woman, triggers ovulation.[6,7,27,45] There is no evidence that the output of other trophic hormones by the pituitary is affected, or that permanent structural changes in the pituitary or hypothalamus are induced by long-term use. The rapid return to normal ovarian function, even after prolonged cyclic use of oral contraceptives, indicates the equally prompt return of normal pituitary gonadotrophin release.[26,42,43]

With regard to thyroid function, oral contraceptives increase the protein-bound iodine in the blood,[54] an effect attributable to the accompanying increase in thyroxin-binding globulin (TBG).[13] An increase in TBG is also seen in pregnancy[35] and during oestrogen administration.[11] It is not progressive and returns to premedication values soon after stopping treatment.[13] There is no evidence that oral contraceptives cause either clinical hyperthyroidism or hypothyroidism, but little is known of their use in women with thyroid dysfunction.

Coming to the adrenal cortex, the estrogen component of oral contraceptives raises the level in the plasma of cortisol-binding globulin or transcortin, and this in turn leads to increased plasma levels of bound cortisol.[22,31] As a consequence, the release of ACTH is stimulated to maintain normal levels of diffusible cortisol. The cortisol clearance rate is at the same time reduced and so is the excretion of corticosteroids in the urine.[36] All these changes are of a minor order, the adrenal responsiveness to ACTH is apparently unimpaired, and no evidence for the development of adrenal deficiency has been encountered among women using oral contraceptives.

Concerning the pancreas and carbohydrate function, although unexpectedly high frequencies of abnormal glucose tolerance have not been encountered by most observers of women using oral contraceptives, Gershberg and his colleagues[15] have reported differently. These workers found that, of sixty women taking norethynodrel with mestranol for from five months to three years, 10 per cent had elevated fasting-blood-sugar levels, while after a glucose load 20 per cent had elevated one-hour levels, and 46 per cent elevated two-hour levels. It could be argued, however, that these figures were compared with those of a so-called normal control group and not with those of the patients themselves before they went on oral contraceptives. In the case of women who had family histories of diabetes, the incidence of abnormal glucose tolerance appeared to be greater than for those without such histories, and one of the patients, evidently a pre-diabetic, developed permanent diabetes under treatment. Wynn and Doar[58] found 18 per cent of oral and 15 per cent of intravenous glucose-tolerance tests were abnormal in a group of 105 women taking oral contraceptives. Though the mean fasting-plasma-glucose was unchanged the levels of fasting-plasma-nonesterified fatty acids were elevated and the fall after glucose administration was delayed. The most striking change observed was an increased fasting-blood-pyruvate level and/or increased maximum pyruvate increment following glucose, occurring in some 20 per cent of the oral contraceptive users. The abnormalities enumerated resemble those of steroid diabetes. Nevertheless, the use of oral contraceptives by women with established diabetes does not in the majority of cases appear to affect the severity of the diabetes, as judged by insulin requirements, and the risk that they might in prediabetic women hasten the onset of frank diabetes is probably less than such an effect from pregnancy.

After only one cycle of treatment with oral contraceptives the appearance of the ovary on direct examination is altered: its size is decreased, it looks inactive, and superficially it resembles a postmenopausal ovary;[29] however, it apparently reverts very promptly to normal, even after six or seven years of treatment.[14] The urinary excretion of ovarian estrogen metabolites is reduced and assumes a pattern consistent with suppression of ovulation, at a level characteristic of the postmenopausal state, but the return to normal levels consistent with ovulation on cessation of treatment is prompt.[26,42,43] Corpora lutea are characteristically absent from the ovaries of treated women but reappear on cessation of treatment. The rate of follicle atresia does not seem to be affected, and deleterious effects on primordial follicles have not been observed. But, of course, data on these points are necessarily limited.[29,36] No pathological changes in ovaries have been reported.

The possibility of genetic damage to the oocytes certainly deserves further investigation, but these possibilities are probably slight.

Coming now to some of the systemic effects of oral contraceptive use, I will deal first with effects on the liver. It may be said that Bromsulphalein® (BSP®) storage in the liver may be increased and its transfer maximum decreased during the last trimester of normal pregnancy, following the administration of estrogen, certain C-17 alkylated steroids, and oral contraceptives, in which the estrogen component is probably responsible for the observed effects. These findings are also seen in certain hereditary disorders of hepatic function such as the Dubin-Johnson and Rotor syndromes. Except in the hereditary disorders, the alteration in BSP metabolism is reversible, transient and disappears even with continued medication, as the liver becomes adjusted to the altered hormonal milieu (see Mears[29] for references). Abnormalities in conventional liver function tests are not encountered with increased frequencies in long-term oral contraceptive users.[25,39,48,50,52] Although abnormal values during the first cycle of treatment of postmenopausal women in Finland have been reported, and this is possibly true in women from other Scandinavian countries too, [2,12,34,44] such an effect has not been seen in a larger series of women reported on from the United States.[4] Possibly the livers of older Scandinavian women are not as well adapted to estrogen inactivation as those of women elsewhere during the reproductive years. At all events, oral contraceptives have not been specifically associated with the production of jaundice, hepatic necrosis, or progressive liver disease in normal women, but their effects in women with acquired liver disease, particularly hepatitis and cirrhosis, have not been investigated systematically. I have myself seen a woman using oral contraceptives (and I have heard of others) who developed infective hepatitis but did not stop using the medication. The jaundice ran its normal course and after it had subsided, liver function tests were normal. The balance of opinion is that, though hepatic excretory function may be affected, this is of little or no significance at clinically used dosage, except in patients with hereditary or acquired defects. Such defects are considered to be a contraindication to oral contraceptive use.[55]

Oral contraceptives cause changes in the blood clotting mechanism, but there are very considerable differences in the reports of different observers,[49] and whether any of these changes have any significance for an increased risk of thrombophlebitis is open to considerable doubt. Although states of hypocoagulability can be defined in terms of deficiences of clotting factors, states of hypercoagulability cannot be defined in terms of excesses of these factors. Alterations in blood circulation, in the state of the vessel wall, and in platelet stickiness and numbers[56] are probably of a more fundamental importance in intravascular thrombosis. As might have been expected, thromboembolic disease has been encountered among women using oral contraceptives, just as it is in nonusers. Though it has often been supposed that this disease has an increased incidence during pregnancy, and a relationship to the augmented sex hormone levels has been assumed, such is not the case. It is only during the puerperium that the incidence is increased by some four to six times,[57] and at this time, of course, the hormone levels are low. There can be no doubt that the high incidence of puerperal thrombosis, like postoperative thrombosis, is primarily due to trauma and to local alterations in blood circulation. The incidence of thrombophlebitis in nonpregnant women between the ages of fifteen and forty-five is not known with certainty but the best estimates place it between one and three per thousand; an investigation carried out by the College of Practitioners in Britain elicited a figure of 2.2 per thousand per annum.[9] The incidence in women using oral contraceptives is also uncertain because of incompleteness of reporting and bias in the selection of patients, but in no reported series has it exceeded the above figure. It was not possible to establish a statistical relationship between thromboembolic death and the use of oral contraceptives in the United States,[57] and the same is true for deaths from thromboembolic disease in the United Kingdom as judged by a report from the Committee of Safety on Drugs.[8] In the "twenty-five month club" study in the United States covering 11,700-odd women who have used norethynodrel-mestranol for twenty-five months or more, the crude thrombophlebitis rate, reported as two per thousand per annum, does not differ from the expected rate. In the United States, although vital statistics show an increase in the age—specific death rates attributed to thromboembolic diseases for the period from 1950 to 1964 inclusive, the rise has been similar for males and females. Moreover the trend for females shows no inflection during the 1960's when oral contraceptives came increasingly into use. In the United Kingdom there has been no change in the age—specific death rates for this condition for persons of either sex under the age of forty-five during the past ten years.[55] Recent reports[16,32,38,41] on the occurrence of arterial thrombosis, mainly cerebral and coronary, among oral contraceptive users have suggested that this may represent a different and more serious hazard than venous thrombosis. Once again the authors of these reports have, in general, ignored the expected frequency of comparable events among nonusers of similar ages, for in fact the death rates show no significant difference.[8] It has been estimated that in the United States during 1964 one tenth of the 40,000,000 women of child-bearing age were using oral contraceptives and yet the death rate from cerebrovascular accidents for women of this group has shown no significant change during the period from 1950 to 1964 inclusive.[55] In fact, cerebrovascular lesions are a common cause of death in women of child-bearing age in the United States as is shown by the vital statistical data for 1960, a year well before the use of oral contraception became widespread. They rank as fourth to sixth, by half decades of life, among white females aged twenty-five to thirty-nine and as first and second causes for nonwhite females of the same age group.

Up to May, 1967, though it could not be said that thromboembolic disease was definitely excluded as a consequential risk of oral contraceptive use, neither did there appear to be any evidence that such use increased the risk. Then a subcommittee of the Medical Research Council, under the chairmanship of Lord Platt, reported the results of three investigations, all retrospective, into a possible relationship.[30] In one study, organized by the College of General Practitioners, the results indicated that the risk of venous thrombosis or pulmonary embolism was approximately six times greater during pregnancy or the puerperium (no distinction appears to have been made between these two states) than in nonpregnant controls, and approximately three times greater for women using oral contraceptives. The second study was based on women who had been admitted to hospital with venous thrombosis or pulmonary embolism without evident medical cause and indicated that a higher proportion of these had been using oral contraceptives (fourteen out of twenty-nine) than of controls (three out of thirty-six). The third study, carried out by the Committee on Safety of Drugs (the Dunlop Committee), concerned the use of oral contraceptives by women who died in 1966 of pulmonary embolism or infarction, coronary thrombosis, or cerebral thrombosis, the results being compared with those of control women selected from the same doctors' practices. There was no evidence of association of death from coronary thrombosis with the use of oral contraceptives, but there appeared to be a relationship with death from pulmonary embolism or infarction in the absence of predisposing medical conditions and possibly also with cerebral thrombosis. The mortality from these conditions attributable to the use of oral contraceptives by married women aged fifteen to forty-four years was estimated to be about three per 100,000/year. Even though the statistical methods used in arriving at these results were of a high degree of sophistication, the fact that relatively small samples were involved leaves open to some doubt the validity of the conclusions reached in each of the separate studies. However, the fact that these conclusions were substantially confirmatory in all three compels respect.

With regard to weight change, both gains and losses in weight occur in oral contraceptive users; although the proportion experiencing weight gain is probably greater. The proportion of women gaining three pounds or more in weight varies from 4 to 50 per cent with different preparations and with different observers.[36] It is higher with higher dosage and with those progestogens which have a greater nitrogen anabolic activity. It is maximal between six and twelve months and declines thereafter.[28] The cause of weight change is undoubtedly complex and is related to psychological factors affecting appetite as well as to possible anabolic and other metabolic effects of the administered steroids. In some patients minor degrees of edema may contribute to weight gain.

Few studies have yet been made on the effects of oral contraceptives on lipid metabolism, but the possibility of effects of importance is raised by recent observations. For example Aurell *et al.*[3] have reported a significant rise in serum lipids, especially in the low-density lipoproteins, in women after a year's use of ethinyl oestradiol and norethindrone acetate. The level of low-density lipoprotein reached was said to be typical of that found in postmenopausal women, the effect, it was suggested, implying either an androgenic action of the progestogen or an antiestrogenic action of the combination. Whether other estrogen-progestogen combinations used in oral contraceptives have similar action is not known. Wynn *et al.*[59] found elevated serum-triglyceride, cholesterol, and low-density and very-low-density lipoprotein levels among oral contraceptive users, 31 per cent of whom had fasting-serum-triglyceride levels above the highest values observed in a control group of seventy-five women. These changes in serum lipids and lipoproteins produced a pattern said to resemble that seen in males and were thought possibly to predispose to the development of atherosclerosis.

Characteristic effects on the endometrium are produced by the combined estrogen-progestogen oral contraceptives, and have been described by numerous observers.[29,36] They differ in only minor degree with different formulations, especially after several cycles of treatment. After several cycles of treatment, the endometrium becomes thin and hypoplastic, though on discontinuation there is prompt return within one to three months to the normal appearance. The incidence of endometrial dysplasia among users of combined oral contraceptives is greatly reduced.[36]

Increase in the size of preexisting fibroids has been reported in some oral contraceptive users, but the significance of this is uncertain, especially since the natural history of fibroids involves continued growth until the menopause. An increased incidence of cervical erosion is fairly well established, but I doubt whether this is of importance because erosion per se is not a pathological condition.

The effects on the menstrual cycle are now so well known that it will suffice to state that, in general, women using oral contraceptives have very

regular cycles once they have become established on the regimen.[36] Therefore, the occurrence of irregular uterine bleeding in a woman who has
been using oral contraceptives with regular menstrual cycles for a long
time is unlikely to be an effect of the treatment and requires the same gyne-
cological investigation as it would in a nonuser. A number of observers
have administered oral contraceptives to lactating women,[29] but the effects
of these agents on lactation have not yet been adequately studied. Though
some suppression of lactation probably results when higher dosage is used,
with lower dosage there is little, if any, effect. For example, in one study
reported by Pincus[36] with norethynodrel-mestranol, at 20 mg per day 77
per cent of the women alleged diminished lactation, and 5 per cent an
increase; whereas at the 2.5 mg dosage the corresponding figures were 15
per cent and 50 per cent respectively. Little is known about the possibility
of the excretion of the hormones present in oral contraceptives or their
metabolites into maternal milk and the consequent effect on the baby, but
the likelihood of harmful consequences does not seem very probable.[29]

Perhaps more anxiety over the long-term use of oral contraceptives has
been expressed in relation to the possibility of inducing cancer in the genital
tract than any other consequence. The twelve or more years' experience
with these compounds is sufficient to cover most long-term consequences
but, it can be argued, not enough in respect to carcinogenesis, where long
latent intervals between stimulation and its effects may apply. The theoretical background, however, offers no convincing evidence for the probability of a carcinogenic risk. Progestogens appear to have an antitumor action
on the endometrium and possibly also the cervix and breasts.[36] The estrogens, though undeniably carcinogenic when administered continuously in
supraphysiological dosage to experimental animals, have never by exogenous administration been convincingly shown to have such an action in the
human.[5] Cancer of the cervix does not appear to have any definite hormonal background but coordinates most closely with low socioeconomic
status and early age of first coitus, implying, in effect, low standards of
hygiene. Though rather less common in nulliparous women, it is no more
common in grande multiparae than in women who have had only one or
two pregnancies, and so is clearly not influenced by the hormonal plethora
of pregnancy. There is thus no fundamental reason why combined oral
contraceptives should increase the risk of cancer of the cervix, and as yet
there is no evidence that they do. In fact a decrease in the incidence of
cytological smears suspicious for carcinoma has been found in a part of the
world where cancer of the cervix has a high endemic rate.[29,36,40] Cancer of
the endometrium, on the other hand, is thought by many to be related,
among other things, to high and persisting levels of endogenous estrogens.

It appears to be likely to occur in women with cystic and adenomatous glandular hyperplasia and with granulosa-cell tumors of the ovary. Since the characteristic endometrial pattern in women using combined oral contraceptives is one of endometrial hypoplasia with glandular inactivity, a pattern exactly opposite to that which is considered by some to be a precancerous state, it may be concluded that, instead of being likely to cause cancer of the endometrium, oral contraceptives of the combined type are more likely to prevent it. This view is further supported by the accumulating evidence from a number of observers that progestogens may have value in the treatment of existing endometrial carcinoma.[17-21,24,46,47,53] In so far as endometrial cancer, previously a relatively uncommon malignancy, is becoming decidedly more common, the possibility of a prophylactic effect from oral contraceptives is potentially of considerable importance.

The endocrine background to mammary cancer is complex and not entirely understood. Its incidence is higher in nulliparae than in parous women,[23] so that, as in cervical cancer, the hormonal plethora of pregnancy is in no way causative. On the other hand, since delay of the menopause until after fifty is found in 55 per cent of women with breast cancer as compared with only 28 per cent of unaffected women,[33] persistent estrogenic stimulation, especially unopposed by progesterone, may have some etiological significance. There is no doubt about the estrogen-dependence of some breast cancers in premenopausal women as well as the antitumor action of estrogens in some postmenopausal women with breast cancer. No increase in the incidence of cancer of the breast has been encountered in oral contraceptive users, in spite of evidence in the United Kingdom of an increasing incidence in women in general.[1] On balance there seems to be no probability that oral contraceptives would increase the risk of breast cancer, although the possibility remains that once it has occurred, their use might adversely affect its growth. On the other hand, Stoll[47] has demonstrated the beneficial effects of oral contraceptives in some menopausal women with breast cancer.

It has been suggested that because oral contraceptives inhibit ovulation they would delay the age of the menopause and so leave women potentially fertile, on stopping treatment, at ages well beyond those at which fertility normally ceases. There is no basis at all for this view which overlooks the fact that the principal cause of follicle loss from the ovaries, which eventually leads to the menopause, is atresia, not ovulation. Atresia continues, evidently at much the same rate, whether the ovary is at rest or is regularly undergoing the changes involved in ovulation. The most obvious illustration of this is that women who have had large numbers of pregnancies and in whom ovulation has therefore been inhibited for a total of many years, do not have correspondingly delayed menopauses. There is equally no reason to suppose that the onset of the menopause, with its associated permanent sterility, would be hastened by oral contraceptive use. The possibility that in postmenopausal women oral contraceptives might be hepatotoxic requires further investigation.

Finally, I would like to say a few words on contraindications. We know little with certainty about these, mainly because, in general, oral contraceptives have been prescribed for women believed to be in good health, and few studies have been made on their possible effect in women suffering from various diseases. There are very few conditions which are known to be aggravated by oral contraceptives. They are the acquired or hereditary defects of hepatic excretory function to which I already referred. In addition, jaundice has redeveloped when oral contraceptives have been given to women who have had idiopathic recurrent jaundice of pregnancy. Another group of conditions, in which adverse reactions to oral contraceptive use have not actually been encountered, but which on *a priori* grounds give rise to some uncertainty and hence the need for caution, includes the history or suspicion of cancer of the genital tract and breasts and past or present liver disease without evidence of impaired excretory function. Because of the possible adverse consequences of sodium and fluid retention in cardiovascular diseases, the use of oral contraceptives in these conditions may also require some caution. In yet a further group of conditions the suggestion has been made from time to time that they are contraindications to oral contraception, though without convincing evidence of cause-and-effect relationships and without *a priori* reasons, from considerations of pathology, for assuming such relationships. This is the largest group and includes thromboembolic disease; varicose veins; cerebrovascular accidents; various ophthalmological manifestations such as papilledema, retinal artery thrombosis, retrobulbar neuritis, diminished visual acuity, and restriction of peripheral vision; and psychic depressive states. The possibility of rare individual idiosyncrasy as a cause cannot be overlooked, but apart from this, there seems at present to be no justification for regarding any of these conditions as contraindications.

In conclusion, it may be said that the vast amount of clinical information and laboratory data that have accumulated since the introduction of steroidal oral contraceptives some eleven or more years ago, together with what is known from the clinical use in gynecology of compounds of this type extending back to more than twenty-five years, leaves no doubt that the safety of this class of compound compares favorably with that of most drugs in widespread use. Although the laboratory studies have shown that oral contraceptives produce changes in many body systems, it is doubtful if any of these have any pathological significance. Serious adverse reactions, such as thromboembolic disease, have been reported in women using oral contraceptives, but the available statistical evidence does not firmly establish a cause-and-effect relationship and neither as yet does the experimental evidence. In the United States alone, where the extent of oral contraceptive use has been greatest, there can be little doubt that the risk of death in childbirth following the unsuccessful use of other methods of birth control is greater than that from the use of oral contraceptives.

REFERENCES

1. ADAMS, M. J. T., and SPICER, C. C.: Recent mortality from breast cancer. *Lancet, 2:* 732, 1965.
2. ADLERKREUTZ, H., and IKONEN, E.: Oral contraceptives and liver damage. *Brit Med J, 2:*1133, 1964.
3. AURELL, M.; CRAMER, K., and RYBO, G.: Serum lipids and lipoproteins during long-term administration of an oral contraceptive. *Lancet, 1:*291, 1966.
4. BAKKE, J. L.: Hepatic impairment during intake of contraceptive pills: Observations in post-menopausal women. *Brit Med J, 1:*631, 1965.
5. BISHOP, P. M. F.: Hormones and cancer. *Clin Obstet Gynec, 3:*1109, 1960.
6. BROWN, J. B.; FOTHERBY, K., and LORAINE, J. A.: The effect of norethisterone and its acetate on ovarian and pituitary function during the menstrual cycle. *J Endocr, 25:*331, 1962.
7. BUCHHOLZ, R.; NORKE, L., and NORKE, W.: The influence of gestagens on the urinary excretion of pituitary gonadotropins, estrogens and pregnanediol in women in the post-menopause and during the menstrual cycle. *Int J Fertil, 9:* 231, 1964.
8. CAHAL, D. A.: Safety of oral contraceptives. *Brit Med J, 2:*1180, 1965.
9. College of General Practitioners and General Register Office Survey (Morbidity Statistics from General Practice, 1958-62). London, H. M. Stationary Office.
10. DODDS, S. C.: Rhime and reason in endocrinology. *J Endocr, 23:*1, 1961.
11. DOWLING, J. T.; FREINKEL, N., and INGBAR, S. H.: Effect of diethylstilbestrol on the binding of thyroxine in serum. *J Clin Endocr, 16:*1491, 1956.
12. EISALO, A.; JÄRVINEN, P. A., and LUUKKAINEN, T.: Hepatic impairment during the intake of contraceptive pills. Clinical trial with post-menopausal women. *Brit Med J, 2:*426, 1964.
13. FLORSHEIM, W. H., and FAIRCLOTH, M. A.: Effects of oral ovulation inhibitors on serum protein-bound iodine and thyroxine binding proteins. *Proc Soc Exp Biol Med, 117:*56, 1964.
14. GARCIA, C.-R.: In *Seminar on Human Fertility and Population Problems.* Boston, American Academy Arts Sciences, 1963, p. 43.
15. GERSHBERG, J.; JAVIER, Z., and HULSE, M.: Glucose tolerance in women receiving an ovulatory suppressant. *Diabetes, 13:*387, 1964.
16. HARTVEIT, F.: Complications of oral contraception. *Brit Med J, 1:*60, 1965.
17. KELLEY, R. M., and BAKER, W. H.: Progestational agents in the treatment of carcinoma of the endometrium. *New Eng J Med, 264:*216, 1961.
18. KENNEDY, B. J.: A progestogen for treatment of advanced endometrial cancer. *JAMA 184:*758, 1963.

19. KISTNER, R. W.: Histological effects of progestins on hyperplasia and carcinoma *in situ* of the endometrium. *Cancer, 12:*1106, 1959.

20. KISTNER, R. W.: The prevention of endometrial cancer. *Obstet Gynec Observer, 3:* 2, 1964.

21. KISTNER, R. W., and BAGINSKY, S.: Observations on the use of 17-alpha-hydroxy-progestrone caproate on primary and metastic endometrial carcinoma. *Surg Forum, 12:*424, 1961.

22. LAIDLAW, J. C.; RUCE, J. L., and GORNALL, A. G.: The influence of estrogen and progesterone on aldosterone excretion. *J Clin Endocr, 22:*161, 1962.

23. LANE-CLAYPON, J. E.: A further report on cancer of the breast. *Report on Public Health and Medical Subjects No. 32.* London, H. M. Stationary Office, 1926.

24. LIGGINS, G. C.: Progestogens as clinical anti-oestrogens. *New Zeal Med J, 63:*383, 1964.

25. LINTHORST, G.: Liver function after long-term progestational treatment with and without oestrogen. *Brit Med J, 2:*920, 1964.

26. LORAINE, J. A., *et al.:* Oral progestational agents: effects of long-term administration on hormone excretion in normally menstruating women. *Lancet, 2:*902, 1963.

27. MATSUMOTO, S.; ITO, T., and INOUE, S.: Studies on ovulatory inhibiting effects of 19-norsteroids in laparotomized patients. *Geburtsh Frauenheilk, 20:*250, 1960.

28. MEARS, E.: In Austin, C. R., and Perry, J. S. (Ed.): *Agents Affecting Fertility,* London, J. & A. Churchill, 1965, p. 211.

29. MEARS, E.: *Handbook on Oral Contraception.* London, J. & A. Churchill, 1965.

30. Medical Research Council: Risk of Thrombo-embolic disease in women taking oral contraceptives: A preliminary communication to the Medical Research Council by a Sub-committee. *Brit Med J, 2:*355, 1967.

31. METCALF, M. G., and BEAVEN, D. W.: Plasma-corticosteroid levels in women receiving oral contraceptive tablets. *Lancet, 2:*1095, 1963.

32. NEVIN, N. C.; ELMES, P. C., and WEAVER, J. A.: Three cases of intravascular thrombosis occurring in patients receiving oral contraceptives. *Brit Med J, 1:*1586, 1965.

33. OLCH, I. Y.: The menopausal age in women with cancer of the breast. *Amer J Cancer, 30:*563, 1937.

34. PALVA, I. P., and MUSTALA, O. O.: Oral contraceptives and liver damage. *Brit Med J, 2:*688, 1964.

35. PETERS, J. P.; MAN, E. B., and HEINEMANN, M.: In *The Normal and Pathological Physiology of Pregnancy.* Baltimore, Williams Wilkins, 1948.

36. PINCUS, G.: *The Control of Fertility.* New York and London, Academic, 1965.

37. PINCUS, G., *et al.:* Fertility control with oral medication. *Amer J Obstet Gynec, 75:* 1333, 1958.

38. READ, D. L., and COON, W. W.: Thromboembolism in patients receiving progestational drugs. *New Eng J Med, 269:*622, 1963.

39. RICE-WRAY, E.: Oral contraceptives and liver damage. *Brit Med J, 2:*1011, 1964.

40. SATTERTHWAITE, A. P., and GAMBLE, C. J.: Conception control with norethynodrel: Progress report of a four-year field study at Humacao, Puerto Rico. *J Amer Med Wom Ass, 17:*797, 1962.

41. SCHATZ, I. J., *et al.:* Thromboembolic disease associated with norethynodrel. *JAMA, 188:* 493, 1964.

42. SHEARMAN, R. P.: Excretion of ovarian steroids in patients treated with an "ovulation inhibitor." *Lancet, 1:*197, 1963.

43. SHEARMAN, R. P.: Diagnostic ovarian stimulation with heterologous gonadotrophin. *Lancet, 2:*557, 1964.

44. SOTANIEMI, E.; KREUS, K. E., and SCHEININ, T. M.: Oral contraception and liver damage. *Brit Med J, 2:*1264, 1964.

45. STEVENS, V. C., and VORYS, N.: Gonadotropin secretion in the normal cycle. In Greenblatt, R. B. (Ed.) : *Ovulation.* Philadelphia and Toronto, Lippincott, 1966.

46. STOLL, B. A.: A new progestational steroid in the therapy of endometrial carcinoma — a preliminary report. *Cancer Chemother Rep, 14:*83, 1961.

47. STOLL, B. A.: Effect of Lyndiol, an oral contraceptive, on breast cancer. *Brit Med J, 1:*150, 1967.

48. SWAAB, L. I.: Oral contraceptives and liver damage. *Brit Med J, 2:*755, 1964.

49. SWYER, G. I. M.: The safety of oestrogen/progestogen oral contraceptives. *Excerpta Med Int Congr, Series No. 132* p. 111. *Proceedings of the Second International Congress on Hormonal Steroids.* Milan, May 1966.

50. SWYER, G. I. M., and LITTLE, V.: Absence of hepatic impairment in long-term oral contraceptive users. *Brit Med J, 1:*1412, 1965.

51. TAYMOR, M. L.: Effect of synthetic progestins on pituitary gonadotropin excretion. *J Clin Endocr, 24:*803, 1964.

52. TYLER, E. T.: Eight years' experience with oral contraception and an analysis of use of low-dosage norethisterone. *Brit Med J, 2:*843, 1964.

53. WENTZ, W. B.: Effect of a progestational agent on endometrial hyperplasia and endometrial cancer. *Obstet Gynec, 24:*370, 1964.

54. WHEELER, H. O.; MELTZER, J. I., and BRADLEY, S. E.: Biliary transport and hepatic storage of sulfobromophthalein sodium in the unanaesthetized dog, in normal man and in patients with hepatic disease. *J Clin Invest, 39:*1131, 1960.

55. World Health Organization: Clinical aspects of oral gestogens: Report of a WHO scientific group. *WHO Techn Rep Ser, 326,* 1966.

56. WRIGHT, H. P.: In Ruck, T. C., and Fulton, J. P. (Eds.) : *Medical Physiology and Biophysis.* Philadelphia, Saunders, 1960.

57. WRIGHT, I. S.: *Final Report on Enovid by the Ad-Hoc Committee for the Evaluation of a Possible Etiologic Relation with Thromboembolic Conditions.* Food and Drug Administration, Department of Health, Education and Welfare, U.S.A., 1963.

58. WYNN, V., and DOAR, J. W. H.: Some effects of oral contraceptives on carbohydrate metabolism. *Lancet, 2:*715, 1966.

59. WYNN, V.; DOAR, J. W. H., and MILLS, G. L.: Some effects of oral contraceptives on serum-lipid and lipoprotein levels. *Lancet, 2:*720, 1966.

Chapter 9

THE SEQUENTIAL PILL

ROBERT H. H. RICHTER

EDITOR'S NOTE: The experimental data presented in this paper are part of a collaborative study performed by M. Arnold, Marianne Mall-Haefeli, F. Roth, H. Stamm, H. Wyss, Stella Cloeren, E. Morf, P. Weis, and the author. [2,24,25]

MAN'S DESIRE to control his fertility is worldwide and undoubtedly as old as life history. Limitation of population even by primitive peoples is an established fact and reaches far back into the dim past. We have to assume that even Adam and Eve practiced some kind of birth control, since for many years they had only two sons, Cain and Abel. And Eve brought forth her third son, Seth, only after Cain had murdered his brother.

Today the challenging stimuli for family planning and birth control are two fold: one is the unique biological phenomenon of population explosion; the other, the personal right of every woman or every couple to decide when to have children and how many to have. On the other side, we have the impression that today more provoked abortions are performed than ever, legally or illegally, all over the world. What can be done to meet the demands and challenge of our time?

Of course, education in sexology, ethics, and human relations; social welfare, and improvement of economic situation are of great help. *The Time Has Come,* a book by the famous American Catholic gynecologist John Rock, tells us with doubtless clarity that everybody concerned with these problems has to work hard and seriously so that we may come to a full understanding of the processes of human reproduction and more acceptable methods of contraception. Of course, these methods have to be adapted, selected, and modified for every population according to religious, moral, cultural, and social conditions.

In this connection, for instance, we may discuss, What is a natural and what is an unnatural method of contraception? What method is and what method is not? Some may even ask, "Is not contraception per se an unnatural, unphysiological, and dangerous intervention? However, we human beings for thousands of years have changed the natural conditions in a way that a further interference obviously appears not only permissible but obligatory. "Deceiving, cheating nature has been often necessary for the survival of mankind," said Father Flynn,[6] professor of ethics at the Catholic College of St. Thomas in St. Paul, Minnesota, U.S.A. We just have to think of how dramatically modern medicine has cut the death rate, particularly of the newborn; then we can imagine, and must understand, that correcting the birth rate in a corresponding manner must come next in the line of consequences.

However, the next question will then be, What is the best or the most suitable, the most acceptable contraceptive, or to be specific, *oral* contraceptive? The original idea of Gregory Pincus was to inhibit ovulation by the administration of progesterone. For various reasons an estrogen was added — and the so-called classic pill was created. Somewhat later, progesterone was replaced by the more efficient and cheaper artificial progestational steroids, either derivatives of 19-nortestosterone or of 17α-hydroxyprogesterone acetate. Still later on, the original doses of progestational components in the "pill" were decreased, and this trend is still going on. About 1961 the idea received impetus that the estrogen is the effective and more important agent as far as ovulation inhibition was concerned. Thus was born the *sequential* regimen. Greenblatt[14] and Aydar and Greenblatt[3] reported their first results with the sequential therapy for contraception in 1961; although Greenblatt et al.[13,15] used a sequential estrogen-progestogen therapy for the suppression of ovulation in the treatment of membranous dysmenorrhoea as far back as the early fifties. Rudel and Martínez-Manautou[20,26] have shown that mestranol in dose of 80 μg daily consistently inhibited ovulation. These data constituted the experimental basis for broad-scale trials as reported later by Goldzieher et al.,[8,9,10,11] Board and Borland,[5] Board,[4] Lean,[18] Tyler et al.,[29] and Abrams.[1]

This idea of sequential therapy was particularly impressive, since by administering an estrogen alone for fifteen or sixteen days followed by the usual "classic" combination of estrogen plus a progestational steroid for five days it was possible to mimic the natural events of the menstrual cycle more closely. Two preparations became available in the United States of America known as Oracon® and C-Quens®.* Soon other preparations employing the sequential regimen came on the market in many countries of the world: Ortho-Novum®, Serial-28, and Feminor-Sequential®, and many more are available for clinical investigation at the present time. The preparations now on the market consist of fifteen or sixteen tablets containing 80 or 100 μg of mestranol or ethinyl estradiol and of five or six tablets (of a different color) containing an estrogen combined with a progestin (cf. Table 9-I). Other sequential regimens are an estrogen alone for eleven days and a combination for ten days, or an estrogen alone for fourteen days and a combination for seven days, or an estrogen for seven days and a combination for fifteen days; but thus far not much data have been published on these latter three regimens.

---

*In some countries this preparation is called Sequens®, in Germany, Estirona®.

TABLE 9-I
SEQUENTIAL PREPARATIONS

| Name | Estrogen therapy | | Combined therapy | |
	Days	Agent and dosage	Days	Agents and dosage
C-Quens	15	mestranol 80 μg	5	mestranol 80 mcg + chlormadinone acetate 2.0 mg
Oracon	16	ethinylestradiol 100 μg	5	ethinylestradiol 100 mcg + dimethisterone 25.0 mg
Ortho-Novum	15	mestranol 8 μg	6	mestranol 80 mcg + norethisterone 2.0 mg
Serial-28	16	ethinylestradiol 100 μg	5	ethinylestradiol 100 mcg + megestrol acetate 1.0 mg
Feminor Sequential	15	mestranol 100 μg	5	mestranol 75 mcg + norethynodrel 5.0 mg

It is difficult to decide what is a natural and what is an unnatural method. However, if we agree with Lord Brain, Parkes, and Bishop[19] of Great Britain, that the pill in the "classic" sense, the Pincus-type of pill, is a physiological method of contraception, then we must admit that the sequential type is more so for the following reasons:

1. The administration of the two steroid hormones in a sequential manner follows more closely the normal pattern of the endogenous hormones as they are secreted by the ovaries during the menstrual cycle.

2. During a cycle under sequential treatment the histological pattern of the endometrium differs only little from that of normal untreated cycles. No decidual or pseudodecidual reaction follows; thus it differs from the combination-type therapy, and no regressive changes of the endometrium occur, a phenomenon frequently observed on combination therapy.

3. The bleeding phenomena were expected to follow a more normal pattern on the basis of theoretical reflections, and the clinical reports have shown that this is actually true.

Of course, only clinical trials can finally decide on advantages or disadvantages. At the Sixth Pan American Congress of Endocrinology last October, Goldzieher[11] presented the results he had collected from seventeen centers. The data from 6,000-odd patients and 82,000 cycles were computerized. Dr. Goldzieher's collective data may appear impressive but misleading. Results from two or more preparations cannot be compared, when these preparations are not dispensed simultaneously, at random, by the same investigators, and under absolutely identical conditions. If these demands are not fulfilled, statistical analyses such as the t-test, Chi Square test, and variance analysis cannot be used to compare two or more preparations.

To get a bias-free comparison, we started about two years ago to perform our own studies. Since we in Berne had obviously not enough women for the trials, we asked our colleagues in Basel, Zürich, Olten, and Baden to collaborate.

TABLE 9-II
PREPARATIONS USED IN TRIAL CONTRA-63

	Progestin (mg)		*Estrogen*	
Etalontin	Norethisterone ac	2.5	EE	0.05
Lyndiol	lynestrenol	2.5	EE3ME*	0.075
Ovulen-0.5	ethynodiol diac.	0.5	EE3ME	0.1
Planovin				
Volidan	megestrol acetate	4.0	EE	0.05
C-Quens				
Sequens	chlormadinone ac.	2.0	EE3ME	0.08
Estirona	(5 days)		(20 days)	

*Mestranol or ethinyl estradiol-3-methyl ether.

In our collaborative trial (Contra-63) we decided to compare Lyndiol®-2.5, Ovulen®-0.5 (containing 0.5 mg ethynodiol diacetate), Planovin® (or Volidan®), and Etalontin® (Table 9-II). After six, twelve, and eighteen treatment cycles each woman switched to another preparation according to the design shown in Table 9-III.

TABLE 9-III

Patient No.	1st period (1-6)	2nd period (7-12)	3rd period (13-18)	4th period (19-24)
1	Lyndiol-2.5	Ovulen-0.5	Planovin	Etalontin
2	Ovulen-0.5	Etalontin	Lyndiol-2.5	Planovin
3	Planovin	Lyndiol-2.5	Etalontin	Ovulen-0.5
4	Etalontin	Planovin	Ovulen-0.5	Lyndiol-2.5
5	C-Quens			

Somewhat later on, we added to our trial a fifth preparation, Sequens, (C-Quens or Estirona) in order to get a preliminary idea about the difference between a sequential regimen and the combination therapy when both treatments are given under identical conditions. The formula for chlormadinone acetate, the progestational agent of Sequens, is shown in Figure 9-1.

Let us have a look at the problems of *side effects* first, considering only two of them: nausea and change of libido. First-cycle nausea varied from one preparation to the other also in our trial. However, the differences were not significant, although the incidence was lowest with Sequens. In only 19 per cent of all first-treatment cycles did nausea occur (Table 9-IV).

CHLORMADINONE ACETATE

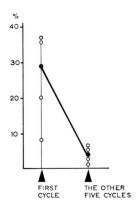

FIGURE 9-1.

TABLE 9-IV
FIRST — CYCLE NAUSEA (FOUR CENTERS)

Drug	%
Lyndiol	28
Ovulen-0.5	26
Planovin	28
Etalontin	22
Sequens	19

The differences among the centers were even much greater than the difference among the preparations. Figure 9-2 shows the enormous scattering from one center with the lowest incidence (8 per cent of all cycles with all preparations) to the one with the highest value (37 per cent of all cycles). In the center, showing a figure of 8 per cent, only private patients were in the study. The mean incidence for all centers and all preparations taken together was 29 per cent; whereas the same average value for the other five cycles (cycles 2 to 6) was found to be 4.5 per cent only.

INCIDENCE OF
NAUSEA

FIGURE 9-2.

A quite similar scattering of first-cycle-nausea incidence was reported by Goldzieher and Maas[11] for Sequens varying from almost 0 to 33 per cent in the seventeen centers.

On the other side Adelaide Satterthwaite[27] has shown the specific effects associated with a research project. When a new research project was initiated to study two new contraceptive preparations together with the old one which had been in use for quite a time, the incidence of first cycle nausea went up from 4 to 9 per cent.

We have observed similar findings: when the incidence of nausea was calculated for every cycle number separately (1st, 2nd, 3rd, and so forth), a surprising picture was found (Fig. 9-3). The incidence rose considerably every sixth cycle, namely during the seventh, thirteenth, and nineteenth cycle. However, the reason for this appears to be quite obvious: the women had to switch to another preparation every six months. The women lost some of their confidence in the different-appearing tablet and the result of this was an increase of nausea every sixth cycle.

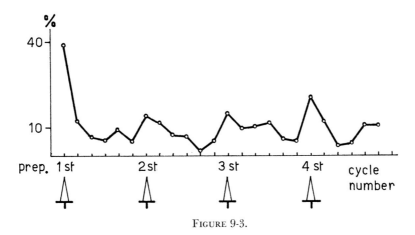

FREQUENCY OF NAUSEA IN 24 Cycles
(all preparations, one center only)

FIGURE 9-3.

This explanation is further supported by an observation we made concerning the change of libido. At the beginning of the treatment — that is in the first cycle — we found the highest number of women with decreased libido and the smallest number of women with increased libido (Fig. 9-4). With time, when the women gradually gained confidence in the pill, this picture changed; more women noted an increase of libido, fewer women a decrease. However, when the preparation was changed, the reverse picture could be seen; the number of women with increased libido dropped, the number of women with decreased libido increased. These two observations, on libido and on nausea, clearly show the importance of psychic factors. They also show that the patient's confidence in the pill or in the doctor or in both may be a considerable factor.

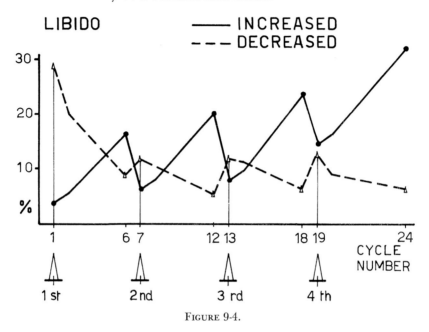

FIGURE 9-4.

Now, I should like to turn to the bleeding phenomenon. The *lag time,* that is the time lag in days between the last tablet and the onset of menstrual bleeding, appears to be a relatively consistent characteristic for a given preparation; although there are some slight differences among the centers, so that the differences among the preparations are somewhat blurred when all centers are taken together (Table 9-V). However, significantly different are the values for Lyndiol (3.4 days) and for Sequens (4.4 days). These figures mean that the cycle is longest under Sequens, on the average 27.4 days in our study.

TABLE 9-V

LAG TIME

Drug	*Average (All centers) Days*	*Average (Center no. 2) Days*
Sequens	4.40	4.40
Lyndiol	3.35	3.49
Etalontin	2.77	2.93
Planovin	2.72	2.60
Ovulen-0.5	2.35	2.07

Silent menstruation occurs in a certain proportion of cycles for all products. The scattering among Goldzieher's seventeen centers is especially impressive: from 0 to 30 per cent; on the average 7.1 per cent*, at the end of the first treatment cycle, later on 2.5 per cent.[11]

In our study the incidence of silent menstruation — or six-day-pseudo-amenorrhea, respectively — was 7 per cent for Sequens; Lyndiol ranks second, seen in about 6 per cent, followed by the other combination-type preparations (Table 9-VI). However, if we waited seven days (instead of six only) before we started with a new treatment in the event menstruation failed to occur, we obtained a much lower incidence, since — as we have seen — the bleeding often started on the seventh day.

TABLE 9-VI
SILENT MENSTRUATION

(6 days pseudoamenorrhea) (All centers)	
Drug	%
Sequens	7.01
Lyndiol	5.96
Ovulen-0.5	3.35
Planovin	2.64
Etalontin	2.03

The average *bleeding time* in days was similar under all preparations except for the sequential regimen with Sequens. This bleeding time (5.1 days) differs significantly from all others (Table 9-VII). The menstrual flow, on the average, did not change noticeably under Sequens.

TABLE 9-7
BLEEDING PERIOD IN DAYS

Drug	Days
Sequens	5.1
Lyndiol	4.2
Planovin	4.2
Ovulen - 0.5	4.2
Etalontin	3.8

As to the incidence of *bleeding during treatment* (breakthrough bleeding or spotting) a clear-cut difference could be found between the patients treated with Sequens and all other patients ,Table 9-VIII). So far, in only 1.8 per cent of all cycles, bleedings occurred under treatment with Sequens. The average values calculated from all centers for the combination-type preparations were 12.1, 15.8, 18.1, and 23.6 per cent respectively. This figure of 1.8 per cent for Sequens compares favorably with Goldzieher's average incidence of 2.3 per cent.[11]

---

*Later on, it was shown that this value reflects the frequency of amenorrhea at the end of the *pretreatment* cycle, first-cycle amenorrhea occurring in 2.3 per cent of the cycles only.[16]

TABLE 9-VIII
SPOTTING AND BREAKTHROUGH BLEEDING

Drug	Average (all centers) Total %
Lyndiol	12.1
Ovulen-0.5	18.1
Planovin	23.6
Etalontin	15.8
Sequens	1.8

A significant *weight gain* was seen after the treatment with Lyndiol and Etalontin, but no significant change was found with Ovulen -0.5, Planovin, and Sequens (Table 9-IX). Since we have found that Sequens distinctively differed from all the combination preparations in many respects, we recently started another trial we are calling Contra-65. In this trial, we compared the sequential regimen with the combination-type therapy by using the same compounds and same dosages. These problems are now under investigation with nine preparations. Preliminary data show that we probably will get the same differences between the sequential and the combination regimen already observed in our Contra-63 trial.

TABLE 9-IX
AVERAGE WEIGHT CHANGES WITHIN
SIX MONTHS OF TREATMENT

Drug	Change (in kg)
Lyndiol	1.22
Ovulen - 0.5	0.08
Planovin	0.19
Etalontin	1.10
Sequens	0.00

Comparing Sequens with CTB, that is a preparation consisting only of twenty *red* tablets unlike Sequens with five (i.e. consisting only of combination tablets of 80 μg of mestranol plus 2 mg of chlormadinone acetate), we found the following: under Sequens (in this very small series), *no* breakthrough bleeding; under CTB, 24 per cent; lag time under Sequens, 4.05; under CTB, 3.58; bleeding time under Sequens, 4.86 and under CTB, 3.96 days. These results are already significant in the Chi Square and the t-test. These findings give proof that these effects (less breakthrough bleeding, longer lag time, and longer bleeding time) are characteristic for the sequential regimen as such, at least when chlormadinone acetate is used as the progestational agent.

Although psychic factors play an important role in the incidence of bleeding phenomena and side effects, we think we have proved that the regimen (sequential or combination) is an important factor influencing the results. Some of the differences are without doubt due to the chemical structure of the progestational component.

I hope that my colleagues who oppose sequential therapy will be convinced that side effects are fewer. However, as to effectiveness, some will see red, and the cold war turns into a hot one. In our own trials we never had the intention to prove effectiveness, since in Switzerland we have not been able to obtain enough women to study this feature. Actually we have not had a single failure as yet.

Nevertheless, in order to discuss effectiveness I have to rely completely upon the work of other investigators. From a theoretical standpoint we cannot prove that a difference does *not* exist; therefore, we would have to prove that a difference *does* exist. As long as we cannot prove this by well-known statistical tests, we have to take for granted that there is *no* difference. This situation corresponds exactly to the situation in court — at least in a democratic society as we are convinced we are: the defendant is considered to be not guilty as long as his guilt could not be proved. The defendant is not obliged to prove his innocence.

Hence, I try to show that, at least up to now, nobody could significantly prove that there is a difference between the combination and the sequential therapy as far as effectiveness is concerned. In his presentation, Goldzieher[11] showed a graph on which he has compared the pregnancy rates found with Sequens in his seventeen centers, varying from 0 to 2.5, with eighteen published reports[12,17,21,23,28] on combination-type preparations, varying from 0 to 3.1 (Fig. 9-5). Each of these reports can be presented by a bar. Figure 9-6

PREGNANCY RATE PER 100 WOMAN-YEARS

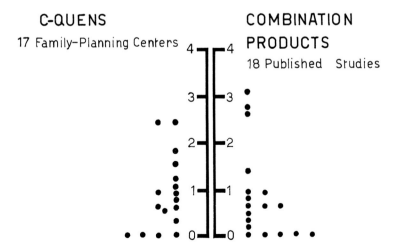

FIGURE 9-5. Taken from lecture presented in Mexico by Goldzieher[9].

shows the pregnancy rates found under treatment with Sequens. Figure 9-7 shows the figures found under a combination-type therapy. The bars in Figures 9-6 and 9-7 fit very nicely into each other (Fig. 9-8). From this obvious fact and also from the fact that four centers with a total of over 8,000 cycles still had a zero use-effectiveness pregnancy rate, Goldzieher has concluded that the limiting factor in effectiveness is the reliability of the women in taking their pills, and that there is no difference between the sequential and the combination regimen. Since it is obviously difficult or impossible from a scientific standpoint to evaluate between tablet failure and patient failure, the overall failure rate was considered in these last-mentioned figures. Nobody ever can prove or disprove whether a woman who became pregnant has taken all her tablets correctly.

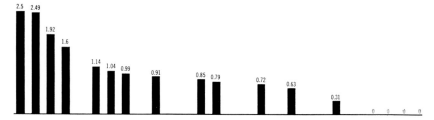

Figure 9-6. The chart shows the pregnancy rates for various combination-type oral contraceptives as reported in eighteen published studies (as cited by Goldzieher[9]).

With all regimens — sequential and combination — tablet failures cannot be entirely denied, since there is, at least in my mind, a possibility that variation in the individual response may be so great that, although very rarely, a particular woman must take a much higher dose for ovulation inhibition. However, many if not all so-called tablet failures are suspected of being patient failures.

However, Goldzieher's position has been attacked. Eleanor Mears[22] presents a pregnancy rate of 5.0 per one hundred women years, that means

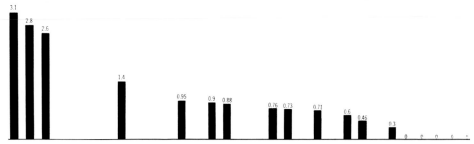

Figure 9-7. The chart presents data derived from seventeen family-planning centers that conducted trials with C-Quens. Each bar represents a center. Its height signifies the pregnancy rate per one hundred woman-years (1,200 cycles) (as cited by Goldzieher[9]).

five pregnancies in 1,200 treatment cycles, a rate which is really high. However, this rate is based on a rather small scale trial (1513 cycles) and dates partly back to the first investigations started in Great Britain about two or three years ago.

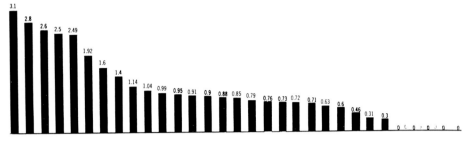

FIGURE 9-8. This chart presents a combination of Figures 9-6 and 9-7.

Some calculations on trial size were done to show the meaninglessness of small-scale trials when it comes to decide on features like effectiveness. On the basis of the published reports of Goldzieher, a pregnancy rate of 1.019 for the sequential therapy and rate of 0.898 for the combination therapy was calculated. If this difference of 0.12 were a real difference, then it would be necessary to study 600,000 treatment cycles in each group (together 1,200,000 cycles) in order to get a significance in the Chi Square test. This example may show the almost insurmountable difficulties in attempting to calculate and prove very rare events.

From a theoretical standpoint pregnancies could occur sooner or are more probable under a sequential-type therapy than under a combination regimen. To explain this possibility it is necessary to discuss the mechanism of action. However, I should like only to mention that it appears safe to say that for the control of fertility under the sequential regimen, mechanisms other than ovulation inhibition must hardly receive any consideration. The endometrium looks far more physiological than under a combination-type therapy and, although we do not know what milieu and conditions a fertilized egg likes, it is quite conceivable that this more physiological secretory endometrium would more readily accept a blastocyst for implantation. Also it is not probable that the relatively low estrogen dose as used in sequential therapy would have any effect on the transport of the egg, fertilized or not, on its way down the tube, or on the correct function of the early corpus luteum of pregnancy. These two effects were, however, considered to be possible under the combination-type therapy, particularly when the progestational component is given in a relatively high dose. Also the estrogens given alone act on the cervical mucus in such a way that sperm migration is not hindered; whereas progestational agents and also combinations of progestogens with estrogens tend to change the cervical mucus so that the sperm are more or less hindered in their passage. Another sequential regimen (e.g. ten or eleven days of an estrogen alone and an estrogen combined with a progestogen for the ten days thereafter) was believed to be able to circumvent the somewhat higher pregnancy rate when some tablets were omitted.[22] If this were so, it might be concluded that a progestin added to the estrogen directly after ovulation has occurred, would have some deleterious effect on the fertilized egg, on the egg transport, or on the function of the corpus luteum.

No oral contraceptive available today is the final answer to the control of world population and to the need of individual family planning. We cannot be certain which methods will be discarded and which will stay, more or less in a modified form. Without doubt other types of oral contraception will be tested in the future; for example, implantation-inhibiting pills, which would be taken only after sexual intercourse. Compounds will be developed which act against egg transport, migration, capacitation, and penetration of the sperm or have an antimitotic activity on the fertilized egg. Enormous work in research covering all fields stands before us in the years to come. We are here to accept this challenge. Some may think that the future is bright; some see it rather gloomy; of course, it is uncertain as always.

REFERENCES

1. ABRAMS, A. A.: Sequential estrogen and progestogen therapy. *Amer J Gynec Obstet,* *96*:1005, 1966.
2. ARNOLD, M., *et al.:* Vorläufige resultate vergleichender versuche mit oralen kontrazeptiva. *Gynaecologia (Basel), 162*:447, 1966.
3. AYDAR, C. K., and GREENBLATT, R. B.: Clinical and experimental studies with a new progestogen-dimethisterone. *J Med Ass Alabama, 31*:3, 1961.
4. BOARD, J. A.: Sequential mestranol-norethindrone for oral contraception. *Obstet Gynec, 27*:217, 1966.
5. BOARD, J. A., and BORLAND, D. S.: Endometrial effects of mestranol-norethindrone sequential therapy for oral contraception. *Obstet Gynec, 24*:655, 1964.
6. FLYNN, F. E.: Natural law and the problem of overpopulation. In *Catholic Messenger,* Davenport, Iowa, June 16, 1960, cited in Rock, J.: *The Time Has Come.* London, Longmans, Green & Co., Ltd., 1963.
7. GARCIA, C. R., and PINCUS, G.: Hormonal inhibition of ovulation. In Balderone, M. S. (Ed.): *Manual of Contraceptive Practice.* Baltimore, Williams & Wilkins, 1964, p. 209.
8. GOLDZIEHER, J. W., *et al.:* Use of sequential estrogen and progestin to inhibit fertility. *Western J Surg, 71*:187, 1963.
9. GOLDZIEHER, J. W.: Newer drugs in oral contraception. *Med Clin N Amer, 48*:529, 1964.
10. GOLDZIEHER, J. W., *et al.:* New oral contraceptive. Sequential estrogen and progestin. *Amer J Obstet Gynec, 90*:404, 1964.

11. GOLDZIEHER, J. W., and MAAS, J. M.: Clinical evaluation of a sequential oral contraceptive. *Sixth Pan American Congress of Endocrinology.* Oct. 10-15, 1965, Mexico City.

12. GOLDZIEHER, J. W., and RICE-WRAY, E.: *Oral Contraception: Mechanism and Management.* Springfield, Ill., Thomas, 1966.

13. GREENBLATT, R. B.: *Office Endocrinology, 4th ed.* Springfield, Ill., Thomas, 1952, p. 200.

14. GREENBLATT, R. B.: Antiovulatory drugs and indications for their use. *Med Clin N Amer, 45*:973, 1961.

15. GREENBLATT, R. B.; HAMMOND, D. O., and CLARK, S. L.: Membranous dysmenorrhea: studies in etiology and treatment. *Amer J Obstet Gynec, 68*:835, 1954.

16. HINES, D. C.; GOLDZIEHER, J. W., and KING, E. P.: A large-scale study of conception control: facts and fancies. *Fifth World Congress of Fertility and Sterility.* June 16-22, 1966, Stockholm.

17. KIRCHHOFF, H., and HALLER, J.: Klinische erfahrungen mit einer ovulations-unterdrückenden östrogen-gestagen-kombination (Anovlar®). *Med Klin (Barc), 59*: 681, 1964.

18. LEAN, T. H.: Sequential formulae and serial regimes of oral contraceptives. *Bull Kandang Kerbau Hospital Singapore, 5*:64, 1966.

19. LORD BRAIN, PARKES, A. S., and BISHOP, P. M. F.: Some medical aspects of oral contraceptives. *Lancet, II*:1329, 1964.

20. MARTÍNEZ-MANAUTOU, J.: Antiovulatory activity of several synthetic and natural estrogens. *In* Greenblatt, R. B. (Ed.): *Ovulation: Stimulation, Suppression, Detection,* Philadelphia, Lippincott, 1966.

21. MEARS, E.: Ovulation inhibitors: large-scale clinical trials. *Int J Fertil, 9*:1, 1964.

22. MEARS, E.: Comparison of combined and sequential oral contraceptives. *Second International Congress on Hormonal Steroids.* May 23-28, 1966, Milan, Italy.

23. PINCUS, G.: Research involving aspects of mammalian egg development. In Mudd, S. (Ed.): *The Population Crisis and the Use of World Resources.* The Hague, W. Junk, 1964, p. 258.

24. RICHTER, R. H. H. *et al.*: Comparative trial with five oral contraceptives. In Cassano, C. (Ed.): *Research on Steroids. Transactions of the Second Meeting of the International Study Group for Steroid Hormones,* vol. 2. Rome Il Pensiero Scientifico, 1966, pp. 441-444.

25. RICHTER, R. H. H., *et al.*: Report from five Swiss centers on two comparative trials with oral contraceptives. Preventive Medicine and Family Planning. *Proceedings of the Fifth Conference of the Europe and Near East Region of the IPPF.* Copenhagen, July 5-8, 1966. Hertford, Stephen Austin and Sons, Ltd., 1967.

26. RUDEL, H. W. and MARTÍNEZ-MANAUTOU, J.: Animal and clinical pharmacology techniques in drug evaluation. In Nodine, J. H., and Siegler, P. E. (Eds.): *Antiovulatory Drugs Evaluation,* Chicago, Year Bk., 1964.

27. SATTERTHWAITE, A. P.: Cited by Venning, G. R.: Oral contraceptive research with special reference to problems of population control. Lecture presented in Augusta, Georgia, U.S.A. (March 1964), and in Stockholm (March 1964).

28. TYLER, E. T., *et al.*: Long-term usage of norethindrone with mestranol preparations in the control of human fertility. *Clin Med, 71*:997, 1964.

29. TYLER, E. T., *et al.*: Oral contraception by the sequential approach. *JAMA, 197*: 943, 1966.

Chapter 10

SEQUENTIAL ESTROGEN AND PROGESTOGEN THERAPY FOR CONCEPTION CONTROL

ARCHIE A. ABRAMS

Eight thousand women were followed for 130,000 cycles on a sequential regimen in twenty-seven maternal health and university clinics, twenty-five of them in the United States.

Naturally, such an intensive study required a specific design, and the protocol for this investigation was both uniform and strict. Patients were required to keep menstrual calendars and to report to their respective clinics monthly. At each visit, the interviewer transferred the menstruation data and the tablet intake from the patient's own calendar and put this on a monthly report form and, in addition, procured specific answers required.

These forms were later sent to one of the two centers in the United States for coding, and the data was then processed and transferred to magnetic tape in Indianapolis; as of now, we have on tape over two million items of information.

Only women with proven fertility (a woman who has had at least one child within the five previous years) and (except for one case I shall mention later), has not reached the age of forty-one, in order to exclude patients with diminishing ovarian function.

Cycles were disqualified for the following reasons:

1. Patient's failure to take eleven pills during a cycle, or the ingestion of a tablet after the twenty-fourth day.
2. Conflicting hormone therapy.
3. Patients who had cycle lengths of less than sixteen days.
4. In addition, we disqualified all those patients who became pregnant.

The percentage of disqualified cycles varied between the twenty-seven centers and amounted to 9.9 per cent of all cycles. The centers with the lowest patient population appeared to have the highest percentage of disqualified cycles.

In addition, an effort was made to exclude from this study those patients who revealed a lack of ability or the motivation to follow the simple directions requested. In addition, we had many dropouts because of family opposition, religious scruples that were belated and came to the fore, or the effects of adverse newspaper publicity. Although the same pattern was observed in all centers, the absolute rates of dropouts differed from center to center. Such differences would seem to reflect variations in population composition and, in part, were due to the attitude of the clinic personnel. One of the most revealing observations to me was the high percentage of reliability noted in patients which we consider comprising the lower socioeconomic group.

The program consisted of the administration of mestranol, 80 μg daily for twenty days supplemented by the progestogen, chlormadinone, 2 mg for the last five. This regimen was started on the fifth day and continued for twenty consecutive days.

The following are some of the results that we have witnessed with this program. In the first place, in this correlated study, we had 123 pregnancies. The crude rate, therefore, seems to be about one per one hundred women-years. This does, however, compare favorably with published data for other oral contraceptives. Five unplanned pregnancies occurred in my center comprising 6,000 cycles to date. Interestingly enough, approximately all of them occurred in the first three thousand cycles, and for some reason there have been no pregnancies since. All these patients were closely interrogated by me, personally. I should like to report some of my findings. One admitted starting her program on the ninth postmenstrual day. Two of them admitted intermittent pill failure of ingestion. One patient, para III, had lupus erythematosus and was treated actively with cortisone. If you will recall, two of the distinguished lecturers, Dr. Greenblatt and Dr. Dorfman, alluded to the effects of cortisone upon triggering release of the eggs from the ovary. I raise the question whether or not conflicting therapy allowed for this pregnancy to occur. For medical and psychiatric indications, a therapeutic abortion was performed on this patient. The fifth patient was a clinic patient on the program for some time who became pregnant the month that her brother was released from jail and was killed in a gang warfare forty-eight hours later. One can question whether or not the hypothalmic pituitary stimulation altered her physiology sufficiently to allow for pregnancy.

All the babies were term babies and perfectly normal. However, going back to the 123 pregnancies, we are trying to obtain more precise information as to when these people became pregnant by studying the birth weight of the children born and other indications that can more precisely explain the pregnancies.

In this study we had six deaths. Four of these deaths were attributable to preexisting conditions ranging from fibrosarcoma to chronic cardiovascular-renal disease. One death was diagnosed as carcinoma of the cervix that developed during the course of the twenty-third cycle of therapy. The sixth death occurred in my study group. This forty-three-year-old girl was paralyzed following a spinal anesthetic on the occasion of her first birth sixteen years previously. I delivered this patient two years later of a second baby. In 1962, after being a bed patient more or less constantly because of her disability, she became pregnant, and because of certain other conditions existing at the time, a therapeutic abortion was considered appropriate. The patient and her husband apparently maintained an active sexual life and three months before her demise requested that she be put on the oral medication as she could no longer handle the diaphragm. During the third cycle she developed a massive pulmonary infarct and died. This patient was autopsied at the Massachusetts General Hospital, and at that time a massive infarct of the lung was revealed. In addition, she had organizing and organized clots elsewhere in her body, and had extensive plaque formation in the arterial tree.

In addition, there were altogether ten cases of thrombophlebitis reported. This would suggest an incidence of about one case per thousand woman-years, including the fatal case above described; this is consistent with the rates usually quoted for this complication in women of the childbearing age.

All patients had annual Papanicolaou smears, which were found to be well within normal limits. Most revealed a good to marked estrogenic effect. In only a small number of the cases was the presence of inflammatory cells reported.

Altogether, there were six certain and two possible malignancies of the cervix and the corpus while on therapy. An incidence of less than one per thousand woman-years. In my six thousand cycles, I had but one case of carcinoma, and that was an epidermoid cancer of the mons veneris treated satisfactorily by vulvectomy. Interestingly enough, there were no cases of breast cancer reported in this large series nor in my own smaller series.

Six cases of hepatitis were reported. In the four with hepatitis who continued to take C-Quens for as long as thirty-two cycles, there were no recurrences reported. All the investigators considered hepatitis as unrelated to the drug.

There is therefore no evidence from 10,000 woman-years of the use of this drug that any patient had a complication threatening health or life that she was not equally likely to have had if she had refrained from taking the drug.

The majority of the endometrial biopsies obtained from these patients during the latter end of the mestranol ingestion revealed a very distinct proliferative endometrium with a loose stroma similar to that already described by Martinez-Manautou. However, on several occasions, on the fifteenth day of therapy, there were evidences of a focal hyperplastic proliferation, and in some cases these were read as endometrial polyps. There were no clinical alterations of the menstrual cycle in those patients that revealed such hyperplasia. Secretory endometrium was diagnosed in all cases after three days or more of progestational therapy.

CYCLE LENGTH ———— IN DAYS

18	19	20	21	22	23	24
.1 %	.1 %	.1 %	.1 %	.2 %	.5 %	1.2 %

25	26	27	28	29	30	31
3.8 %	14.8 %	29.1 %	25.8 %	14.6 %	6.6 %	2.8 %

FIGURE 10-1.

It is a matter of observation that with the sequential pill the cycle lengths tend to be uniform in contrast to the irregularities encountered in untreated women (Fig. 10-1). The withdrawal (Fig. 10-2) interval for most patients is three to four days and the bleeding interval, as seen in Figure 10-3), is three to five days for the majority of patients.

WITHDRAWAL INTERVAL BEFORE BLEEDING
(QUALIFIED CYCLES ONLY)

NUMBER OF PATIENTS— BY NUMBER OF DAYS INTERVAL										
0	1	2	3	4	5	6	7	Sub Total	Un-known	TOTAL
53	179	821	1,495	1,775	1,087	545	145	6,100	588	6,688
.8 %	2.9%	13.4%	24.5%	29.0 %	17.8 %	8.9%	2.3%	100.0 %		

—— 71.3 % ——
—— 93.6% ——

FIGURE 10-2.

Breakthrough bleeding, it was noted, appears to be strongly influenced by tablet omission (Fig. 10-4).

Dysmenorrhea clinically is distinctly more infrequent in the pill population (Fig. 10-5).

Of all patients, 85.5 per cent were without complaints. Symptoms complained of by the remaining 14.5 per cent were varied. Premenstrual abdominal fullness occurred in 0.7 per cent of the cycles, and breast tenderness occurred in an equal number of cycles. Acne noted in 4.2 per cent of pretreatment patients was found to occur in 0.1 per cent of all cycles. Nausea was noted in 123 cycles (3.5%) and rarely was noted after the second cycle. Nervousness was recorded as only 0.6 per cent of the cycles. In fifteen cycles (0.4%), appetite was increased with weight gains recorded.

DURATION OF WITHDRAWAL BLEEDING

(QUALIFIED CYCLES ONLY)

	No Menses	1	2	3	4	5	6	7	8	9 or More	Sub Total	Unknown	TOTAL
	NUMBER OF PATIENTS — BY NUMBER OF DAYS DURATION OF MENSES												
Pre-treatment	≗ 36 11.7%	1 .3%	3 1.0%	13 4.2%	32 10.4%	187 60.9%	22 7.2%	11 3.6%	2 .7%		307 100.0%		
On Rₓ	113 †1.8%	5 .1%	15 .2%	97 1.5%	346 5.5%	5,328 84.1%	269 4.2%	128 2.0%	29 .5%	5 .1%	6,335 100.0%	353	6,688

93.8%

97.3%

≗ Pre treatment "No Menses" values connote a history of one or more missed periods exclusive of pregnancy some time during the patient's potentially reproductive period.

† On treatment "No Menses" values pertain to failure to experience withdrawal bleeding following completion of any given therapeutic cycle.

FIGURE 10-3.

INCIDENCE OF BREAKTHROUGH BLEEDING (BTB) OR SPOTTING
IN RELATION TO TABLETS OMITTED - ALL CYCLES

Number of Tablets Omitted	Number of Patients - By Bleeding Related to Number of Tablets Omitted				Unknown	TOTAL
	Breakthrough Bleeding	Spotting Only	No BTB	Sub Total		
0	92 1.5%	77 1.3%	5,822 97.2%	5,991 100.0%	106	6,097
1	24 3.7%	14 2.2%	605 94.1%	643 100.0%	11	654
2	3 2.9%	1 1.0%	99 96.1%	103 100.0%	2	105
3		3 6.3%	45 93.8%	48 100.0%	3	51
4	3 2.7%	1 .9%	108 96.4%	112 100.0%	7	119
5	6 11.1%	1 1.9%	47 87.0%	54 100.0%	2	56
6-10	5 9.3%		49 90.7%	54 100.0%	4	58
11-20	2 2.2%	1 1.1%	89 96.7%	92 100.0%	60	152
Sub Total	135 1.9%	98 1.4%	6,864 96.7%	7,097 100.0%	195.	7,292
Unknown	12	5	153	170	236	406
TOTAL	147	103	7,017	7,267	431	7,698

FIGURE 10-4.

A weight decrease associated with an increase in appetite occurred in only two cycles. Headache was complained of in approximately 2 per cent of the patients in this series.

DYSMENORRHEA

	None	Slight	Moderate	Severe
Pre treatment	50.5 %	31.5 %	11.2 %	6.8 %
On Treatment	91.2 %	6.1 %	1.5 %	1.2 %

FIGURE 10-5.

Tiredness was mentioned by patients in a total of forty-one cycles (1.2%). Reported less frequently were vaginal discharge, bloating, malaise, itching, menstrual cramps, and edema.

Close scrutiny of the data suggests that the highest incidence of side effects occurs during the earlier cycles and diminishes rapidly thereafter.

Hematologic studies performed in our laboratories on every fifth patient at six-month intervals failed to reveal any significant abnormalities. The only factor which did reveal a definite upward trend was the PBI. On continued therapy, a leveling off was noted and in some cases returned to normal. This not-unexpected result is related to the known property of estrogen to increase the circulating thyroxine-binding protein.

In conclusion, sequential therapy appears to mimic the normal menstrual cycle with the production of a normal-appearing endometrial pattern. Adverse symptoms are infrequent and are rare beyond the second and third cycles of therapy.

REFERENCES

1. MARTINEZ-MANAUTOU, J.; ALVAREDO-ZAMORA, R., and CORTES-GALLEGOS, V.: *Prensa Med Mex, 27:*272, 1962.
2. GARCIA, C. R., and PINCUS, G.: Hormonal inhibition of ovulation. In Calderone, M.S. (Ed.) : *Manual of Contraceptive Practice.* Baltimore, Williams & Wilkins, 1964.
3. GOLDZIEHER, J. W., and MAAS, J. M.: Clinical Evaluation of a Sequential Oral Contraceptive. Presented at Sixth Pan American Congress of Endocrinology, Mexico City, October 10-15, 1965.

Chapter 11

CONTINUOUS PROGESTOGEN THERAPY CONTRACEPTION WITHOUT OVULATION INHIBITION

HARRY W. RUDEL AND JORGE MARTINEZ-MANAUTOU

EARLIER INVESTIGATORS HAVE MAINTAINED that ovulation inhibition with either estrogen or progestogen, or a combination of both of these gonadal hormones, was necessary to insure contraception in women. Considering the complexity of the reproductive process, this degree of interference has seemed excessive to thwart the normal process of fertility. Instead of suppressing endogenous gonadotrophin and, consequently, ovulation and gonadal hormone production, we have evolved, as a working hypothesis, the concept of creating a hormonal imbalance in the menstrual cycle. Consideration has been given to progestogens for this purpose, since they are anti-estrogens or antagonists of the peripheral action of estrogens on the secondary organs of reproduction[6] (Fig. 11-1). We have found that progestogens can, indeed, produce an antifertility effect in women in doses which do not interfere with the normal cyclic histological development of the endometrium[7] and ovulation, as evidenced by a urinary pregnanediol excretion and culdoscopic visualization of recent corpora lutea.[1] The number

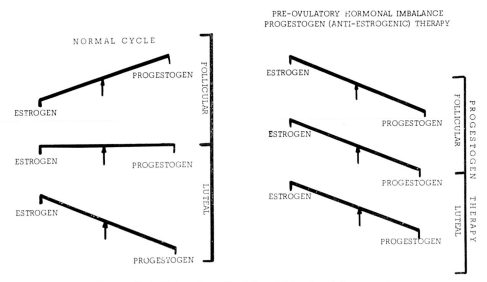

FIGURE 11-1. Taken from Rudel and Martinez-Manautou[6].

TABLE 11-I
99.9 PER CENT EFFECTIVE DOSE AND CONFIDENCE INTERVAL FOR INHIBITION
OF PREGNANCY WITH CHLORMADINONE ACETATE

Threshold (%)	(Dose, μg)		
	$ED_{99.9}$	95 per cent confidence limits Upper	Lower
70	379	474	284
75	362	450	273
80	336	427	246

of women protected by this antifertility action is directly related to the dosage of progesterone, and an effective contraceptive dose for a given percentage of the population may be determined from the dose-response data, using the technique of probit analysis.[5] In this analysis, it is assumed that in any given month, between 20 and 30 per cent of women not using contraception, who are exposed, become pregnant, representing a natural contraceptive threshold of between 70 and 80 per cent. The 99.9 per cent effective contraceptive doses ($ED_{99.9}$) for chlormadinone acetate, a synthetic progestogen, for thresholds of 70, 75, and 80 per cent are given in Table 11-I, and the 80 per cent threshold data are graphically represented in Figure 11-2.

In a population of women, a dose of progestogen which produces a significant antifertility effect may cause a suppression of the endometrium in some, and in a lesser number, suppression of ovulation[3] (Fig. 11-3). The extent and intensity of the endometrial glandular suppression in a group of women is also a direct function of the progestogen dose.[4] Not only can these data be used to assay the antiestrogenic potency of a progestogen on the endometrium, but they can also show the amount of interference with endometrial development which may occur with various contraceptive doses.

As an example, the contraceptive $ED_{99.9}$ of chlormadinone acetate (Table 11-I) may be expected to produce some endometrial suppression in approximately one half of the patients (Fig. 11-4). Such an interruption in the normal development of the endometrium is very likely the basis of vaginal spotting and intermenstrual bleeding seen in clinical studies with continuous low-dose chlormadinone acetate contraceptive programs (see below). A more intense degree of inhibition, characterized by discrete to absent glandular tortuosity and secretion, has been seen in some women. This is a reflection of more than a local antiestrogenic action, probably representing gonadotrophic and gonadal hormone suppression associated with ovulation inhibition or deferral. This is thought to relate to long cycles and amenorrhea also reported in clinical contraceptive trials with continuous progestogen therapy.

A new concept of hormonal contraception has evolved from these clinical pharmacologic findings — a concept based upon the continuous

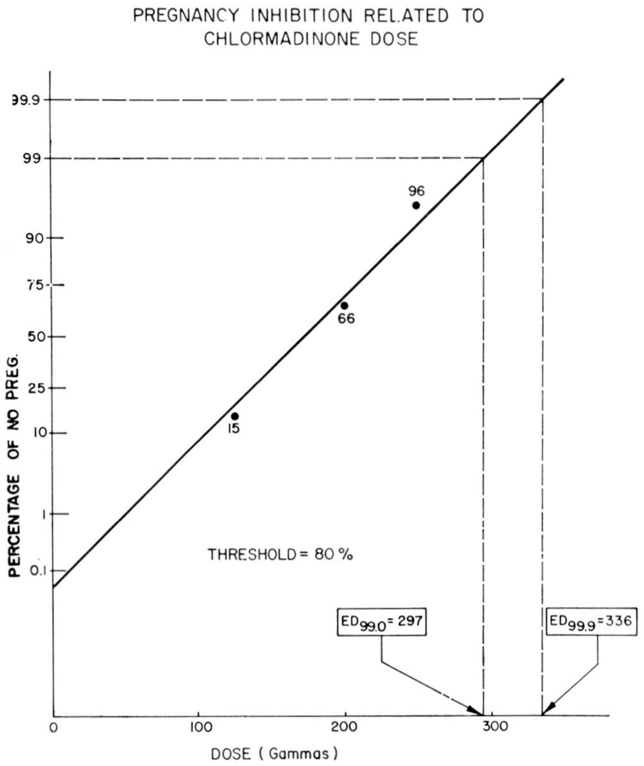

PREGNANCY INHIBITION RELATED TO
CHLORMADINONE DOSE

FIGURE 11-2. The computations, consisting of transforming the response data into "probit" units and then fitting a straight line to the transformed data by least square techniques were performed twice, once with the dosages in natural units and again with the dosages in logarithmic units. The straight line fit the data better when dosage was expressed in natural units. The goodness-of-fit criteria was based on the Chi Square statistic. Here, the percentages of pregnancy inhibition are shown for dosages of 100, 200, and 250 μg using a natural pregnancy threshold of 80 per cent.

daily use of progestogens in doses which will produce an antifertility state with minimal interference with endometrial development and ovulation. In theory, this method would permit endogenous hormonal control of menstrual cycling.

Using such an uninterrupted oral dosage regimen, chlormadinone acetate (0.5 mg daily) has been studied as a contraceptive in a group of 945 fertile nonlactating women, during a total of 8,091 cycles of treatment, representing a median duration of five cycles.[2] Fourteen pregnancies occurred; however, in thirteen of these, women failed to take medication for several days. The pregnancy rate (the number of pregnancies per 100 women-years of experience) adjusted for these patient failures is 0.2. The "use effectiveness pregnancy rate," where all pregnancies are included, is

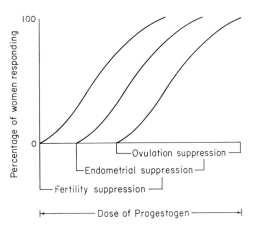

FIGURE 11-3. Taken from Rudel[3].

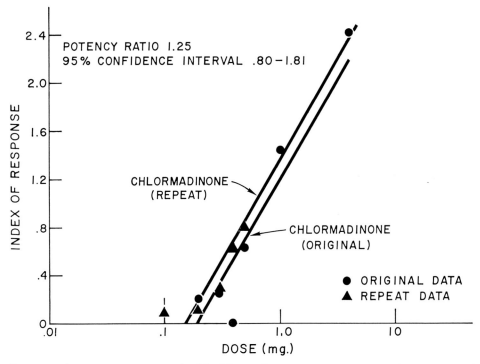

FIGURE 11-4. Women were treated with chlormadinone acetate, 0·2, 0·3, 0·4, 0·5, 1·0, and 4·0 daily for twenty days, starting on day five of the menstrual cycle. A biopsy was taken from each patient between the twenty-first and twenty-seventh day and classified. A value of zero has been assigned to secretory and proliferative endometria. Irregular secretory, irregular and inactive endometria are the consequence of increasing inhibitory effects of the progestogens, and in turn have been given values of 1, 2, and 3 respectively. An index of response for each dose was calculated as a weighted average of the values. The above graph represents results obtained from replicate experiments with chlormadinone acetate.

2.1. Approximately one-third of these patients were completely free of cycle irregularity. The remainder of them had one or more randomly occurring cycles of shorter than twenty-five or longer than thirty-five days' duration. In any given month of treatment, between 60 and 74 per cent of women had a cycle length of twenty-five to thirty-five days. Intermenstrual (breakthrough) bleeding was seen in 20.5 per cent of the patients in the first cycle. This decreased gradually to 11.9 per cent by the fifth cycle. Amenorrheic cycles of sixty days or longer occurred 169 times, or 2.4 per cent of all cycles.

These clinical findings, both as to antifertility action and menstrual cycle behavior, were predictable from clinical pharmacologic assays. In this respect, 118 (58%) of the 202 endometrial biopsies performed in the study showed varying degrees of endometrial suppression (Table 11-II). It is quite clear that the intensity of biologic response to chlormadinone acetate (0.5 mg) is randomly distributed in a population of women. Some will experience only an antifertility effect, while others show some degree of endometrial suppression, or even ovulation inhibition (Fig. 11-3). A compound must be sought which will have a broader separation between the dose producing satisfactory contraception for the population and the dose causing menstrual cycle irregularities through interference with endometrial development and ovulation.

TABLE 11-II
RESULT OF ENDOMETRIAL BIOPSY IN 202 CASES

Classification of Endometria	Patients No. %
Secretory	61 (30•2)
Irregular secretory	71 (35•2)
Irregular	35 (17•3)
Proliferative	23 (11•4)
Inactive	12 (6•0)

In the meantime, there are ways which theoretically could improve the menstrual pattern reported in the clinical trial with chlormadinone acetate. In the course of development of oral contraceptives, there has been an adherence to the principle that one dose must satisfy all women. This is a departure from therapeutic practice in which a dose of drug is adjusted to the patient's needs. It seems logical that, if a patient experiences irregular bleeding, it is an indication that the dose of progestogen is excessive and that the individual should be given a smaller amount of drug. The fact that the contraceptive action of chlormadinone acetate and other progestogens is a function of dosage and not an all-or-none phenomenon, lends support to this theory. We are tending away from individualization of therapy in modern medicine, but until we find the perfect drug, it would seem to be the easiest way to obtain the maximum therapeutic benefit with the minimal physiologic insult to the patient. One dose daily, rather than divided doses, presents further difficulties, since this method requires that the level of compound not drop below the critical antifertility level and that it does not encroach upon levels which would produce changes in endometrial development or hypothalamic-pituitary interrelationships. A rapid rise to the desired therapeutic blood level, a maintenance of this level for twenty-four hours, then a sharp decline to zero level is not a characteristic of oral therapy with any drug. The slope of the blood level curve, following a single oral dose, is relatively steep until reaching peak levels. This is followed by a less steep disappearance curve. The shape of this curve would be modified by several factors, including the amount of drug administered, the efficiency of gastrointestinal absorption, concomitant food ingestion, intestinal disease, fat storage or depoting, rate of metabolic inactivation and enterohepatic recirculation. If the dose of the progestogen is too small, or if its disappearance rate is too fast, then contraceptive coverage may not be complete for an entire twenty-four hours. This deficiency could be compensated by the women taking medication within several hours of the time the couple usually engages in sexual intercourse. Increasing the dosage would, of course, prolong the duration of effectiveness, but the progestogen level may be increased to the point where there is interference with menstrual cycle regularity. Further, if there is not complete disappearance within twenty-four hours, a buildup of the progestogen may occur.

These problems inherent to oral medication are exaggerated by an irregular schedule of tablet ingestion, the most extreme case being omission, but the failure to take the progestogen at the same time daily might also create difficulties. Long-acting progestogen implants which have a narrow range in day-to-day release rates offer the most satisfactory solution. This type of formulation was originally envisioned for the continuous progestogen technique of contraception. Daily uninterrupted oral therapy has been used primarily as a model for the development of a steroid implant. Such a dosage form would fulfil many of the physiologic, pharmacologic, medical, and administrative criteria for a contraceptive method.

REFERENCES

1. MARTINEZ-MANAUTOU, J., *et al.*: Low doses of progestogen as an approach to fertility control. *Fertil Steril, 17*:49-57, 1966.
2. MARTINEZ-MANAUTOU, J., *et al.*: Daily progestogen for contraception: a clinical study. *Brit Med J, 2*:730-732, 1967.
3. RUDEL, H. W.: The mechanism of action of hormonal antifertility agents. In

Pharmacology for Physicians, a monthly publication of the American Society for Pharmacology and Experimental Therapeutics. Philadelphia and London, Saunders, (in press).

4. RUDEL, HARRY W., *et al.:* Assay of the anti-oestrogenic effects of progestagens in women. *J Reprod Fertil, 13:*199-203, 1967.

5. RUDEL, H. W., and MARTINEZ-MANAUTOU, J.: 1966 The importance of the antiestrogenic property of progestogens in the hormonal control of fertility in women. *Proceedings of the Second International Congress on Hormonal Steroids.* Excerpta Med Int Congr Ser 132, Milan, May, 1966.

6. RUDEL, H. W., and MARTINEZ-MANAUTOU, J.: Hormonal fertility control: a working hypothesis for population control. *Fertil Steril, 18:*219-222, 1967.

7. RUDEL, H. W.; MARTINEZ-MANAUTOU, J., and MAQUEO-TOPETE, M.: The role of progestogens in the hormonal control of fertility. *Fertil Steril, 16:*158-169, 1965.

Chapter 12

MECHANISM OF ACTION OF
ORAL CONTRACEPTIVE AGENTS

W. INGIULLA, MODERATOR

W E HAVE ALREADY considered the results of clinical trials involving the use of various steroid preparations for birth control and I hope that it may now be of value to discuss their mechanism of action. In opening the discussion I should like to mention an important point and this is the extent to which these antiovulatory agents are antigonadotrophic. At the same time, I think that you will agree that due to technical problems in gonadotrophin assay our knowledge of this aspect of the mechanism of action is of a limited nature and much remains to be learned about the effect of antiovulatory agents upon the production or action of the gonadotrophins.

For the present, I should like to refer briefly to some of the results obtained in my Institute.

As an essential preliminary to the study of the effect of various preparations, it is essential to investigate the gonadotrophins in relation to the normal menstrual cycle by the methods of hormone assay which are currently available. This is also a matter of practical importance in view of the advent of new preparations for the replacement of gonadotrophin deficiency. It is apparent from the study of published data that there are considerable discrepancies in the literature both with regard to the excretion of total urinary gonadotrophins and of individual activities. Thus, although there is general agreement that the former are excreted in increased amounts in patients with an ovarian deficiency (Turner's syndrome, surgical and physiological menopause), the information about the normal menstrual cycle is conflicting (see Fig. 12-1). To some extent these differences may be explained by the nonspecificity of the mouse-uterine-weight technique which is affected by the different ratios of FSH to LH in the urinary extracts. It might have been hoped that less contradictory results would be obtained by the estimation of the individual gonadotrophins of pituitary origin but, although there is general agreement about the existence of a peak in LH excretion close to the time of ovulation (by either biological or immunological methods) reports upon FSH excretion are extremely variable (Figs. 12-2 and 12-3).

We have assayed the urinary excretion of FSH and LH by serial analyses in the following types of subject:

1. Throughout two consecutive cycles in a healthy young woman.
2. In three consecutive ovulatory cycles in a woman who had suffered from phases of amenorrhoea.
3. In a healthy woman six years after a physiological menopause (twenty-eight-day study).
4. In a patient seven years after a surgical menopause (sixty-six-day study).

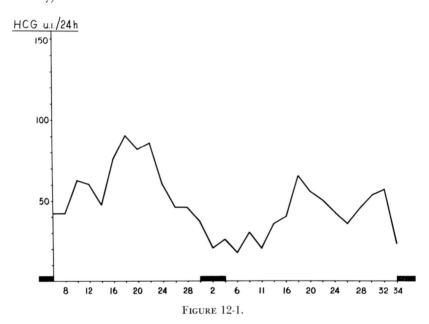

FIGURE 12-1.

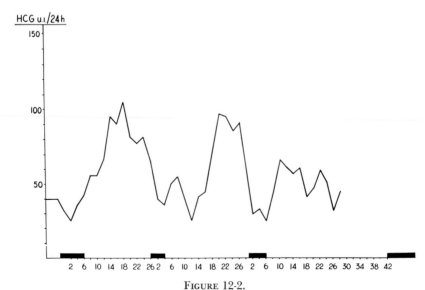

FIGURE 12-2.

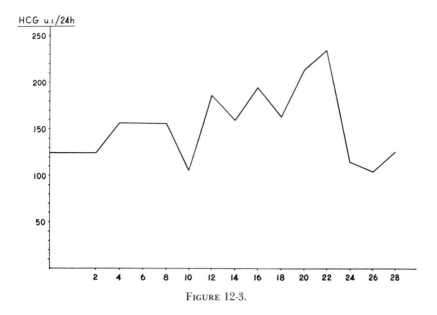

FIGURE 12-3.

Urine specimens were collected daily and stored at 4°C. The urine was adsorbed on kaolin and precipitated with acetone according to Albert's method. The precipitate was washed with alcohol and ether, dried, and the powder further purified by ammonium acetate and alcohol, reprecipitated, washed several times, and dried. The extract was dissolved in physiological saline and a portion corresponding to thirty-hours excretion was used for the determination of FSH and the remainder corresponding to eighteen-hours excretion was used for the determination of LH. FSH was determined by P. S. Brown's bio-assay, based upon the increase in weight of the ovary of prepubertal female mice treated with an excess of HCG. All results are expressed in terms of the second IRP HMG standard with calculation by the method of Gaddum and a four-point assay. LH was determined by the method of Butt *et al.* for the immuno-assay of HCG — the urinary extract being concentrated to increase the sensitivity of the immunological system and the anti-HCG antiserum was treated with a preparation of urinary proteins extracted from patients with Simmonds' disease to absorb non-specific antibodies. The excretion values were plotted in terms of the average excretion per twenty-four hours, and results which were not statistically significant were omitted.

LH Excretion

In the normal menstrual cycle the major peak of excretion was found to occur in the ovulatory phase with minor peaks in the premenstrual phase of the cycle (Figs. 12-1 and 12-2). Following a physiological menopause there were irregular fluctuations in excretion, but these were always at a high level (Fig. 12-3). In the study of the patient seven years after a surgical menopause, there was a high excretion of LH throughout the long period of investigation with marked fluctuations but no definite rhythm (Fig. 12-4).

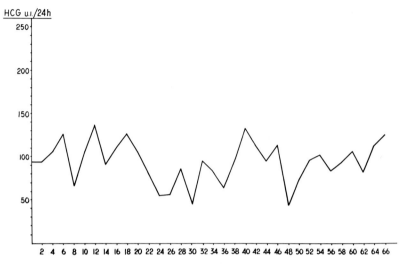

FIGURE 12-4.

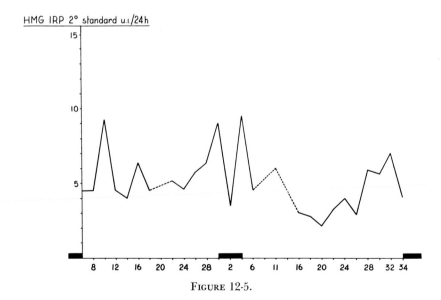

FIGURE 12-5.

FSH Excretion

In the young woman with normal menstrual cycles there was considerable daily variation in FSH excretion, and this did not appear to be related to any phase of the cycle. Moreover, the pattern varied throughout the two consecutive cycles but there was some evidence of an increased excretion at the time of menstruation (Fig 12-5). In both postmenopausal women, variable amounts of FSH were excreted with no definite rhythm and this was more apparent in the patient following surgical menopause (Figs. 12-6 and 12-7). The FSH excretion in the older woman who was still ovulating (after phases of amenorrhoea) showed a peak at the time of menstruation, but there were wider variations in other phases of the three consecutive cycles than were found in the younger woman (Fig. 12-8).

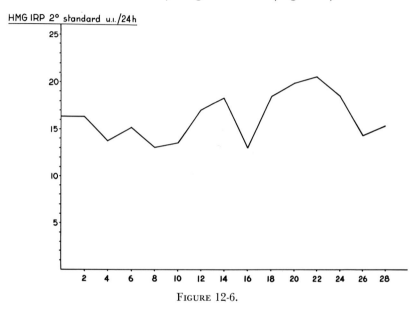

FIGURE 12-6.

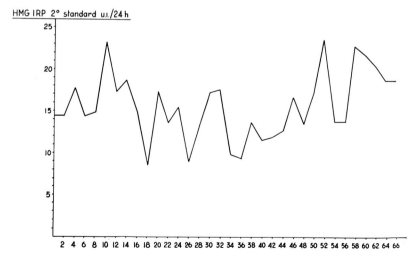

FIGURE 12-7.

With regard to any correlation between the excretion of FSH and LH when assayed concurrently in the same women, our results confirm the presence of an LH peak in the ovulatory phase and an FSH peak in the premenstrual phase in both younger and older subjects, but there was no consistent pattern for the excretion of either factor at other times of the cycle. In some specimens there was a concurrent peak in the excretion of both gonadotrophins and in others changes of excretion were completely independent.

It will be seen that the average excretion of both gonadotrophins fluctuates in subjects with ovulatory cycles but that the levels of excretion and the extent to which they vary are less marked than those which we have observed in postmenopausal women.

In addition to these preliminary studies involving serial analysis of FSH and LH, we are investigating the relationship which should be demonstrable between gonadotrophin excretion and ovarian hormone secretion. This approach is becoming more practicable with the development of new techniques for the determination of plasma steroids in addition to the determination of urinary excretion of oestrogens and pregnanediol. It is hoped, in this way, to throw some light upon the homeostatic system represented by the dynamic regulation of ovarian function during the normal menstrual cycle and to attempt to investigate the manner in which inhibiting or exciting factors may act upon this system.

DISCUSSION

DR. INGIULLA: Granted that oral contraceptive agents are effective, I must ask, How do they work? Is it by inhibition of ovulation? Will gonado-

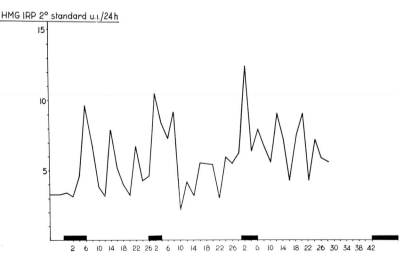

FIGURE 12-8.

trophic assays help or confuse us in learning about the mechanism of action? Dr. Lunenfeld, can you shed some light on this point?

Dr. Lunenfeld: As pointed out by Professor Ingiulla, care must be excercised when discussing gonadotrophic assays. We should keep in mind that the inherent errors of bio-assays are so great that it is difficult to detect the delicate changes which take place during the menstrual cycle. It is quite simple to detect inhibition in a menopausal or castrated patient who receives large amounts of steroids, but it is very difficult, using existing methods, to detect the delicate changes which occur during the menstrual cycle. Two drawbacks of gonadotrophic assays are (1) loss incurred during extraction procedures and (2) animal variation in the bio-assays. It is only recently that a few groups have tried to obtain information on gonadotrophic excretion patterns in the menstrual cycle. The data presented by Stevens and Fukushima on the one hand, and the group of Loraine on the other, do not coincide completely. It is difficult, therefore, to reach conclusions on the qualitative and quantitative changes of gonadotrophic excretion in the normal cycle. As a result, the problem of studying the action of oral contraceptives at the pituitary level becomes extremely complicated.

Furthermore, we must take into account that we are not discussing one compound — we are covering very many compounds, tested by many procedures. It is probable that the various progestational compounds may have different sites of action and some compounds may be more inhibiting at the pituitary level, while other compounds may interfere to a greater extent at the ovarian level. We have seen from Dr. Dorfman's work that steroids formed during ovarian biosynthesis have inhibitory actions at the ovarian level. We must remember, however, that in *in vitro* studies the accumulation of such products is probably higher than in *in vivo* conditions. Synthetic compounds may very well simulate such inhibitory action. Therefore, we must consider two possibilities: inhibition at the pituitary level and inhibition of steroidogenesis at the ovarian level.

Dr. Dorfman: In this general area I should like to introduce the subject with some elegant studies from the laboratory of Professor McCann, formerly of the University of Pennsylvania and now in Houston, Texas. Dr. McCann has been working with hypothalamic-releasing factors that trigger the formation and/or release of the follicle-stimulating and luteinizing hormone of the anterior pituitary, which in turn causes the formation of the follicle, the secretion of estrogens and progesterone, and relates it entirely to the menstrual cycle. His studies have been mainly in the rat. The remarkable results that he has attained have been confirmed by others, i.e. that estrogens are highly important in the control of the release and/or formation of the luteinizing hormone.

This is of particular importance to us in this problem because I would like to develop the hypothesis that in the usual conception control the mechanism is basically maintained by the estrogen and that the progestational agent is secondary for the actual inhibition or prevention of ovulation. The estrogens by themselves can cause a remarkable decrease in the amount of hypothalamic-releasing factor of luteinizing hormone. In previous experiments and over the years we have also known that estrogens can control the formation and release of the follicle-stimulating hormone. It is a further point that has been shown very elegantly by Dr. McCann in experiments on the rat that the progestational agent by itself is only partially effective, and I believe the hypothesis must be presented in this manner: estrogens alone as used in the sequential therapy or estrogens in combination with progesterone during the early days of the cycle basically inhibit the hypothalamic area, which in turn inhibits the anterior pituitary, thus preventing ovulation.

There are some studies that have been done in humans, and I agree wholeheartedly with Dr. Lunenfeld in the extreme difficulty of obtaining reproducible data in this field. In the average study using the mouse uterus with two or three animals at a single concentration and by a dilution technique, it is not unusual that the determination by this type of technique could be 200 and 300 per cent in error. If one uses a technique in which ten animals are used at a single concentration, and one works with two concentrations, or a total of forty animals, even then an error of plus or minus 30 to 50 per cent is usually realized if one is fortunate enough to be within the scope of the dose response bio-assay curve, and if qualitatively the material is similar to the material that is used as a standard. I only mention this because these are the difficulties one faces. However, in spite of these difficulties, there is growing evidence that when something of the order of 50 μgs of ethinyl estradiol or more of mestranol are employed per day possibly for five, seven, or eight days as a minimum, one does in fact see a significant decrease in the gonadotrophic hormones of the pituitary, probably both FSH and LH.

The hypothesis I suggest here is not original nor unique nor necessarily new. As a matter of fact, I recall some years ago in Lima, Peru, that Dr. Greenblatt was presenting this very same thought. I should also like to remind you that as early as fifteen, twenty, and twenty-five years ago Dr. Albright and his colleagues were seeing inhibitions of the same type only with estrogens, so I think that this time it might be wise to hear from Dr. Greenblatt and hear his views of the subject.

DR. GREENBLATT: Dr. Dorfman reviewed the concept that the hypothalamus plays a very important role in releasing those factors which allow the pituitary to secrete FSH and LH in its proper sequence. It is well that we appreciate these fine points. Before we knew too much about the hypothalamus, many of us administered estrogens alone from day five to day twenty-five of the cycle to inhibit ovulation for the treatment of dysmenorrhea. Sturgis and Albright as early as 1942 showed that dysmenorrhea could be alleviated for at least one month by the administration of a large intramuscular injection of estradiol benzoate on day eight, ten, and twelve of the cycle through the inhibition of ovulation. Many clinical investigators had learned to inhibit ovulation for the treatment of mittelschmerz, dysmenorrhea, and severe premenstrual tension but failed to think in terms of contraception. For instance, in my book *Office Endocrinology,* 4th edition, published in 1952, I demonstrated the constant inhibition of ovulation by the use of estrogens for the period of one year in the management of membranous dysmenorrhea. Painless menses were induced by interposing three to five days of an oral progestogen.

It remained for Pincus and Rock to apply these principles for conception control. Theirs is the credit for this important contribution, and we shall ever be in their debt. Nonetheless, we must deemphasize the role of the progestogen and stress that of estrogens as the prime factor in ovulation inhibition. It is the estrogen that inhibits the ovulation; the norethynodrel employed in the original "pill" lent constancy to the contraceptive properties of the "classic" pill.

MARTINI: It is quite possible, although it has not been clearly demonstarted so far, that the action of antiovulatory steroids on synthesis and release of gonadotrophins might not be a direct one taking place at the pituitary level, but an indirect one taking place on the hypothalamic centers which control the function of the anterior pituitary. There are two possible approaches to clarify this problem:

1. To inject or to implant micro-amounts of antiovulatory steroids into the pituitary or into several areas of the brain and to study the ensuing endocrine effects.
2. To see whether antiovulatory steroids, when injected systemically, may modify some hypothalamic activity such as the synthesis, the release and the storage of those hormonal mediators (called LH-Releasing Factor or LH-RF) which are believed to be necessary to trigger the release of pituitary gonadotrophins.

The first approach did not prove to be successful in providing clear-cut evidence for a hypothalamic site of action of steroids for the following reasons:

1. Any kind of implantation or injection into the brain will induce a certain degree of destruction of brain tissue. The effect observed

might then not be due to the drug or to the steroid administered but just to the technical procedure employed.

2. Because of the peculiar anatomy of the pituitary portal vessels the technique of hypothalamic implants or injections might provide the best way of distributing a drug or a steroid into the pituitary gland.[1]

3. When brain implantation techniques are used, steroids which do not cross the blood brain barrier may appear effective. The second method of approach should be much more successful. The work which has already been done using this new approach is based on the assumption that if hypothalamic releasers for gonadotrophins play any physiological role in the ovulatory process, their concentrations in hypothalamic tissue should parallel those of the corresponding trophic hormones FSH or LH in the pituitary gland.[2]

FSH-RF in the hypothalamic extracts was measured using the procedure described by David *et al.*[3] This procedure is based on the demonstration that the intracarotid injection of hypothalamic extracts into normal male rats is followed by depletion of pituitary FSH stores of the recipient animal which is related to the amount of FSH-RF present in the extract injected. (Fig. 12-9).

FSH-RF was measured in the hypothalamus of normal female rats, of castrated female rats (two weeks following castration), and of castrated female rats (two weeks following castration) treated with estradiol benzoate ($200\mu g/100$ gm BW per day, subcutaneously). At the same time the hypophyseal FSH content was also assayed in these three groups of animals using the procedure of Steelman and Pohley[4] as modified by Parlow and Reichert.[5]

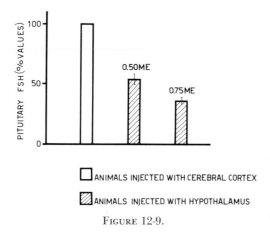

FSH DEPLETION IN MALE RATS

☐ ANIMALS INJECTED WITH CEREBRAL CORTEX

▨ ANIMALS INJECTED WITH HYPOTHALAMUS

FIGURE 12-9.

It has been shown that hypothalamic extracts of castrated animals have a much higher FSH releasing activity than those prepared from normal animals. In castrated animals estrogen treatment reduces the amount of FSH-RF in the hypothalamus, which in these rats contains hardly any FSH-RF (Fig. 12-10).

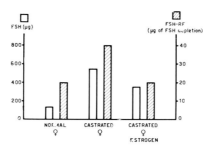

FIGURE 12-10.

The hypophyseal content of FSH in normal rats, in castrated rats, and in rats castrated and treated with estrogens parallel to the content of hypothalamic FSH-RF. Castration induces a definite increase in FSH pituitary content; treatment with estrogens, on the other hand, significantly diminishes hypophyseal content (Fig. 12-10).

These results confirm, with the help of a new approach, the observations made with the implantation technique,[6] i.e. that the inhibiting action of estrogens on the secretion of gonadotrophins is exerted through a nervous inhibition which ends in a reduction of the synthesis and of the secretion of hypothalamic gonadotrophin-releasing factors.

Studies are now in progress which indicate that progesterone and several antiovulatory steroids also decrease the hypothalamic concentration of gonadotrophin releasing factors. This certainly supports the idea that these steroids might block ovulation through a hypothalamic mechanism.

INGIULLA: We appreciate the interesting research that Dr. Martini conducted on animals, but I would suggest we concentrate our attention to the human species, because what happens in rats cannot always be applied to women.

MARTINEZ-MANAUTOU: I am afraid we are extending ourselves in trying to explain the mechanism of action of the "pill." It was very clearly presented by Dr. Lunenfeld and Dr. Dorfman that at best we do not have enough evidence of the effect of the "pill" on the pituitary. We don't know exactly what is happening. We believe that the estrogens suppress the production of FSH, and we have some evidence that the progestogen in certain doses may inhibit both FSH and LH, or in some cases just LH.

We have evidence through some studies of Dr. Diczfalusy that doses of 100μg of norethindrone block the production of LH. In a personal communication he felt that the LH release on treatment with 100μg of norethindrone is decidedly irregular.

Now the other important factor that I would like to mention is that with 100 μg of norethindrone in the first 150 patients studied by us, 50 per cent of the endometrial biopsies were of the proliferative, anovulatory type. This is in agreement, I believe, with the results of Diczfalusy in that we are blocking the production of LH, and I would like to know more about this field, something practical that may explain what is happening or how these compounds exert their effects.

DR. DORFMAN: Dr. Martinez-Manautou certainly made an important point when he said that we have to keep to practical knowledge. I should say first, however, to the direct question of animals and man, rat and human, I think we will all agree that it will be quite unlikely that the mechanisms are different. The mechanisms involved in reproductive physiology probably have some fundamentally similar relationships in various species.

However, I would like to indicate some properties of synthetic progestins. Progesterone is a progestational agent by definition. The uniqueness of progesterone is that it has an action quite distinct from anything that we can call an estrogen. It acts in concert with estrogens. Norethindrone, which has been mentioned, has an action similar to progesterone in many respects, but this compound has certain estrogenic properties. So that norethindrone, norethynodrel, and perhaps related compounds have an action basically progestational plus something else. It is for these reasons that when we talk about a compound of this type, and particularly with emphasis on the hypothalamic anterior pituitary area, that we are talking of a combination action — something quite unique. Unique particularly with respect to the type of activity we see with progesterone or with a compound such as the 17-acetoxy derivative of progesterone, of which there are many examples. One outstanding example is chlormadinone acetate. This compound is unique in that, with respect to estrogenicity, it resembles progesterone more than it resembles norethynodrel or norethindrone.

I bring this to your attention because now I think we need to explore the action of these compounds on the hypothalamic and anterior pituitary region when there is no estrogen present. It is true, as Dr. Martinez-Manautou has pointed out, that they too, in the general category of progestational agents, do influence this mechanism, but preliminary experiments indicate, for example, that the amount necessary to inhibit luteinizing hormone in humans, as measured by testosterone production of the testis, is of the order probably of ten, if not twenty-five times greater than the dose that is used in conjunction with estrogenic agents for inhibition of the same phenomenon. It is in this area that I would contend that it is the estrogen that is the principal inhibitor. In other words, to summarize my feelings, we have only microgram amounts of estrogens in human beings of the order of 50 μg ethinyl estradiol and mestranol on a daily basis and probably in a period of a week to two weeks can cause a significant suppression of gonadotrophins, both FSH and LH. Norethindrone by itself or norethynodrel in definitive doses can cause the same effect, and there we believe it will be the joint action of the small estrogenicity that is generated from the compound plus the progestational agent. But when we come to the pure progestational agent, progesterone or a compound like chlormadinone acetate, we have a compound of different order of activity. Now we need much larger doses.

MARTINI: Let me add a few words before passing to the clinicians. I have been very impressed by the data shown by Professor G. W. Harris, of Oxford. He has implanted in the median eminence region of the brain of the rabbit a small amount of chlormadinone; with such an implant he was able to block copulation-induced ovulation in the rabbit. This apparently indicates that chlormandinone may have a central effect on the brain and that probably this steroid blocks the release of LH-RF which normally triggers the release of ovulating amounts of LH.

DR. DORFMAN: I just wanted to remark that the data of Geoffry Harris are in complete accord with the data that we published some time ago on the antiovulatory effect of chlormandinone acetate in the rabbit to which I just referred. I can only remind you that the compound is some thirty-five times more potent than norethindrone and under certain conditions 3,500 times more active than progesterone. However, this type of activity is a very special one, and as Martinez-Manautou has pointed out, it is unlikely to carry over to humans. We would like to see it, but I fear that it may not.

LUNENFELD: Particular caution must be observed when referring to the hypothalamus with regard to clinical experiments, since at the hypothalamic level, animals might differ from humans. For example, we know that in the rabbit, ovulation comes as a direct effect of coitus, and in the rat ovulation is spontaneous, but corpora lutea become functional following coitus.

SWYER: If I may make one or two entirely clinical observations at this point, I should like first to say that I think all of us with experience in the use of estrogens for the treatment of dysmenorrhea will agree that, with the dosages which we used, although ovulation and subsequent dysmenorrhea were inhibited in many cycles, characteristically every now and then a patient would have a painful period even while under cyclic estrogen treatment. If one kept a basal temperature record, in the cycle during which the period was painful this would be biphasic. I believe that to prevent this from happening, considerably larger doses of estrogen would have been needed. In my opinion, the great innovation which, unwittingly, Pincus introduced by adding an oral progestogen to the estrogen, was to make ovulation inhibition virtually a constant and repeatable phenomenon. Now it could be argued that the progestogen he used — norethynodrel — was simply acting as an estrogen in inhibiting ovulation, and this is not entirely easy to disprove. Nevertheless, I would emphasize that the overall effect of a combination of, for example, norethindrone and ethinylestradiol, as revealed by its clinical action on the patient, is not estrogenic but progestational. So although I do not wish to disagree with what has been said by Dr. Dorfman and by Dr. Greenblatt, I still believe that with combined estrogen-progestogen oral contraceptives, the inhibition of ovulation which they cause, though principally due to estrogen, is not entirely so.

Dr. Greenblatt: Dr. Martinez-Manautou showed us that 3.75 mg of Premarin® inhibited ovulation. Many years ago we used 5 mg because that was the amount we found consistently inhibited ovulation, if given from day five to day twenty-five of the cycle. What we failed to realize is the fact that the withdrawal period on estrogens alone is indefinite; it may take place in two or ten days or not at all. There was an inconstancy to the withdrawal period, and ovulation escaped when the withdrawal period did not take place within a given time. Estrogens alone are adequate, but they do not assure a withdrawal period, and the delay that occurs before starting the next round of therapy may permit ovulation to escape. Whether both estrogens and progesterone are given together or are employed in sequence, it is important that no more than six or seven days elapse before commencement of therapy; otherwise, there may be ovulation-escape. If norethynodrel alone were adequate to inhibit ovulation, why did Pincus and Rock add an estrogen to the original pill? I restate my position, estrogens inhibit ovulation, progestogens enhance this propensity and lend a constancy to the menstrual cycle.

Swyer: I should like to differ in minor detail with my respected colleague, Dr. Greenblatt. I have in my own experience seen the effect that he described, namely, delayed ovulation on estrogen alone; this is well recognized, but I have also seen what I would call breakthrough ovulation, in which ovulation occurs even while the estrogen alone is being given. Of course this is a dose-related phenomenon. From my reading of the literature, I have understood that the main reason for the presence of the estrogen in the original norethynodrel-mestranol combination used by the Pincus group was that, first of all, it was very difficult to remove the mestranol which was present as a contaminant in the manufacture of norethynodrel, and second, that they had found cycle control to be poor when only a little of the contaminating mestranol was present. So, they made a virtue of necessity by leaving the mestranol and indeed increasing it to the level of 0.15 mg in a total tablet of 10 mg. This is only what I had gathered from my reading. It may be that the true story is otherwise.

DR. MARTINEZ-MANAUTOU: The data I presented employing different estrogens alone from day five to day twenty-four were, first, an indication of the antiovulatory activity of the estrogens. Secondly, some of the studies that were made in England with 2.5 mg norethynodrel plus 36 μg of mestranol showed a 50 per cent pregnancy rate. When they increased the dosage to 100 μg of mestranol, using the same amount of the progestin, the results were completely different. This indicated to me the importance of adequate doses of estrogen. It is my belief that in that combination it is the estrogens that are responsible for the inhibitory activity.

DR. DORFMAN: It just so happens that I wanted to quote the same experiment from Birmingham, and I just reiterate that when the amount of estrogen falls to the equivalent of 50 μg. of mestranol per day, difficulties arise. There is another factor involved that complicates the picture. Norethynodrel, norethindrone, chlormadinone acetate, and other of these progestational agents used for this purpose also happen to be anti-estrogenic substances. And though the amount of estrogens necessary for control may be of the order of 10 or 20 μg alone, somewhat larger amounts are frequently necessary to offset this antiestrogenic effect on the anterior pituitary. But I would again suggest to Dr. Swyer that one thing that has to be explained is this Birmingham experiment. We should like to hear his explanation.

SWYER: I am not in the slightest disagreement either with Dr. Dorfman or Dr. Martinez-Manautou over the interpretation of the Birmingham results. It is perfectly clear that when the dosage of norethynodrel is dropped to 2.5 mg the amount of estrogen becomes quite critical. It is not so critical if larger amounts of norethynodrel are given. I don't think we are in any basic disagreement here at all, and I have no hesitation in agreeing with the general concept that as ovulation inhibitors, certainly on a weight basis, estrogens are very many times more potently active than progestogens. This is perfectly clear, and I think there is no disagreement on this point.

The only point that I am trying to make is that older observations had suggested that although synthetic estrogens at a dosage level that was reasonably well tolerated by the patient would inhibit ovulation, they would do so with 100 per cent reliability. And it seems to me that the addition of one of the potent progestational agents, in appropriate amounts, makes the inhibition of ovulation much closer, or let us say, closer to 100 per cent than the equivalent amount of estrogen alone would do.

Perhaps it may at this point be worth mentioning that experiences in different parts of the world suggest strongly that the dose of estrogen needed to inhibit ovulation is not the same for all women. We have reason to suspect that a dose of mestranol of 75 μg, which appears to be quite adequate in some countries, is not enough to inhibit ovulation in British women. We feel that a dose of the order to 100 μg is the minimal level which can be relied upon for this purpose. I think factors of this kind need a good deal more consideration than they have received in the past.

DR. DORFMAN: There appears to be some evidence, particularly by Lunenfeld and his group, that some of the progestational agents in concert with or without estrogens, interfere with the action of gonadotrophins at the ovarian level. Dr. Lunenfeld acknowledges that this is his thesis, and I believe a most attractive one. This has also gained support from the school of Loraine of Scotland. This does, in general, fit with the possible action that I discussed at this meeting. I don't, however, have direct evidence from our own laboratory. This is not because we have tried extensively and failed. I would say that we have not subjected this hypothesis with these particular agents to sufficient tests. I can only say that I believe that this should be tested extensively. I think there is considerable merit that at least a part of the activity is due to this possibility. It is also theoretically possible that there are other agents, perhaps of the same classes with which we are now working, which could accomplish the purpose by this method.

LUNENFELD: I believe it was Dr. Gemzell who showed, for the first time, that progesterone, when given in high doses, inhibited the action of exogenous human pituitary gonadotrophins on the ovary. Further, Dr. Diczfalusy showed that in some patients testosterone acted in the same manner. On the other hand, when Dr. Diczfalusy repeated our own experiment, he demonstrated that high doses of gonadotrophins could overcome this inhibitory effect of certain progestational agents (when given together with estrogens).

We have never claimed that inhibition at the ovarian level is the only mode of action of oral contraceptives. We agree that the primary mechanism may very well be at the pituitary level, but added that there may also be a secondary effect peripherally on the gonads. While on the subject of peripheral effects, we should keep in mind a third effect of these compounds: the creation of an environment which is unfavorable to sperm penetration in the cervical mucus.

ABRAMS: A large number of patients complain of an increase in vaginal discharge. Microscopically, we observe a fern pattern in the very free flowing, clear mucoid discharge from the cervical canal. This is lessened with the onset of progestational therapy.

I should like to direct this observation to Dr. Dorfman: Many years ago when chlormadinone was first available and we were experimenting with it in patients having menstrual disorders, we observed an increase in uterine bleeding with larger doses. Its hemostatic effect was greater in smaller doses. This no doubt fits in with your feeling that it is an antiestrogenic substance.

DR. DORFMAN: I don't think I have anything useful to add to this from the clinical point of view. I think Dr. Greenblatt is the gentleman who originally worked with this.

DR. GREENBLATT: The advocates of the classic or conventional or the "preclassic" pill, as Dr. Martinez-Manautou calls it, claim that the change in the cervical mucus is perhaps the important factor in its contraceptive properties. On sequential therapy the cervical mucus, as Dr. Abrams has pointed out, is rich and watery. It is a haven, a refuge for sperm, staying alive and active there for days. One must not assume that a clear watery mucus contributes to the chances for conception and wholly disregard that other factors are at play which prevent conception.

We have paid too much attention to the importance of cervical mucus. For the patient who produces too much cervical mucus, it is preferable to use the combination type of pill. For those in whom this complication is not offensive, I still feel that sequential therapy has a place, because for many women it is easier to take. They feel better; they do not feel let down. Admittedly the classic pill is virtually 100 per cent effective, the sequential pill, slightly less. Moreover, now the doctor has a choice, the patient has a choice, and we are in a position to provide what best suits the situation and the human condition.

INGIULLA: It has been quite a difficult discussion and time has run out before we could reach any conclusions. I believe that everyone can at the present time conclude that the pills are efficient as contraceptives and are practically free from danger, but nothing else.

We cannot say how the single type of pill acts in contraception. We have very little information from *in vitro* or *in vivo* experiments in humans, and too much has been done in animals. I hope that this discussion will stimulate further work in this very important field.

REFERENCES

1. BOGDANOVE, E. M.: *Endocrinology, 73:*696, 1963.
2. DAVID, M. A.; FRASCHINI, F., and MARTINI, L.: *C R Acad Sci (Paris), 261:*2249, 1965.
3. DAVID, M. A.; FRASCHINI, F., and MARTINI, L.: *Experientia, 21:*483, 1965.
4. STEELMAN, S. L., and POHLEY, F. M.: *Endocrinology, 53:*604, 1953.
5. PARLOW, A. F., and REICHERT, L. E.: *Endocrinology, 73:*740, 1963.
6. SZENTAGOTHAI, J,. *et al.: Hypothalamic Control of the Anterior Pituitary.* Budapest, Akademiai Kiado, 1962.

Chapter 13

SOCIAL, MORAL, AND HISTORIC ASPECTS OF CONTRACEPTION CONTROL

A – MORAL PROBLEMS INVOLVED IN THE EMPLOYMENT OF ANTIOVULATION DRUGS

ALESSANDRO DALL'OLIO, S.J.

IF PROGESTERONE AND its derivatives were drugs used only for the medical treatment of disorders and of the pathologic conditions of the feminine organism, then the moral problem of their employment would not be dissimilar from that of any other medication. In practice, the only two conditions required are that the remedy should cure effectively the proper organ and that it should not injure the whole organism with harmful secondary effects.

But, since it has been established that progesterones have the property of preventing ovulation, new problems have arisen in connection with their use for the purpose of avoiding procreation. We shall briefly examine these problems in a progressive order.

The first point to make clear is whether the problem of birth regulation is really extant, and if so, on what scale (i.e. whether on an individual, a familial, or a worldwide scale). In the affirmative case, one should examine what rules derive from it for the individual, meaning such norms of behaviour that, were they not followed, would expose the person to meet with reprobation.

Let us start with the social aspect of the problem and ask ourselves if there is responsibility of the individual before a world that threatens to become overpopulated. Undeniably there has been, in these last decades, a demographic explosion or rapid increase in world population. That is, however, insufficient to determine the moral obligation of the individual to produce no children above a certain number.

One would have to prove that an increase in the world's population will indubitably continue, and that such an eventuality could prove harmful to future generations. It is not the task of the theologian to ascertain whether there is an impending danger in the density of population, but of the sociologists who study demography. Should one discover with absolute scientific certainty that such a danger exists, then it may be incumbent on the theologian to emphasize the responsibility of the individual regarding limitation of the family.

So far nothing has been said regarding the means to be adopted in carrying out this regulation (it shall be considered later) nor, least of all, was it affixed that it is the state's duty to intervene should a citizen contravene such a moral obligation. One may indeed state at once the Catholic teaching on this point. Let us take for example the case of a marriage deemed inadvisable for eugenic reasons; the state can and must exert moral pressure on individuals in order that they should not take this wrong step and thus create unhappiness for those who shall come after them, yet it may not prevent or punish such a marriage. Likewise in the case of infraction of a birth-regulating norm, issued in view of a dangerous increase in population, the state may not and must not intervene with restraint or punishment. It is the individual's sense of responsibility that must be formed and trained; any direct intervention from the outside is against the dignity of human beings. This doctrine is also founded upon the essential Christian principle that history is not made by man alone but by man and God together. Scientific data are true and acceptable; still they are not the only components to be considered in discussing the problems of human society.

Another phase of the birth control problem is the familial and the individual aspect. In the present world, marked by a technical and industrialized civilization, the family cannot be as large as it could in an agricultural society. The latter required many hands; indeed, the more children there were, the greater was the prestige of the head of the family who always retained the management of the clan or static association of related families tied to the land on which they toiled. The industrial civilization in which we live has imposed a different sociological type of family; the excessive density of settlement and the relative restricted lodgings, the rather mature age at which marriages take place, the mobility of the family subject to frequent displacement by reason of work or by other causes, feminine employment even among mothers in an attempt to increase the family income which is not always sufficient, all these factors make the life of a large family very difficult.

A critical analysis would be necessary to evaluate the importance of these changes. Consult, for instance, L. Beirnaert.[1]

If one adds to the above, contraindications to further pregnancies due to the health of the mother or to the risk of hereditary disorders (nowadays easily identified; whereas a few decades ago they were almost unobserved or unknown), one can easily realize the changed circumstances under which the question is raised. In the past, numerous offspring could be an index of family soundness both from the human and the Christian point of view, but today the situation has changed, and the Catholic Church itself has acknowledged, in Vatican Council II, that a married couple may for various reasons consider the question of how many children they should produce.

One should note that the Council starts from a presupposition, namely, the tendency of a Christian family towards fecundity, for otherwise one falls in a hedonistic conception of matrimony. (Incidentally, numerous offspring do not per se exclude such a hedonistic concept.)

Assuming the existence of such fecundity in the love of two spouses, the latter should, however, judge how many children they can rear. In a measure, this Catholic attitude toward the family problem is new, in as much as it leaves the decision as to the number of children to the parents, yet the precept of fertility remains unchanged.

In this connection one should also bear in mind the warning given by the Council* which, in praising a large family, requests of the parents maturity, prudence, and mutual agreement before producing more children.

To conclude this point, we emphasize that although the opinion of the Church has not changed (praise of fertile marriage), it takes into consideration the changed sociological factors (by which a marriage can be deemed generously fertile even with very few children) and the changed structure of the individual human being in the sense that, being more responsibly mature, the individual must not receive detailed precepts regarding his fertility in the family, but must judge by himself whether this precept is truthfully put into practice.

Up to now I have said nothing about the means by which a married couple may achieve conscious procreation control by the reflection of a mature conscience. Much can be said in this field; in order to frame the ideas, we may affirm that there are some sure means which are good from the point of view of human and Christian morals. There are others which, with equal certainty, are morally bad and repulsive to any conscience. But between the two extremes there is a certain range, still not wholly explored, of means and methods open to discussion which can not yet be catalogued either in the first or in the second of these two classes.

It is certain, for instance, that the Ogino Knaus method is considered morally sound by everybody, though it is not considered by everybody to be fully efficient in obtaining the desired result, and at this point probably many factors are brought into action, among them the intelligence and the constancy of the couple, apart from the perfect normality, or otherwise, of the female organism.

Even recently the Holy Father, speaking about the necessary study of theologians of the new birth rate and family problems, while invoking everybody's patience in awaiting the results of this study, said that limitation of birth can always be obtained by the married couple through that method.

Gaudium et Spes, vol. 50.

It is equally certain that no Catholic and no judicious non-Catholic can accept abortion as the means of birth control either in a family or in a nation. Abortion is a calamity to be fought against by all possible means, among these the spreading of other efficient and morally acceptable methods, to avoid such terrible infanticide inside the mother's womb.

The moral evaluation of both methods of birth control stated above is clear, but one should also note that, as a general rule, families are anxiously on the lookout for science to provide something better. Knowledge of the human body's structure and physiology has sharpened this problem; it is not rare to hear from a good mother of a family, not particularly versed in biological studies, that she has no confidence in the use of the Ogino Knaus method for fear of secondary ovulations. Thus the terms of the problem are better known, and immoral methods like abortion are normally shunned. But as modern life becomes too weary and complicated for a mother to allow the bringing-up of many children, one understands the almost morbid interest stirred up by news of the discovery of progesterone derivates, known under the general journalistic name of "the pill." Thus procreation becomes an act controlled by biological technique and depending on the will of the married couple and not on chance.*

We have immediately asked ourselves if the use of such remedies is morally lawful. The writings of Catholic and non-Catholic theologians on this subject have multiplied day by day. Their chief consequence has been the enlargement of the field of discussion, shifting the interest of research from the limitation of birth to the intervention of technique in the physiologic phenomena of the human body, down to the fathoming of the ultimate significance of human sexuality.

Starting from the first question on the lawfulness of the use of progestogenics for the purpose of birth control and excluding the examination of possibly harmful secondary effects brought by their use, the position of the Catholic theologians is as follows: at first, in 1958, some theologians, e.g. Van Kol,[5] identify the use of such drugs with direct sterilization (i.e. the ablation of reproductive organs or some such hindrance to their function as the tying of uterine tubes). Pius XII condemned such methods that same year.[4] But in the immediately following years, the field of knowledge widened and one perceives a great variety of cases in which this pharmacological technique may be used. Moral judgment becomes more complex and is subject to distinctions. Two cases, for instance, lend themselves to discussion: the use of drugs to regulate the menstrual cycle and to maintain the

---

*Moral legality is under discussion not only for the "progestogenic" remedies. The recent discovery that insertion of small plastic spirals in the uterus prevents pregnancy has likewise set a problem for this system. Uncertainties as to moral evaluation depend on our ignorance of their function.

anovulatory state in a woman who nurses her child after parturition (a state existing normally when nature follows its normal course). Catholic opinion still remains contradictory; however, the problem becomes clearer year after year, and the group of theologians who accept the use of antiovulation drugs in such cases is increasing.*

Other facts occur which propose new questions; such is the case of the rape to which many nuns have been subjected in the Congo. We dealt with the following problem, It is right for a nun or any other unmarried woman to take protective measures with antiovulation drugs to prevent pregnancy in consequence of carnal violence?

Articles appeared in many specialized magazines, written by Catholic theologians — some of whom were opposed and others approved.†

The latter, more numerous, justified their statement in different ways. Father Hurth, for instance, makes a distinction between sterilization in itself and sterilization in a relative sense, that is in relation to the sexual acts or sexual duties ensuing from the matrimonial state of a person. In the first case there are qualifications of ethics, and therefore if a person who, not being married and having neither the right nor the duty, and not even the wish to accomplish sexual acts, uses antiovulation drugs to prevent possible pregnancy consequent to forcible action from other people, that person does not transgress any moral principles. It is merely a judicious administration of one's bodily faculties such as, for instance, a temporary suspension of the digestive faculty.

Lambruschini, on the contrary, omits all distinctions in sterilization and invokes a different principle: the one of a person's total well-being. In fact, a married couple has more means at hand in order to avoid fecundation, the Ogino method, for instance, or even abstention; whereas an unmarried woman who wishes to avoid an unwanted pregnancy imposed on her by violence has no other means. And, like in the case of a subordination to a whole, one might justify even body mutilation, thus sterilization by drugs, comparable to a temporary mutilation obtained on purpose, is in this case morally licit, for the fact that the wholeness of spiritual welfare is far more superior to mere physical well-being. Therefore, priority must always be given to the preexisting right of spiritual choice, rather than to a physiological process, when contrasts arise.

Having reached this point, one can easily foresee a further step in the discussion. If the biologic sphere is subordinate to the totality of a person's

---

*The theologians who approve are, for instance, Connel, Gibbons, Connery, Lynch, Haring, O'Collaghan, Fuchs, Nalesso. Contrary: Perico, Guzzetti, Zalda, Navarro.

†Amongst those in favour are Fuchs, Snoek, Ford, Kelly, Demmer, Palazzini, Hurt, Lambrischini. The last three have expressed their views in the magazine *Studi Sattolici*, December 1961, pp. 63-72.

spiritual well-being, then the question arises as to the limits imposed by God on man in the utilization of the generative faculty.

Since 1963 a new chapter is therefore open to discussion, the one of the ultimate significance of human sexuality and the lawfulness of interference by surgical and medical techniques of the physiologically natural processes of the human body.

It would be necessary to outline a brief history of the Christian point of view on sexuality and of the changes undergone by it through the centuries. Something of the sort has been done by Canon Janssens[2] and Father Schillebeeck in a conference at the Stensen Institute of Florence, which was later published in various magazines. These scholars have stressed the fact that during the early age of Christianity the biologic conjugal intercourse that was not directed towards procreation was not morally good (though not sinful, provided it was accomplished within legitimate matrimony). An accurate study of St. Augustine's texts can prove that the opinion then upheld was not founded upon the identification between biological moral laws, but upon the conceptions of Hellenistic culture passed into Christianity. To the Greek, a real man was one who had subdued the senses and lived by abiding to an intellectualistic vision of life.

Thus the sexual activity, which presents conducts of pure, irrational instinct, was considered as a return to the animal state, and this was an improper condition in the eyes of Greek humanism. Christianity felt this influence, and therefore there had been a tendency (of which St. Augustine is an authoritative exponent) to consider any form of sensual pleasure as a deteriorating factor never to be indulged in by a man in that he was a man and a Christian. Consequently, the purpose of procreation was set forward and assumed the importance of the primary aim in matrimony.

In the centuries following, however, scholastic philosophy emphasized this fact too much by identifying the biologic laws of sexual intercourse = procreation with those of sexual ethics. By extending this principle it would follow that it is immoral to go against the spontaneous biological order that takes place in the human body. The physicians' task would be to reestablish the natural biological equilibrium, to bring back into the stream of spontaneity the phenomena which occur in the human individual without modifying in the least their physiological trend.

This identification between the spontaneous biological order and the ethical order of the human individual is no longer supported by theologians. The trend is more and more towards morality founded upon the dignity of the human being, i.e. on his total well-being considered within its emotional and spiritual biological sphere.

One may assert that the appearance of antiovulation drugs in the medical field has set forth even more urgently a question which already existed. To what point is the intervention of technique and progress licit in the biological phenomena of the human body?

So far, a serious query has received no answer from the highest authorities of the Catholic Church; one should, however, note that this answer is not conditioned by uncertainty in the field of those moral principles which they profess. Rather it is science that fails to give sufficient evidence to formulate sure judgments. Theologians ask the scientists which techniques are humanizing (i.e. lead toward improvement, perfect the person) and which are destructive. After that they will answer the question of whether an action is moral or immoral, basing themselves on the principle that the dignity of the human being, taken in its totality, must be safeguarded. Should there be techniques which diminish and degrade such dignity and reduce man to the animal level, they shall be condemned.

But if, on the contrary, such innovatory techniques exist (or will be invented) that shall render man more and more complete and bring harmony to biologic, psychologic, and spiritual responses (and here we cannot pass over in silence that man's destiny is not purely earthly, but raised to Grace and released from the limits of time), then the theologians will be able to accept them as moral. Indeed it is, in a way, desirable that new ways of living should be discovered to allow man to move more freely toward those values that alone justify his life. This pertains to God's commandment, quoted in the first page of the Scripture, to dominate over everything by his intelligent action.

But to conclude, there is yet another very important point brought into focus in the moral polemic that has been stirred up by the advent of anti-ovulation drugs, namely, the significance of human sexuality. There have been some important studies by Catholic theologians, partly instigated by Freud's theories, but the decisive thrust has come from the appearance of certain drugs. The result has been the fall of the medieval theory that the primary purpose of matrimony is procreation. Recent studies[3] that examine the value of sexuality in wedlock emphasize the insufficiency of procreation as the only ground of intercourse between husband and wife. There is a value which, as stated in Council's Constitution *Gaudium et Spes,* remains unaltered even when there is the impossibility of producing children, and this is identifiable in that intermediation to which the human body must consent in order to attain emotional fusion, the only one that achieves the Scripture's precept: "They shall be two in one flesh." The procreative function, by itself, does not blend two persons; only an outward tie is formed: the presence of children. Pleasure can unite a couple even less; psychology has made quite clear that each party objectifies the other and lends it the quality of a thing. In a way, the search for pleasure as an end is love's grave.

But man acts in a truly human way when he makes use of sexuality as a language expressing deep affection, so deep that it cannot find a proportionate manifestation either in words or in a simple gesture, but only in conjugal intercourse significant of a loving gift of oneself in view of the fusion of two spirits. The bodily fusion (which clearly contains a large base of instinctivity, i.e. irrationality) is purely the means of fulfilling the affective possibilities (which are by no means irrational, but belong to the sphere of sentiment, typically modal of the human spirit) of the two parties at issue. One can say that the spouses, who have matured their affectivity in sufficient integration of their personality, have likewise reconstructed their person. They have obtained through the performance of sexuality that affective completion of their own persons which makes them quiet, self confident, responsible, innerly satisfied although life reserves trials and sorrows.

But all this is the result of the judicious use of sexual activity in wedlock; it must be taken as a language of affectivity implying an integrity of actions (each departure therefrom expresses no more the gift of oneself, but rather a selfish exploitation of the other party) and a consistency of these feelings in all daily circumstances.

Almost every day some new book appears on the problems that we have pointed out. One can therefore imagine the difficulty of synthetizing them in a few words. I am content with stressing but one fact: today, more than ever, the Church does not judge in the moral field on the ground of preconceived spiritualistic and intellectual positions. But demands much of science. Obviously not all, since the Church is well aware of the human condition, that incarnate spirit whose materiality is by no means despicable or degrading but which forms with the spirit one entity of eternal duration. From the physicians, the scientists and those married couples who have given evident proof of building an effectively solid family, the Church requires today the support that will enable it to form, in the light of Revelation, an ethically exact judgment suitable to the various circumstances of modern man.

Second Intervention

I would insist upon the collaboration which must exist between the theologians and the scholars of medicine and psychologists. The Church does not fear science, rather it expects from science many clarifying elements which are necessary in order to deliver moral judgment. For instance, the hypothesis expressed by the Hon. Matteotti, that free love is the progressive aim of humanity, we believers reply that we know how God has created man and therefore free love is immoral since it is contrary to the structure of human individual and prevents his perfection. But we do not exclude the argument of science, for by studying psychology without preconceptions, one discovers that monogamous love is a necessity for the individual. Through monogamy the individual achieves that full height which gives concrete form to human dignity.

Within that field of the human individual's dignity there are not only the arguments of the authorities, but likewise scientific proof. Let us look for them together and let us decide upon our aim: what kind of man do we want to realize? In a pluralistic society like our present one, such a study can be advantageously carried out in collaboration with theologians and scientists, believers and nonbelievers.

There is also another fact, we priests await even more anxiously than you for some results of this research on the licit means of birth control, which will be morally good and scientifically safe. We know what tragedies of conscience burst forth and torture married couples. We want young people to step into the path of matrimony with optimism and confidence. We desire even more than you do, the collaboration of doctors and theologians, the technicians of the body and the technicians of the soul, to help with the problems of man — man, that mysterious reality, made of body and spirit.

REFERENCES

1. BEIRNAERT, L.: Regulation des naissances et sexualité humaine. *Etudes, 1:*23, 1966.
2. CANON JANSSENS: Morale conjugale et progestigenes. In *Ephemerides Theologicae Lovaniensen.* 1963, pp. 781-826.
3. FATHER PIERRE: Sens de la sexualité humaine. In *Sexualité Humaine.* Paris, Laennec.
4. POPE PIUS, XII: Paper read at The Seventh International Meeting of Haematologists. *Acta Apostolica Sedis.* 1958, p. 734.
5. VAN KOL, A., S. J.: Progestiene hormon-praeparaten. *R Kathol Artsenbald, 37:*323-331, 1958.

B — SOME THOUGHTS ON MORAL PROBLEMS INVOLVED IN CONCEPTION CONTROL

A. A. BUZZATI-TRAVERSO

The problem of birth control, as I see it, must be considered from different perspectives according to whether one considers it as a phenomenon that interests the human population as a whole (the three billion and over alive today) or a limited fraction of it. The problem referred to the human population as a whole, as Father Dall'Olio has explained, arises in its very gravest form in that part of the world which has come to be called "underdeveloped," where the birth rate is two or three times higher than that of the technologically advanced nations. This fact has been caused, in the first place, by the introduction of antibiotics and insecticides on a large scale that have brought about a drastic and rapid lowering of mortality. The problem assumes other aspects in the technologically advanced countries, and in particular among the nations in which the Catholic religion prevails.

Until recent times the Catholic Church has expressed itself in negative terms on birth control, with methods different from the Ogino Knauss; one would then expect that predominantly Catholic nations would have a high birth rate. This is not true, because nations of the West, like our own, have a low mortality as compared with the rest of the world. The Italian birth rate in 1964 was 18.6 per 1000, which can be compared with a birth rate of 40, 48, 50 per 1000 in nations predominantly Catholic, like those of South America. What is true for Italy is true also for other European countries; for example, in 1964 the birth rate in Belgium was 17.1; in Luxembourg, 15.7, and in Austria, 18.8 (per 1000). There does not seem to be an immediate correlation between the religious ideology prevalent in a population and its birth rate.

On the contrary, the correlation which has been ascertained and discussed most is that between birth rate and the so-called standard of living. This must not be taken only in terms of amount of money available individually or to the average family, but on a more general condition, namely scholastic instruction.

Thus we see that those nations which, from this point of view, are very advanced, like those of Northern Europe, have for some time now stabilized their birth rate (or nearly so) on the basis of the criteria of family planning. This is justifiable by the preoccupation of parents to give their children the possibility of good living conditions, of being educated, and of becoming good citizens. However, in some of these nations we note that, particularly in this postwar period, there has been a return to higher birth rates. The most remarkable case, also because it is that of a very large population, is that of the United States of America, where there was noted a rise in the birth rate; however, this is now diminishing.

From the point of view of the Italian case, we find ourselves in a very serious situation, arising more from the Italian laws than from the Catholic Church. The fact is that we are still subject to a legislation which, if applied severely, could lead us all — we who speak and you who listen — to prison. Hon. Matteotti has in times past — and more than once — proposed in Parliament, along with others, the abolition of certain articles of the penal code and police regulations, but without any success. Therefore, we must try to obtain this first of all, something which, from what I hear, would not be entirely contrary to the affirmation of the Catholic Church today.

If now we come to the question of means, there is one that Father Dall'Olio did not mention, and I was astonished, in a way, since I believe it to be permitted by the Catholic Church, and that is abstinence. Historically there is a case, although *prima facie*, of a nation which succeeded in notably reducing its birth rate through this measure, a measure which came about in good part by late marriage. This nation is Ireland, which not much more than a century ago, following the national famine produced by the fall in the production of potatoes, had to face the tragic situation which is today actually being faced by the underdeveloped countries. Instead of resorting to unallowed contraceptive methods, Ireland partly solved the problem through migration, mainly to the United States, and partly through persuading individuals to marry late, because it is known that the fertility of women falls rapidly with age.

The other way is that pointed out by Father Dall'Olio — the method of Ogino Knauss; however, at the individual level, this does not give too much guarantee. Then there are other methods, the permissiveness of which requires discussion on a moral basis. In the Catholic religion the last word has not yet been spoken on what are and are not the so-called means against nature. This is an expression that I personally have never succeeded in understanding. If interventions of technology, biological or medical, are considered contrary to nature when they change the facts of life at the level of the birth rate, why is it not also against nature to intervene at the level of the death rate? In the past the problem of birth control was not posed because men were not controlling death, and therefore there was an equilibrium — so-called natural — between these two aspects of the biology of the human race. We have upset the equilibrium through the development of biology and medicine. We have upset it above all by the utilization of chemical products which have brought about a fall in infant mortality; the result is a perturbation of the natural equilibrium, to which we are now seeking to find a remedy by an intervention in the opposite sense, whose permissiveness and naturalness, to me as an individual, seem as acceptable as the first. In Italy, as I have said, the average birth rate is low. It is at its minimum in Northern Italy, especially in Piemonte, which, I believe, is perhaps the part of the world with the lowest birth rate (below the death rate). In other regions, notably Campania, Puglia, and Sicily, the birth rate is much higher. The result is that our population has grown in the last year to more than 52,000,000. From this viewpoint one can take two attitudes: that of saying that with the development of industry there will be an ever greater need for a labour force as the economists call for, and that therefore we do not have to be worried. Or it is possible to take another attitude; we must remember that in Italy today we already have a considerable number of unemployed. From my own point of view, I have never seen the sense of having too many people, that is to say, I cannot forget the horrors of which we are victims in Italy; the absurd assemblages of people in the large cities, such as on the periphery of Rome, are in large measure the product of this excess of population, which is concentrated in these horrid urban agglomerations and produces harmful effects at the biological and medical levels. One has read recently of an inquiry carried out on Roman babies; the results show that in certain boroughs there are twenty malformed babies per one hundred, due to the fact that they had not had the possibility of romping through the fields, as we of the older generation were able to do, more or less. I think, therefore, that birth control should become more widespread in Italy. The fact that there are meetings such as this, without the police putting us to jail, is a notable step forward — considering what used to happen not so very long ago. I remember immediately after the war, while living in Milan at the end of 1945, I proposed that the Circolo Filologico Milanese, a cultural association, should hold a debate on this subject. It was the late Professor Malcovati, who sustained the thesis of the inopportunity of birth control by whatever technique adopted, and I, on the other hand, sustained the timeliness of birth control in Italy by every possible technique, though possibly not with abortion, a technique which is unfortunately very widely used. Then the two of us were accused, even in the newspapers, of completely lacking a sense of morality. I recall that a colleague at the University of Pavia, a Catholic jurist, insulted me just for this fact. Today this could not happen and for this we cannot be anything but collectively pleased, but the relatively low average Italian birth rate should not make us think that planned birth control does not concern us. It concerns us, as it concerns all countries, although in smaller measure than in the developing countries. These latter find themselves in front of the acute problem, of which the Italians heard an echo recently when the Holy Father invited the population to collect goods, money, and provisions to send India. On that occasion we should not have limited ourselves to sending this help, but we ought to have offered to the suffering Indians also the most efficacious means of contraception and to have facilitated their distribution in every possible way. There is another step that we can take: When this problem is being discussed in international circles and in particular at the United Nations, the Italian Government should take up an attitude adequate to the situation. They ought to stop always voting systematically No when discussing the necessity of the United Nations as a body bringing the modern results of biology, medicine, and pharmacology to the knowledge of those people who badly need it. To conclude, my opinion is that today in Italy it is justifiable for the citizens to concern themselves with this problem.

C — CONTRACEPTION AND THE POPULATION EXPLOSION
ROBERT B. GREENBLATT

The headlong flight into disaster, resulting from the population explosion, should be of deep concern to all of us. If unchecked, it will pose irremediable problems to future generations. For the sake of our children and their children's children, world measures must be adopted now. Time is running out.

In 1650 the world population was one-half billion; by 1850 it had risen to one billion, and by 1930 to 2 billion. Demographers predict four billion by 1980. At this rate there will be standing room only unless measures are taken to curb the population explosion. This phenomenal growth in population was brought on by rapid development in medical science, the reduction in the infantile death rate, and the eradication of disease.

Let us look at the situation in my country. About eighty years ago when the Statue of Liberty was erected at the entrance to the New York harbor there was inscribed on its pedestal a poem by Emma Lazarus:

> Give me your tired, your poor,
> Your huddled masses yearning to breathe free,
> The wretched refuse of your teeming shore,
> Send these, the homeless, tempest toss'd, to me:
> I lift my lamp beside the golden door.

This generous offer by the United States of America to the oppressed, the dispossessed, and the underpriviledged people of the world is no longer in force. The immigration policy has been modified and greatly limited. Our ability to feed the starving masses throughout the world is being tested. Our wheat bins are being rapidly emptied. The population of the United States today is 200 million and will exceed 300 million by the end of this century. By the middle of the next century it is predicted that we will have 600 million people, and if this happens we will be burdened with the same socioeconomic conditions common to India and China.

Famine and poverty and the need for living space are the factors that breed war — they are the spoiled fruits of overpopulation. Hitler was motivated not only by a compulsive drive for conquest but also for Lebensraum — living room. His *drang noch osten* was to conquer the Ukraine — the wheat basket of Europe — in order to feed his growing Teutonic masses. Even laboratory rats, packed too many in one cage, become socially maladjusted and soon will devour one another.

Every child-bearing mother has a right to space her family and not be burdened by one child after another. It is in the interest of her health that she choose the time for her family increases. Every unborn child has a right to be properly fed, properly clothed, properly educated, and properly prepared for a place in the society in which he is to live. Every married couple has a right to conjugal love and happiness, unhampered by the fear of an unwanted child.

What can we do to control conception? Historically one of the first contraceptive measures is mentioned in Genesis. Onan was forced to marry his brother's widow according to Hebrew law. He wished to avoid the entanglement of paternity, and so the Bible records that *he spilled his seed upon the ground.* "Onanism," or "coitus interruptus," is the most widely used contraceptive technique employed to this day in both the civilized and uncivilized world. It is a practice that weighs on the conscience of man, and does violence to an act that should engender tenderness, fulfillment, and the sublimest of emotional nuances. A great deal of illness among women, manifested in a dozen different ways, may be traced to such and other unsatisfactory sexual experiences.

Various mechanical barriers have come into vogue from time to time: diaphragms, sheaths, and jellies. The lowly camel driver, aware that his transportation system might break down should one of his camels become pregnant, prevented their conception by inserting a pebble into the uterine cavity. In the 1920's, Berlin's Ernst Graffenberg, now residing in Israel, transmuted the Arab cameleer's stone into a ring of spun gold or silver, gentle enough for the human womb. This was in preantibiotic days. The use of the ring fell into disrepute as much from enmity of his colleagues as from corrosion and infection. Now a plastic device has become available which has proved safe and quite effective. The intrauterine contraceptive device, known as the IUCD, may be the answer for countries where literacy is low and the population explosion dangerously high. Expulsion of the device, uterine bleeding, cramps, and discomfort occur in 10 to 15 per cent of the users.

Of course, complete continence is the only method 100 per cent sure to control birth despite the recent claims of two English women that their conceptions were parthenogenetic. A London newspaper scornfully challenged their claims. One of the offended women brought suit in the courts of law claiming that her virtue and good name were sullied. The courts awarded her damages of several thousand pounds.

The rhythm method — that is, abstinence during the fertile period of a woman's cycle — is a method condoned and encouraged by the Roman Catholic Church. Not until 1930 did the Vatican modify the Augustinian rule that sex must be for procreation alone; then Pope Pius XI approved the rhythm method. A mandate for temporary abstinence, it would appear, is apparent in the Apostle Paul's Epistle to the Corinthians:

> Defraud ye not one the other, except it be with consent for a time, that ye may give yourselves to fasting and prayer; and come together again, that Satan tempt you not for your incontinency (I Corinthians, 7:5).

The "pill," now in use by some six million women in the United States, has been found to be safe and virtually 100 per cent effective. The modern advances in contraception are the result of newer knowledge in hormonal physiology and in the science of endocrinology. The study of endocrinology has revealed the mechanism involved in ovulation and menstruation. Now that we have discovered these secrets, and pharmaceutical laboratories have synthesized the very hormones produced by the ovary (and many other steroid preparations that simulate the action of these hormones), we can utilize our knowledge to the betterment of mankind. We have harnessed these hormones so that we can imitate the menstual cycle; we can reproduce some of the hormonal changes that take place early in pregnancy.

Soon after conception, the ovary produces hormones to support the developing embryo and at the same time prevent further ovulation, so that a woman will not conceive during her pregnancy. Nature has shown us the way, and we have applied these principles in the management of family planning. The contraceptive pill mimics this natural phenomenon. We have two regimens of the pill — a combined estrogen-progestogen pill and the sequential form. Some women may have side effects, and the physician may have to switch from one type of pill to another. At any rate, the patient and the doctor have a choice and it has proved a blessing not only to the women in the United States but the world over. Furthermore, the contraceptive pill may be employed to great advantage in the management of many gynecologic disorders.

It has been conjectured that the rhythm method discovered in this century as a method of limiting the family was not new but merely a reaffirmation of what the Apostle had advised. Many years before the time of Paul, the Preacher (Ecclesiastes 3:2-5) spoke of "A time to be born, and a time to die; . . . a time to embrace, and a time to refrain from embracing . . ." To read into this passage some contraceptive plan is to reach beyond the realms of reason. The rhythm method — according to Dr. Edward Tyler, an eminent authority on planned parenthood — is only 75 per cent effective. Because of its relatively low efficacy, many conscientious women who have tried rhythm and failed have given the method the sobriquet of "Roman roulette." Nonetheless, it is the only technique available to millions of practicing Catholics. When in 1954 Pope Pius XII made the statement that it was the responsibility of each family not to have more children than it could take good care of, he, in effect, struck a blow for birth control. Considerable dialogue is taking place among lay Catholic intellectuals, progressive bishops, the clergy, and the Vatican with a view of finding a solution to the birth control problem.

Whether or not the church plays a constructive role in planned parenthood depends, according to sociologist Charles Henry, on whether religious institutions are used to suppress or to release man's capacity to exercise moral responsibility. Reinhold Niebuhr believes that the function of religion is to help people develop and maintain their basic faith in the meaning of life, in man's dignity, infinite worth, and destiny. I have long felt that if the rhythm method is employed to circumvent conception, how can it differ from the "pill" or the other contraceptive devices? The intent is the same, God is not deceived. Whatever methods are used for family spacing and limitation of the population explosion are also good for the family unit, the existing children, the health of a future child, and of the mother-wife. God is on the side of man.

The ultimate goal of contraceptive measures is to provide the means whereby the destiny of man and the welfare of our world are not left to chance and sexual desire alone. Every child should be wanted, planned, with a design for his future welfare — not just born like sheep or goats. All of us are born *inter feces et urinam,* unfortunately far too many remain forever with the feces and urine.

Chapter 14

THE USE OF HUMAN PITUITARY GONADOTROPHIN IN SOME ASPECTS OF OVARIAN PATHOLOGY

A. C. CROOKE

Human pituitary follicle stimulating hormone (FSH) has been used in clinical trials in this department for the last six years. The material is supplied from the Medical Research Council's collection of human pituitary glands which totals between twenty and twenty-five thousand glands or 2 and 2.5 kg of dry powder per annum. This yields a very considerable amount of FSH. Most of it is being used for chemical and immunological studies and about a third for the treatment of patients.

Previously we had been working with gonadotrophins from urine, and in 1958 we reported a method for extracting human menopausal gonadotrophin (HMG) which could be used instead of pituitary FSH. The pituitary fraction used in most of our clinical trials[3] is called CP 1.

TABLE 14-I
TYPICAL ASSAY OF CP 1*

Standard	FSH	LH	FSH/LH
IRP-HMG	3004	516	5.9
	(1830-4300)	(230-906)	(4.8-11.0)
IU	429	258	1.7
NIH	16.9	0.17	

*The potency of FSH (CP 1) expressed in terms of the First International Reference Preparation of Human Menopausal Gonadotrophin (IRP-HMG), the new international standard, and the National Institutes of Health (NIH), Bethesda, standards. Results from five different batches.

Table 14-I shows a typical assay of CP 1 expressed in terms of the new international units and also in terms of the first International Reference Preparation (IRP) and of the NIH standards. The potency measured as FSH is between 400 and 500 IU. The preparation also contains luteinizing hormone (LH) and the ratio of FSH to LH is shown in the last column. The potency and the ratio have been remarkably consistent throughout about forty consecutive preparations.

The parameters which have been used to assess the response are the excretion of oestriol and of pregnanediol. Figure 14-1 shows the normal pattern of excretion of oestriol and of pregnanediol measured by an adaptation of the method of Brown and of Klopper, respectively,[1,8] and adjusted for treatment starting on day one. It will be seen that the oestriol peak occurs about day ten and the pregnanediol peak about day eighteen when there may be a secondary peak of oestriol also.

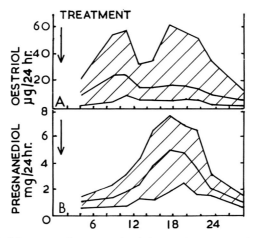

FIGURE 14-1 A and B. Mean, maximum, and minimum figures (shaded) for the excretion of oestriol and of pregnanediol by healthy women in selected specimens of urine. The first day of menstruation is adjusted to occur on day twenty-four. (Crooke *et al.: Obstet Gynaec Brit Comm, 70:*604, 1963.

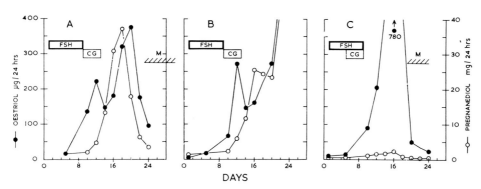

FIGURE 14-2. Abnormal patterns of excretion of oestriol and pregnanediol after treatment with follicle stimulating hormone and chorionic gonadotrophin. A, multiple ovulation; B, multiple ovulation with pregnancy; C, multiple follicular development without ovulation. M = menstruation. (Crooke *et al.: J Obstet Gynaec Brit Comm, 70:*604, 1963; *Acta endocr, (Kobenhavn), 46:*292, 1964) .

Abnormal patterns may be studied quantitatively and qualitatively. Figure 14-2A shows a quantitatively exaggerated but qualitatively normal curve. It is shown here because the exaggerated peaks demonstrate the time relationship to treatment more clearly and this time relationship is re-

markably constant from one treatment to another. There is a rise of
oestriol on about day ten, followed by a fall. It represents the secretion of
oestrogen by a developing follicle which then ruptures. Simultaneously
with the fall in oestriol, the follicle becomes converted into a corpus luteum
producing progesterone and this is reflected in the rise in excretion of
pregnanediol.

In this case there is also a striking secondary rise in excretion of
oestriol which reaches a peak almost simultaneously with the peak in
excretion of pregnanediol. Both steroids return to control values before the
end of the month unless the patient is pregnant. This is demonstrated in
Figure 14-2B. We believe that the secondary rise in the excretion of oestriol
is derived from other developing follicles and represents multiple follicular
development. The steroid pattern in Figure 14-2B was associated with the
subsequent birth of twins. Figure 14-2C shows a qualitatively different pattern. Here there is a quantitatively enormous rise in the excretion of oestriol
which again returns to control values before the end of the month, but there
is no midcycle peak followed by a fall and there is no corresponding rise in
pregnanediol. Laparotomies on patients who have shown this sort of pattern
have revealed multiple follicles which have failed to rupture. It is a pattern
which is sometimes seen when a patient has been given unsuitable treatment, but it is interesting because it shows that follicles cannot secrete
oestrogens for longer than about two weeks even though they may persist
unruptured for much longer.

Figure 14-3 shows a series of qualitative changes induced in the same
patient when given different kinds of treatment in different months. In the
first month she had gelatin followed by chorionic gonadotrophin (HCG) as
a control and both the oestriol and pregnanediol failed to rise (Fig. 14-3A).
In the next month she was given a highly potent preparation of FSH, and
there was a normal midcycle rise of oestriol, followed by a fall and a simultaneous rise of pregnanediol (Fig. 14-3B). There was no secondary rise of
oestriol, probably indicating that only one follicle had ruptured, and she
menstruated for the first time in seven years. Next she received a urinary
preparation supplied by Organon which contained a relatively high concentration of LH, but it was given in exactly the same dose (measured as
FSH) as in the previous month. She therefore received more total gonadotrophin than before, but she showed a very poor rise of oestriol at midcycle
and practically no rise of pregnanediol. There was, however, a curious
secondary rise of oestriol and she failed to menstruate (Fig. 14-3C). We
suspect that this represents the development of more than one follicle but
no luteinization. Lastly the same preparation of FSH in the same dose as
had been used in the second month (Fig. 14-3B) was repeated, but she had

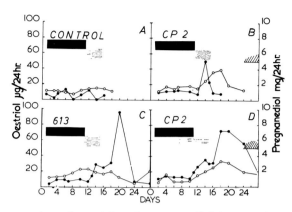

FIGURE 14-3. The excretion of oestriol and pregnanediol by a patient with amenorrhea treated with gelatin control or different preparations of follicle stimulating hormone and chorionic gonadotrophin. A, gelatin control; B and D, FSH (CP 2); C, FSH (613). M = menstruation. (Crooke *et al.: J Obstet Gynaec Brit Comm, 70:*604, 1963).

HCG for eight days instead of four and it overlapped treatment with FSH. Again she showed the typical midcycle rise and fall of oestriol, then a secondary rise associated with a considerable rise of pregnanediol, and she menstruated for the second time (Fig. 14-3D). We believe this again represents the development of more than one follicle, at least one of which ruptured. These qualitative changes suggest that when the FSH contained too much LH or when HCG was given for too long, it caused the development of multiple follicles.

For our quantitative studies we used a series of experiments of factorial design and investigated a number of variables. These were differences between patients, between successive months of treatment, between replication of treatment, between different preparations of FSH, between different daily and total dosages and number of injections of FSH, and between different total dosages, numbers, and timing of injections of HCG.

Figure 14-4 shows the results of one of these experiments. In this particular instance four patients received the whole dose of FSH in one injection or divided into two, four, or eight equal injections at two different dose levels. The HCG also was given in one or four equal injections simultaneously with the last dose of FSH or after it, again at two different dose levels. This is a half replicate design which enables many variables to be studied simultaneously.

Figure 14-5 shows some of the results assessed by a method of scoring.[3] It summarizes the results obtained in all four patients when given the whole dose as a single injection, or divided into two, four, or eight injections in different months. The top line shows the results when a high dose of FSH

The Ovary

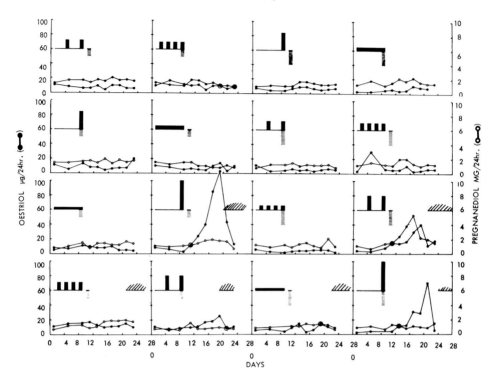

FIGURE 14-4. The excretion of oestriol and pregnanediol by patients given different treatment with follicle stimulating hormone and chorionic gonadotrophin. ▬▬▬, follicle stimulating hormone; ⅢⅢⅢⅢ, chorionic gonadotrophin. The dosage of each substance is proportional to the area of shaded surface. Uterine bleeding is indicated by diagonal hatching. (Crooke *et al.: J Obstet Gynaec Brit Comm, 71*:571, 1964).

was given; the bottom line shows when a low dose was given. There is a straight line relationship between the score or response and the number of injections at both the high and the low dose levels. It shows that the same effect is obtained with a dose of FSH given in a single injection as twice that dose will produce when divided into eight equal daily injections. From previous experiments, however, we concluded that a single injection of FSH tends to produce that qualitative pattern of steroid excretion which represents the development of follicles without luteinization. We concluded that three injections of FSH over eight days followed by HCG in the tenth gives the best results and uses only two-thirds of the material which would have had to be used if it had been given daily for eight days. This therefore became our routine treatment.

Figure 14-6 summarizes the results obtained in patients used in a number of previous experiments. Here also the results were assessed by a method of scoring. The first thirteen patients had prolonged secondary amenorrhea and

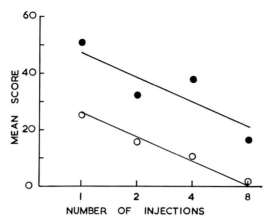

Figure 14-5. Regression of mean score on the number of injections at high and low dosages of follicle stimulating hormone. High dose ● = 571 IU Low dose ◯ = 343 IU. (Crooke *et al.: Acta Endocr (Kobenhavn), Suppl 111*, 1966).

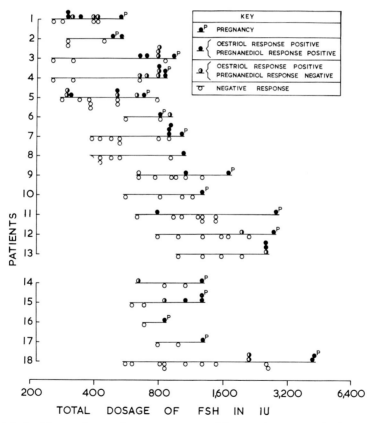

FIGURE 14-6. Positive and negative responses to different dosages of follicle stimulating hormone in thirteen patients with secondary amenorrhoea (numbers 1 to 13) and five patients with anovular cycles (numbers 14 to 18). (Crooke *et al.: Acta Endocr (Kobenhavn), Suppl 111*, 1966).

the remaining five had anovulatory cycles. Some had Stein-Leventhal syndrome. Different responses are shown by different symbols, and the dosages of FSH at which they occurred are given on the abscissa. There is obviously a striking difference in the dosages at which the different patients responded, and when pregnancy occurred it was nearly always at the highest dosage used for that individual patient.

Next a measure of the sensitivity of each of the patients was obtained by the method of Spearman and Karber described in Finney.[6] This gives an estimate of the ED 50, or that dose which, if it was repeated, would give a positive response 50 per cent of the time and a negative response 50 per cent of the time. Both groups of patients are arranged in ascending order of ED 50.

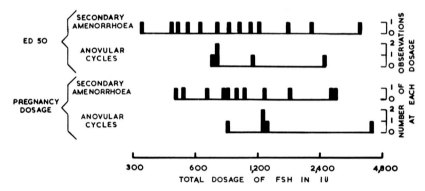

FIGURE 14-7. Distribution of ED 50's and dosages at which pregnancy occurred in patients with secondary amenorrhoea and with anovular cycles. (Crooke *et al.: Acta Endocr, (Kobenhavn), Suppl 111, 1966)*.

Figure 14-7 shows the distribution of the ED 50's and of the doses at which pregnancies occurred. There is no significant difference between the two groups of patients. There is at least a sevenfold difference in sensitivity between patients, but these patients comprise only one quarter of the total number of patients treated. Others had to be excluded because there was insufficient data to establish their sensitivity. Many had had only one treatment prior to operation; others became pregnant with the first dose, yet others never responded at all. Clearly the distribution of the ED 50 may be wider than is shown in this illustration.

We next expressed every dose given to each patient as a percentage of that patient's ED 50. This enabled us to superimpose all ED 50's. All doses given to all patients are shown in Figure 14-8. The ED 50 is at 100 on the abscissa. All positive responses are shown above the upper line and negative ones below the lower line. A dose-response line was then fitted which shows that at a dose of half the ED 50 a positive response would be expected to occur less than once in ten treatments, and at a dose of twice the ED 50 a positive response would be expected more than nine times in ten treatments. We believe, however, that at a dosage of twice the ED 50 there is considerable risk of an excessive response.

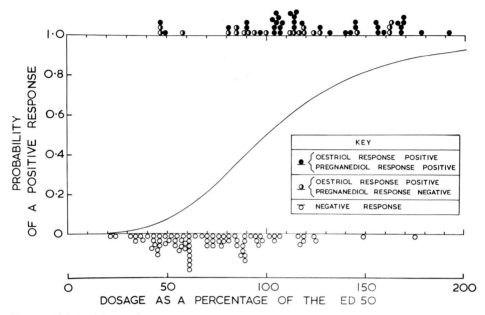

FIGURE 14-8. Positive and negative responses of the eighteen patients at dosages expressed as percentages of each patient's ED 50, and the resulting dose-response line. (Crooke *et al.: Acta Endocr (Kobenhavn) Suppl, 111,* 1966).

Figure 14-9 shows all the positive oestriol and pregnanediol responses which we have obtained in the series. The solid spots represent positive responses when pregnancy failed to occur. They tend to be to the right of the ED 50. The crosses are positive responses with pregnancy. These are still further to the right. The arrows are excessive responses with pregnancy. Obviously there were too few of these to draw firm conclusions, but they appear to be still further to the right of the ED 50.

There were three patients who responded excessively. They had abdominal pain and swelling with great enlargement of the ovaries, but their symptoms soon subsided. They are similar to patients with moderate "hyperstimulation syndrome" described by Lunenfeld.[10] In this paper, Lunenfeld reported six moderate and six severe cases in a comparable number of months of treatment. His severe cases had, in addition to these symptoms, ascites and pleural effusions, symptoms which we have never seen. Two had hemoconcentration and thrombosis, one had gangrene of a leg, and one died of cerebral thrombosis.

We believe that these severe complications can be greatly reduced by measuring each patient's sensitivity and adjusting the dose accordingly.

A sensitivity test has therefore been developed. Each patient is given a single injection of FSH, and if no response occurs, this is repeated at intervals with increasing dosages until a positive one is obtained, measured by a rise in excretion of oestriol. Figure 14-10 shows the positive responses of a group of patients to the first effective doses of FSH. The peak in excretion occurs between about days ten and twelve.

The dosage schedule[5] which we now use is shown in Table 14-II. The

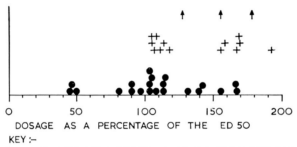

KEY :–

↑ PREGNANCY WITH SYMPTOMS OF EXCESSIVE RESPONSE
+ PREGNANCY WITHOUT SYMPTOMS OF EXCESSIVE RESPONSE
● POSITIVE OESTRIOL AND PREGNANEDIOL RESPONSE

FIGURE 14-9. Distribution about the ED 50 of dosages producing evidence of ovulation. (Crooke *et al.: Acta Endocr (Kobenhavn), Suppl. 111, 1966)*.

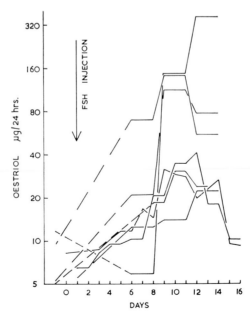

FIGURE 14-10. Excretion of oestriol by seven patients in response to effective test dosages given on day one. (Crooke *et al.: Acta Endocr (Kobenhavn), Suppl 111, 1966)*.

first dose is 500 IU, and if no response is obtained it is increased to 750 IU, and so on. The injection of FSH is invariably followed by 4,000 IU, HCG on day nine or ten. In this way we combine test and treatment, and the patient may become pregnant after the first effective does of FSH.[4]

This method of treatment is in striking contrast to the methods used by other workers. Gemzell gives injections of 108 IU, FSH daily for ten days, a total of 1080 IU, followed by HCG for three days.[7] Figure 14-6 shows that many of our patients were too insensitive to have responded to the dosage used by Gemzell, and many became pregnant at higher dosages than this. Gemzell's low dosage schedule probably accounts, however, for the relatively few instances of hyperstimulation syndrome that he has had.

Other workers prolong the treatment with FSH or increase the dose if they fail to get a response after several daily injections of FSH.[9,11] It can be seen in Figure 14-10, however, that a maximum response does not occur until ten to twelve days after giving an effective dose of FSH, and we believe that it is dangerous to attempt to assess further requirements on a day-to-day basis of response. We consider that this method of treatment is responsible for the high incidence of hyperstimulation syndrome reported by other workers.

We have observed this time relationship with various regimens of treatment. It is remarkably constant (Figs. 14-1 and 14-2), and we believe it represents the duration of the natural life of the follicle. If this is so, then prolonging the treatment with FSH or increasing the dosage during the course of treatment is unlikely to influence follicles which have already started to develop, but it may well stimulate more follicles to start growing and result in hyperstimulation syndrome.

Some insight into the mode of action of the gonadotrophins may be obtained by a study of the effects of FSH and HCG in the polycystic ovary of Stein-Leventhal syndrome, a condition which we have come to regard as one of altered physiology rather than a pathological entity.

Many workers have administered gonadotrophins to patients with Stein-

TABLE 14-II
DOSAGE SCHEDULE

Month	FSH Dosage (IU)
1	500
2	750
3	1,100
4	1,700
5	2,500
6	3,750

The total dose of FSH given on day 1 is increased by 50 per cent each month until a positive response occurs. It is followed by 4,000 IU of HCG on day nine or ten. (*Lancet*, ii:636, 1967.)

Leventhal syndrome. Some have assessed the effects by studying the changes in steroid concentration of the whole ovary, and others by measuring the steroids in ovarian vein blood. In both of these methods it seems likely that some of the steroids which are being measured have come from developing follicles, some from follicles which are regressing, and some from interstitial cells. We have studied this problem from a somewhat different angle and have measured the steroids in the cyst fluid of a number of different follicles from the same patient aspirated at the same time and from which portions of each cyst wall have been taken for histological examination. In some patients, samples have been obtained before as well as after treatment with gonadotrophins.

The typical steroid pattern found in the cyst fluid in Stein-Leventhal syndrome is shown in Figure 14-11, supplied by Dr. Roger Short of Cambridge University, with whom we have been cooperating. It shows a high concentration of androstenedione, little progesterone, and no oestrogens. It is presumably due to an enzymic defect resulting in a breakdown in the synthetic pathway to oestrogens.

The effects of treating patients with classical Stein-Leventhal syndrome are shown in the next three illustrations.[2] In these cases the magnitude of the response is not important, since this study was undertaken before it was appreciated that there are great differences in sensitivity to FSH between patients. No sensitivity tests were performed, and the dosages and dosage schedules were arbitrary. The qualitative changes are the important points, and these varied with the time that elapsed between treatment and sampling. The time relationships between the injections of gonadotrophins and operation are shown in the figures and the responses are demonstrated by the changes in excretion of oestriol and pregnanediol in urine.

Figure 14-12 shows the effect of treatment when samples were obtained at operation performed only a few hours after the injection of HCG. The urinary oestriol was still rising and the pregnanediol was low. Fluid was obtained from nine cysts, and the results are plotted on the right with the mean values shown by the boxes. There was a striking increase in progesterone, 17-hydroxyprogesterone, and oestradiol while the androstenedione was low. The high progesterone was surprising since there was no macroscopic or microscopic evidence of luteinization. Presumably it reflects the rapid turnover to oestrogens, and little found its way into the bloodstream to be excreted as pregnanediol. The remarkable feature here is the similarity in the steroid pattern in the fluid from all the cysts sampled and the striking contrast with that of untreated Stein-Leventhal syndrome.

Figure 14-13 shows the effect of treatment when samples were obtained at operation performed a week after the injection of HCG. The urinary steroid pattern is in keeping with ovulation, and a recent corpus luteum was found. Several small cysts were aspirated, but insufficient fluid was obtained for individual studies to be made. The samples from each ovary were pooled separately and the results obtained with the two pools are shown on the right. Both gave remarkably similar results. There was a

CONCENTRATIONS OF STEROIDS IN FOLLICULAR FLUID

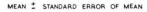

MEAN ± STANDARD ERROR OF MEAN

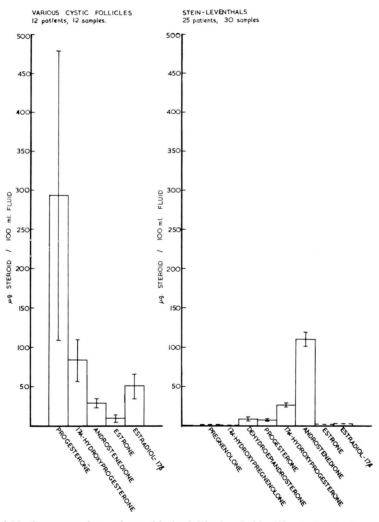

FIGURE 14-11. Concentrations of steroids in follicular fluid. (Short, R. V.: *Proceeding of the Second International Congress on Endocrinology,* London, 1964. ICS 83, Amsterdam Excerpta Medica Foundation) .

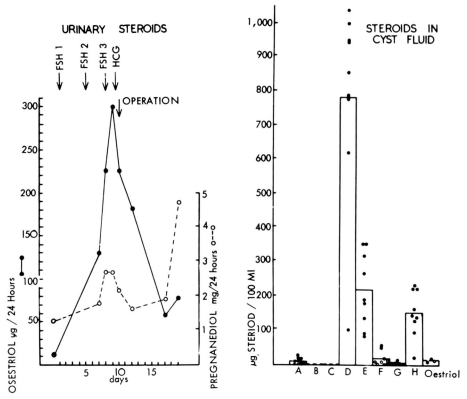

FIGURE 14-12. Concentration of oestriol and pregnanediol in urine following treatment with follicle stimulating hormone and chorionic gonadotrophin and concentrations of steroids in cyst fluid removed at operation eighteen hours after giving chorionic gonadotrophin. Key to cyst fluid steroids in this and following figures: A = pregnenolone; B = 17α-hydroxypregnenolone; C = dehydroepiandrosterone; D = progesterone; E = 17α-hydroxyprogesterone; F = androstenedione; G = oestrone; H = oestradiol-17β. (Reference to this and following figures — Crooke, A. C.: *Proceedings of the Fifth World Congress on Fertility and Sterility*, ICS 133. Excerpta Amsterdam, Medica Foundation, 1967, p. 56.

striking increase in progesterone and 17-hydroxyprogesterone but little androstenedione or oestrogen. It is remarkable that the fluid obtained from the tiny surviving cysts should show such a different steroid pattern to that found in untreated Stein-Leventhal syndrome, but histologically they showed luteinization of the theca interna and frequent haemorrhages.

Figure 14-14 shows an extraordinary contrast with the previous two slides. There was a dramatic rise in the excretion of urinary steroids, but these had returned to control levels as usual before the end of the month, indicating a normal life span in the capacity of the follicles to synthesize oestrogens. The operation was delayed, however, until thirty-three days after the injection of HCG. The ovaries were still greatly enlarged and contained numerous large follicles. Seven of these were aspirated, and all showed a steroid pattern typical of Stein-Leventhal syndrome. This seems to indicate that follicles which had produced enormous quantities of oestrogens for the normal length of time had now lost this capacity and synthesis had become arrested at androstenedione again.

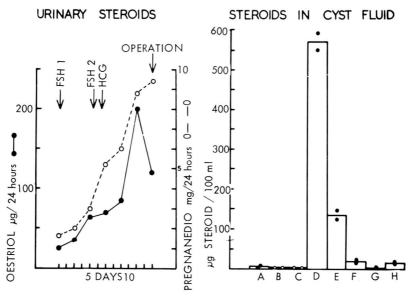

FIGURE 14-13. Concentration of steroids in urine and in cyst fluid removed at operation six days after giving chorionic gonadotrophin.

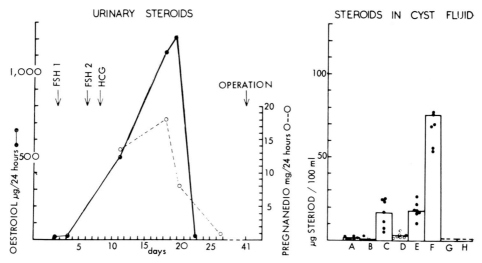

FIGURE 14-14. Concentration of steroids in urine and in cyst fluid removed at operation thirty-four days after giving chorionic gonadotrophin.

We have treated fourteen other patients with polycystic ovaries in a similar way. Some failed to respond to the arbitrary dosage but the others showed similar patterns to these, depending on the time when samples were taken. We believe this indicates altered physiology, as was said earlier, and that it demonstrates rather well the response of the ovary to unsuitable amounts or wrong proportions of the two gonadotrophins or perhaps to poor end-organ response to normal amounts of hormones.

*   *   *

This work was supported by a block grant from the Medical Research Council and a grant from The Ford Foundation.

REFERENCES

1. BROWN, J. B.: Metabolism of oestrogens and the measurement of the excretory product in the urine. *J Obstet Gynaec Brit Emp, 66:*795, 1959.
2. Gonadotrophins in Stein-Leventhal Syndrome in Fertility and Sterility. Proceedings of the Fifth World Congress on Fertility and Sterility ECS 133, Amsterdam, Excerpta Medica Foundation, 1967, p. 56.
3. CROOKE, A. C.; BUTT, W. R., and BERTRAND, P. V.: Clinical trial of human gonadotrophins. III Variation in sensitivity between patients and standardisation of treatment. *Acta Endocr (Kobenhavn), Suppl 111,* 1966.
4. CROOKE, A. C.; BUTT, W. R., and BERTRAND, P. V.: Treatment of idiopathic secondary amenorrhea with single injections of follicle stimulating hormone and chorionic gonadotrophin. *Lancet, ii:*514, 1966.
5. CROOKE, A. C. *et al.:* Treatment of infertility and secondary amenorrhoea with follicle stimulating hormone and chorionic gonadotrophin. *Lancet, ii:*636, 1967.
6. FINNEY, D. J.: *Statistical Method in Biological Assay.* London, Griffin, 1952, p. 524.
7. GEMZELL, C. A.; ROOS, P., and LOEFFLER, F. E.: The clinical use of pituitary gonadotrophins in women. *J Reprod Fertil, 12:*49, 1966.
8. KLOPPER, A. I.: The excretion of pregnanediol during the normal menstrual cycle. *J Obstet Gynaec Brit Emp, 64:*504, 1957.
9. LUNENFELD, B.: Urinary gonadotrophins. *Proceedings of the Second International Congress of Endocrinology,* Part II, p. 814. Edited by S. Taylor, Amsterdam, Excerpta Medica Foundation, 1965.
10. MOZES, M. *et al.:* Thrombo-embolic phenomena following ovarian stimulation with human gonadotrophins. *Lancet, ii:*1213, 1965.
11. VANDE WIELE, R. L., and TURKSOY, N.: Treatment of amenorrhoea and of anovulation with human menopausal gonadotrophins. *J Clin Endocr, 25:*369, 1965.

Chapter 15

THE USE OF HUMAN MENOPAUSAL GONADOTROPINS IN GONADAL PATHOLOGY

B. LUNENFELD

I WOULD LIKE TO DISCUSS our experience in the treatment of gonadotropic insufficiency. I will present our successes and failures and discuss some of the many unanswered questions and obstacles with which we are still confronted. Permit me first to synchronize our definitions — that is, to state what we mean by gonadotropic insufficiency.

We believe that gonadotropic insufficiency is due to lack of production of gonadotropins by the pituitary gland, lack of release of gonadotropins from a normally producing pituitary, or a relative insensitivity of the gonads to a normal stimulus of gonadotropins. In humans, differentiation between lack of production and lack of release is not feasible today. In animals, one can extirpate the pituitary and assay gonadotropic content of the pituitary gland and blood, and obtain information about gonadotropic release mechanisms. Recently, experimental evidence has accumulated, pointing to clomiphene citrate as a potential modifier of pituitary activity, by causing the release of gonadotropins. This question is still being discussed and much controversy exists as to the mechanism of action of clomiphene citrate. Should the findings be confirmed that clomiphene citrate causes the release of gonadotropins, it will be possible to differentiate between gonadotropic insufficiency due to lack of release (those who respond to clomiphene therapy) and those with gonadotropic insufficiency due to lack of production (unresponsiveness to clomiphene, but responsiveness to human gonadotropins).

To differentiate between a relative gonadotropic insufficiency and relative gonadal unresponsiveness to gonadotropins, urinary assays of gonadotropins, in relation to urinary steroids, can be of definite help. To substantiate such a diagnosis, a gonadotropin stimulation test can be performed.[5] Gonadotropic insufficiency due to imbalance of FSH-LH ratio (due to failure of production or release), or specific relative unresponsiveness of certain gonadal elements to FSH or LH, may exist. The evaluation of such a group, if it actually exists, will only be possible by precise, selective FSH and LH determinations. Therefore, in treating gonadotropic insufficiency and considering the above-mentioned, gonadotropic therapy would be useful in all categories and clomiphene, specifically in those cases where impairment of gonadotropic release is anticipated.

First we will discuss gonadotropic insufficiency in female patients. The second part of our presentation deals specifically with the effects of gonadotropins on testicular function in the sterile male. Patients with normally responsive ovaries and a specific gonadotropic deficiency can be treated with combinations of HMG and HCG. Patients with anovulatory cycles associated with hypersensitive ovaries could be treated with HCG or with a combination of HMG and HCG together with an antiovulatory compound. Patients with anovulatory cycles associated with unresponsive or hyposensitive ovaries (possible metabolic block or interfering steroid action) could be treated with HMG and HCG. Patients suffering from sterility, but with ovulatory cycles (prolonged follicular phase with biphasic basal temperature and a normal corpus luteum activity due to diminished ovarian responsiveness) as well as sterile patients with ovulatory cycles and delayed onset of the follicular phase (with biphasic temperature and a normal corpus luteum) could be treated by timing, with HMG, HCG or clomiphene. Sterile patients with ovulatory cycles but insufficient corpus luteum activity could be treated with clomiphene or HCG.

For the past thirty-five years, gonadotropins from various sources (mammalian pituitary glands, serum of pregnant mares, urine of pregnant women and, more recently, from postmortem human pituitaries and human postmenopausal urine), or combinations of them, have been used in clinical trials (see references 3, 15, 16, 17, 21, and 22).

Gonadotropins of animal origin gave inconsistent results which may be attributed to the formation of neutralizing antibodies to heterologous gonadotropins, following repeated or prolonged administration. Usually, initial ovarian stimulation can be evoked.[1] Subsequent response, however, depends upon the time of appearance and the quantity of circulating neutralizing antibodies. The divergency of results can be attributed to treatment schedules and to the individual antibody-production rate. To avoid therapeutic failures due to the formation of neutralizing antibodies, gonadotropins from human sources only should be used for clinical treatment. Human chorionic gonadotropins, which of course will not produce antibodies, have been used extensively. A certain success rate was established, and there are quite a number of "chorionic gonadotropin babies." Today we know that treatment with human chorionic gonadotropins will be effective only in cases of relative or absolute LH deficiency. In these cases, HCG will be effective only after sufficient follicle stimulation. Therefore, proper timing and dosage are essential. In 1958, Gemzell, Diczfalusy, and Tillinger[7] published their first report on the use of human pituitary gonadotropins (obtained from postmortem pituitaries) in the induction of ovulation. We will not elaborate on these findings, since these were discussed by Dr. Crooke. Therefore I will discuss only the experience of the Tel-Hashomer group with the use of human menopausal gonadotropins for induction of ovulation.

More than twelve years ago, we established[4] that human menopausal gonadotropins (HMG) were effective gonadal stimulators in hypophysectomized laboratory mammals. By 1959, Donini had succeeded in purifying such preparations to the extent that they could be used in humans. We succeeded for the first time to show that these preparations, prepared by Donini, were potent stimulators of ovarian activity in the human, as indicated by steroid excretion patterns and endometrial and vaginal morphology.[5]

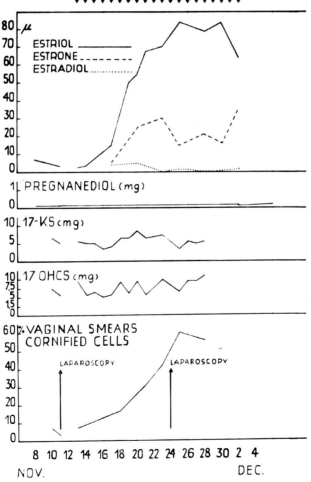

FIGURE 15-1. Urinary steroid excretion patterns and vaginal cytology during HMG treatment in a primary amenorrhea patient.

Figure 15-1 demonstrates laboratory data in treatment using only HMG. Urinary estrogens, pregnanediol levels, vaginal smears, and endometrial biopsies were used as the criteria of ovarian response. A rise of estrogens, without increase in pregnanediol, accompanied by a proliferative endometrium, was considered as definite evidence of follicle response. During the thirteen days of therapy, urinary estriol excretion increased from 8 to 80 μg. There was no increase in pregnanediol. At laparoscopy, on the twelfth day of treatment, the ovaries were found to be hyperemic and contained a number of protruding follicles. Similar hormonal excretion patterns were observed in all patients who received only HMG.

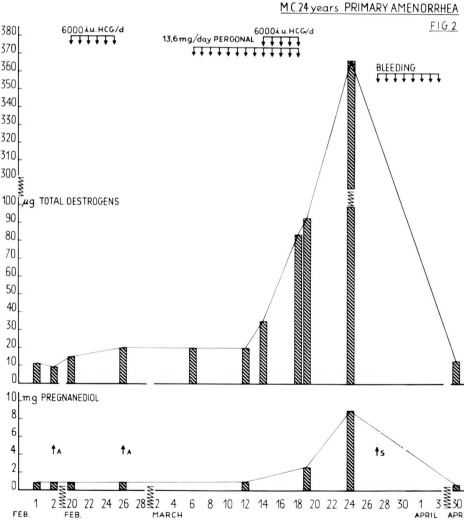

FIGURE 15-2. Urinary steroid excretion patterns during HMG and HCG treatment in amenorrheic patient.

Figure 15-2 presents data on a second case of primary amenorrhea. HCG alone (6,000 IU/day for six days) evoked no ovarian response. Progesterone administration evoked no withdrawal bleeding. HMG evoked a rise in urinary estrogens. When HCG was added on the ninth day of HMG therapy, peak values of 367 µg estrogen and 9 mg pregnanediol were obtained five days after all treatment was stopped. Uterine bleeding appeared fourteen days after the first combined HMG-HCG injection. An endometrial biopsy, at the time of bleeding, revealed a secretory endometrium. Although steroid patterns, endometrial and vaginal morphology, as well as basal temperature changes, seemed to indicate cyclic ovarian function, certain physiopathological conditions might simulate such changes as are seen after ovulation. Therefore, one of the following three criteria must prevail as crucial proof that ovulation has occurred: isolation of the egg, demonstration of the stigmata in the postovulatory follicle or in the fresh corpus luteum, pregnancy resulting from fertilization during treatment.

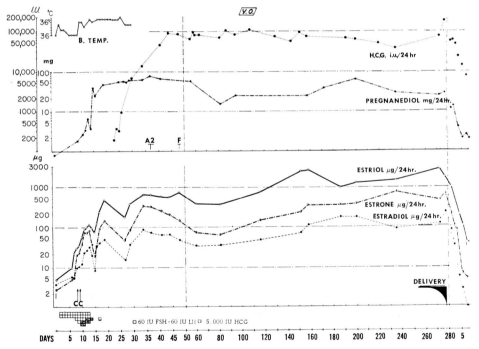

FIGURE 15-3. Urinary steroid excretion patterns during HMG induced ovulation and pregnancy in amenorrheic patient.

Figure 15-3 illustrates the data of our first patient, a twenty-six-year-old woman who became pregnant during HMG-HCG treatment. At the age of fourteen this patient had her first menstruation, which diminished gradually thereafter until amenorrhea, accompanied by galactorrhea, appeared at the

The Ovary

age of nineteen. There had been no previous pregnancies. Repeated gonadotropic assays during the six years prior to treatment gave negative results.
Urinary estrogens (estriol, estrone, estradiol) never reached a level of 10 μg
per day and the pregnanediol excretion never exceeded 1 mg per day. The
uterus was infantile and repeated biopsies showed an atrophic endometrium.
Progesterone evoked no withdrawal bleeding. HCG evoked no ovarian
response. Replacement therapy with estrogens and progesterone provoked
withdrawal bleeding, demonstrating a responsive endometrium. The 17-
ketosteroids and 17-OHCGs were at the upper level of normal and the protein-bound iodine was normal. The expected increase in estrogen excretion,
under the influence of HMG, was followed, after HCG administration, by
a continuous rise of estrogens, to an ovulatory peak of 110 μg per day, a
sharp rise in pregnanediol from 1.5 to 6 mg per day and a basal temperature
shift. Coitus was performed during the two days prior to predicted ovulation
time. The occurrence of ovulation, fertilization, and nidation was made
evident by the appearance of HCG in the urine twenty-three days after the
beginning of the course of treatment and by the birth of a healthy girl nine
months thereafter. The abnormally high values of estrogens and pregnanediol found between days ten and twenty may have been due to cyst formation. Although there was no complaint on the part of the patient, at this
time cysts were palpated in both ovaries. Even though urinary endogenous
HCG excretion went up to 100,000 IU per day, there was no further increase in the cyst formation. Actually, during the second month of pregnancy
the cysts had subsided. The rather flat urinary estrogen and pregnanediol
excretion slopes during the initial stage of pregnancy could be explained by
the fact that the excretion values of these steroids represent the sum of
endocrine activities of cysts and the corpus luteum, where cysts are in regression and the corpus luteum is increasing its function. The pregnancy terminated with normal labor and delivery, and the child is now five years old.
The mother is amenorrheic again.

During initial trials we based our treatment entirely on urinary estrogen
and pregnanediol values. In our subsequent work, we attempted to replace
at least part of the steroid determinations by simpler methods. Comparing
vaginal cytology and cervical mucus crystallization with urinary estrogen
determinations (Fig. 15-4), we were able to obtain some degree of correlation, at least in the sense that a negative ferning pattern never coincided
with high estrogen values. This permitted the reduction of the number of
estrogen determinations in a given treatment cycle to final days of treatment.

Practically the treatment is carried out as follows: The patient is usually
started on 2 ampoulles of HMG (150 IU FSH) daily and this dosage is continued until a positive response is obtained (fern test, vaginal smears and/or
urinary estrogen level). If, after administration of 2 ampoulles of HMG over

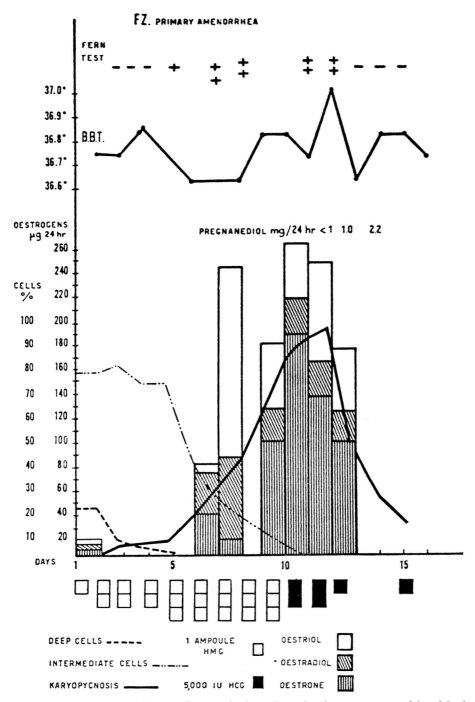

FIGURE 15-4. Urinary steroid excretion, vaginal cytology, ferning patterns, and basal body temperature during HMG/HCG treatment.

5-7 days no response is apparent, the dose is successively increased to 3 or 4 ampoulles daily. If the response to 2 ampoulles daily of HMG is too prompt the dose is decreased by 50% and the treatment is continued.

After the initial response is established the treatment is continued until maturation of follicles can be presumed, i.e. when the crystallization (fern) test is strongly positive (+ +) for 4-5 days and the karyopycnotic index reaches 50-80% and/or urinary estrogens attain the level of 40-80 mcgr/24 h. Then HCG is administered for induction of ovulation. We usually give 25,000 IU over a period of 3 days. The first dose of HCG is usually administered together with the last dose of HMG. Sometimes, however, depending on the patient's response (the size of the ovaries and the appearance of the external cervical os), the administration of HCG is delayed for 24-48 hours after the last injection of HMG. The patient is examined every day or every other day. Some ovarian enlargement and a slight tenderness in the fornices is usually found on vaginal examination. Sizable ovarian cysts have not been found following the administration of HMG alone. These occasionally appear after the HMG-stimulated ovaries are luteinized by the action of HCG.

Using this scheme of therapy we have up to now treated 133 patients throughout 264 cycles. One patient with Sheehan's Syndrome was also treated and conceived during the first course of therapy. She was, however, excluded from this study since she was receiving substitutional thyroid and corticoid therapy. All other patients had no apparent endocrine disorders apart from amenorrhea and/or anovulation.

The patients were classified into groups according to the level of urinary gonadotropins and the presence or lack of endogenous estrogen activity (Table 15-I).

Group I consisted of patients with primary or secondary amenorrhea. None of them responded with withdrawal bleeding to either HCG therapy and/or administration of progesterone-like substances. In none of these subjects could there be detected more than 8 IU of "total gonadotropic" activity in 24 hour urine samples. In some of them lack of ovarian activity was demonstrated by the low and noncyclic estrogen and pregnanediol excretion in the urine.

Group Ia comprised 10 patients with post-partum amenorrhea and galactorrhea (Chiari-Frommel Syndrome).

Group II consisted of patients with either secondary amenorrhea or oligomenorrhea or fairly regular anovulatory cycles. The common features of all patients belonging to this group were urinary gonadotropins in the normal range and evidence of endogenous estrogen activity as indicated by urinary estrogen assays, vaginal smears, fern test and/or the appearance of

TABLE 15-I.
THE DISTRIBUTION OF PATIENTS ACCORDING TO CLINICAL GROUP AND
PRESENTING SYMPTOM AND RESULTS

Clinical group	Presenting symptom	No. of patients	No. of courses	Efficiency of* treatment	Pregnancy** rate %
GROUP I low urinary gonadotropins; no evidence of endogenous estrogen activity	Primary amenorrhea	33	63	2.6	61
	Second. amenorrhea	52	111	2.6	69
GROUP Ia	Post-partum amenorrhea & galactorrhea	10	16	2.0	80
GROUP II urinary gonadotropins in the normal range; evidence of endogenous estrogen activity	Second. amenorrhea (MAP+) Abnormal follicular phase	11	20	3.3	45
	(oligomenorrhea)	10	15	2.5	60
	Anovulatory cycle	17	39	9.7	23
TOTAL		133	264		

*Efficiency of treatment = mean number of treatment courses per pregnancy in a given group of patients
**Pregnancy rate = the percentage of patients who conceived during treatment

withdrawal bleeding following administration of a progestational agent (MAP) *. Patients belonging to the respective Groups I, Ia and II differed significantly so far as the mean requirement of HMG and the mean duration of treatment were concerned (Table 15-II).

TABLE 15-II
COMPARISON OF THE MEAN DOSE REQUIREMENT AND DURATION OF GONADOTROPIC THERAPY IN PATIENTS BELONGING TO THE MAIN CLINICAL GROUPS

Clinical Group	No. of cases	No. of treatment	Mean dose of HMG (amp.)	Mean duration of treatment (days)
Group I	85	174	→ 36	→ 14
			↑ $p > 0.3$ ↓	↑ $p < 0.001$ ↓
Group Ia	10	16	$p < 0.001$ 25	$p < 0.001$ 11
			↑ $p > 0.6$ ↓	↑ $p < 0.05$ ↓
Group II	38	74	→ 17	→ 9

The results of gonadotropic therapy (see Table 15-I), expressed in terms of efficiency of treatment and pregnancy rate, were satisfactory in all subgroups of patients except for those with fairly regular anovulatory cycles. In these cases gonadotropic therapy was much less efficient and pregnancy rate significantly lower ($p < 0.01$). This series of 264 treatment courses given to 133 women resulted in 88 pregnancies. Sufficient data were obtained on 86, but 2 patients were lost for follow up. Table 15-III shows the outcome of these pregnancies.

Analysis of the material covering 264 treatment courses of combined HMG-HCG therapy reveals three significant facts: 1) there was a high abortion rate (29%); 2) excessive twinning occurred (30%); and 3) mild and severe adverse reactions occurred in 3.8% and 2.4% of treatment courses respectively (Table 15-V). It is of interest to note that these findings were not statistically related to diagnostic groups or gonadotropic dosage.

The excessive abortion rate can be explained by mechanical factors. This is not surprising, since most of the patients had a history of long-standing amenorrhea with hypoplastic uteri and atrophic endometria prior to treatment. In some cases the abortions could be explained on endocrinological grounds. During HMG stimulation, urinary estrogen excretion rose, and under HMG-HCG stimulation ovulation occurred. Nidation of a fertilized egg is evidenced by the appearance of endogenous chorionic gonadotropins.

---

*Medroxy-progesterone acetate, a progestational agent with no intrinsic estrogen activity.

Unfortunately, although the magnitude of the HCG seems normal, at the time of its appearance the corpus luteum was already in regression, as evidenced by a sharp decrease of urinary estrogens and prenanediol. The endogenous HCG seems incapable, at this stage, of augmenting the function of this regressing corpus luteum, and the patient aborted.

TABLE 15-III
THE OUTCOME OF PREGNANCIES OBTAINED IN 264 COURES OF
GONADOTROPIC THERAPY GIVEN TO 133 WOMEN

Delivered:		
Single	43	(70.5%)
Twins	15	(24.6%)
Triplets	2	(3.3%)
Quadruplets	1	(1.6%)
TOTAL DELIVERIES	61	
Abortions	25	(29.0%)

*Two patients with no adequate follow-up not included.

In a similar case substitutional therapy with estrogens and progesterone or synthetic progesterone analogues could not prevent abortion. The only difference between these two cases is that in the second instance the abortion was delayed, and ninety days after ovulation a macerated fetus was expelled. It can therefore be concluded that, at least in one group, abortions are due to an insufficiency of corpus luteum reserve at the time of appearance of endogenous HCG.

The excessive twinning rate (30%) and the adverse reactions in 6 per cent of treatments may be explained by hyperstimulation. During the normal cycle the rate and growth of follicles are regulated by a negative feedback mechanism. The growing follicle produces steroids which regulate gonadotropic function and this delicate balance between steroid production and gonadotropic release is probably responsible for the general occurrence of a single ovulation during one cycle in the human. Under exogenous gonadotropic stimulation, this delicate balance cannot be maintained and this is probably the cause of more than one follicle ovulating either simultaneously or successively. Since the range between ineffective dosage and overstimulation dosage is exceedingly small, we obtained single pregnancies only in 70% of the patients who delivered.

The adverse reactions can be explained on similar lines, except that in some instances, the exogenous gonadotropic stimulation evoked either ovulation (s) and cysts or only cysts. We have attempted to classify this hyperstimulation into six grades, according to the clinical and laboratory findings (Table 15-IV). In most of the patients, hyperstimulation was evidenced only by excessive urinary estrogens and pregnanediol, slight enlargement of ovaries, with or without palpable cysts (Grades I and II, Table 15-IV). Patients of these two grades required no treatment. In ten cases, enlargement of ovaries, cysts, low abdominal pains, and/or distension of the abdomen and nausea were noted. Five of these ten patients also vomited and complained of diarrhea. Patients of these two grades (III and IV) required medical observation and no further exacerbations or complications occurred.

TABLE 15-IV
HYPERSTIMULATION CLASSIFICATION

Laboratory and Clinical Findings	I	II	III	IV	V	VI
			Mild		*Severe*	Adverse Reactions
Estrogens >150 μg/24h	+	+	+	+	+	+
Pregnanediol >10 mg/24h	+	+	+	+	+	+
Enlarged ovaries		+	+	+	+	+
Palpable cysts		?	+	+	+	+
Distension of abdomen			+	+	+	+
Nausea			+	+	+	+
Vomiting				+	+	+
Diarrhea				?	+	+
Ascites					+	+
Hydrothorax					?	+
Changes in blood volume, viscosity, and coagulation time						+
	Require no treatment		Require observation		Require hospitalization	

Six patients presented themselves with enlargement of ovaries, cysts, distension of the abdomen, nausea, vomiting, diarrhea, and ascites — four of them with hydrothorax also (Grade V). Three patients of Grade V showed changes in blood volume, viscosity, and hypercoagulability (Grade VI). Grades V and VI needed hospitalization and therapeutic control of blood volume, viscosity, and coagulation time, as well as evacuation of fluids from abdominal and pleural cavities. However, in none of these cases was laparotomy or excision of cysts or ovaries required. Grades V and VI were classified as severe adverse reactions. The difference between this dose of gonadotropins which causes ovulation and that which evokes hyperstimulation is exceedingly small. Therefore it seems practically impossible to predict the occurrence of adverse reaction in any given patient before onset of therapy.

These findings led to a hypothetical assumption that in some cases, hyperstimulation symptoms, (mild and/or severe reactions), are probably due to a metabolic disorder of the corpus luteum. This possibility was investigated in two cases by searching for the presence of abnormal steroids in urine. In both patients, amounts of at least one steroid (pregnanetriol) were excreted in abnormally high quantities. Table 15-VI illustrates one case where pregnanetriol up to 27 mg per twenty-four hours was excreted. Comparable amounts are sometimes found in urine of patients with adrenal hyperplasia

TABLE 15-V
THE INCIDENCE OF HYPERSTIMULATION OF 264 COURSES OF
GONADOTROPIC THERAPY (IN BRACKETS - % OF COURSES)

			Grade of hyperstimulation			
I	II	III	IV	V	VI
	No clinical reaction		Mild adverse reaction		Severe adverse reaction	
?*	19	5	5	3	3
	(7.2)	(1.9)	(1.9)	(1.2)	(1.2)
	Require no treatment		Require observation		Require hospitalization	

*The exact number of courses with laboratory hyperstimulation (Grade I) cannot be assessed, since urinary steroid determinations were not performed in all treatment cycles.

due to adrenogenital syndrome. Since pregnanetriol could not be suppressed by dexamethasone in this case, and also because of its decline to normal values at the end of the first trimester of pregnancy (coinciding with the regression of corpus luteum of pregnancy), it can be assumed that the pregnanetriol found was a metabolite of 17-OH progesterone of ovarian origin. These findings indicate a metabolic defect of the corpus luteum. With this in mind, we are continuing our search for other steroids to obtain a clearer understanding of the factors causing the symptoms of at least part of the patients of Group VI.

TABLE 15-VI
HMG-HCG TREATMENT

Ki. A. 59/149 — Severe Side Effects (during early pregnancy)			
Days Postovulation	Pregnanetriol mg/24 hr	Pregnanediol mg/24 hr	Estriol µg/24 hr
24		38	
28	14	41	784
36	10		
44	27	60	241
64			684
92	9	24	971
99	4	25	805
117	1.9	25	945
146	0.95	17	880
182	0.41	11	7000

It is of interest to note that even excessive amounts of HMG or HCG did not evoke any adverse reactions in patients lacking ovarian responsiveness to gonadotropins, nor in male patients treated with massive doses for periods as long as 150 days. This brings us to our second subject: the treatment of gonadotropic insufficiency in the male. In male patients, gonadotropic insufficiency can lead to a variety of symptoms ranging from complete loss of all testicular functions to either variations in sperm quality or relative

changes in potency. The spermiogenic and androgenic functions are com-
plementary and localized in the same gland. However, fluctuations in their
levels of activities do not always occur simultaneously. Under pathological
conditions it is not uncommon for a testicular disorder to affect selectively
only one of these functions. The symptomatology will therefore depend
upon the nature of the deficiency, on the time lapse between the onset of
the deficiency and its recognition, plus the age of the patient at the time of
onset.

Past history of the patient, physical examination, laboratory findings,
nature of the ejaculate and the morphological appearance of the testes must
influence the choice of therapy.[1,2,9,13,14] Knowledge of biosynthesis of steroids
by the intertubular tissue which contains the Leydig cells has accumulated
since David *et al.* isolated testosterone in its pure form from bovine testes
in 1935, and several pathways of testosterone biosynthesis have since been
proposed. Furthermore, the chronology of events leading from the spermato-
gonium to the spermatid (spermatogenesis) and their differentiation from
mature spermatozoa (spermiogenesis) are fairly well understood. The
kinetics of the germinal epithelium in men have recently been reviewed by
Heller and Clermont.[10] In their elaborate studies of the cycles of human
spermatogenesis, using tritiated thymidine as their tracer compound, they
concluded that the duration of spermatogenesis in man is close to seventy-
four days with a possible variation of four or five days. Heller and Clermont,
considering the views of other authors that spermatogenesis begins with the
formation of new stem cells, postulate that if valid, this would correspond
to the formation of a new type of Ad spermatogonia. If this is the case,
spermatogenesis of man would last ninety days, i.e. sixteen days (one cycle)
more than the previous estimate. However, little is known about the nature
of the factors which control the successive stages of spermatogenesis and
spermiogenesis.

The scarcity of knowledge on testicular physiology may in part have
been responsible for the inconsistent results reported on empirical treatment
of hypogonadism throughout the past thirty years. The lack of suitable
human gonadotropic preparations for therapeutic use has hampered our
understanding of testicular physiology and treatment of hypogonadism. The
divergency of results obtained in the use of gonadotropins of animal origin
may be attributed to the formation of neutralizing antibodies to heterologous gonadotropins following repeated and prolonged administration. Results
with such therapy partly depend upon the time of appearance and the
quantity of circulating antibodies.

Human chorionic gonadotropins (HCG) have been used extensively.
HCG will stimulate androgenic production of the intertubular tissue (Leydig cells) and may thus bring about an amelioration of symptoms which

were due to androgenic insufficiency. The hormonal activity culminates in the production of testosterone which determines both the output of seminal plasma by the accessory organs of reproduction as well as the secondary sex characteristics. HCG should only be administered in cases of seminal plasma insufficiency (ejaculate less than 1.5 ml) and in cases with under-development of secondary sex characteristics. Its effectiveness will depend upon the extent of endogenous FSH stimulation and on the stage of the seminiferous tubules at the time treatment is initiated.

The management of absolute FSH deficiency or a deficiency of both gonadotropic hormones (FSH and ICSH) presents a more difficult problem. Such deficiencies may be overcome by extracts containing both FSH and ICSH activities. An extract of pooled menopausal urine was investigated for its gonadotropic activity[4] in hypophysectomized immature rats. It pro-duced repair of the interstitial cells of the testes and evoked complete spermatogenesis. Since such extracts (Pergonal) for human use have become available, it was possible to investigate their effects in clinical studies. Resto-ration of spermatogenesis in a hypophysectomized patient, by Pergonal, has been reported by MacLeod et al.[19] in 1964. Treatment of this patient was started when the process of involution of the seminiferous tubules was virtually complete. After sixty-seven days of daily Pergonal injections, his-tological investigation of a testicular biopsy revealed that maturation had occurred close to the stage of exfoliation of spermatozoa into the lumen. However, this stage of maturation was achieved only in some of the tubules. A testicular biopsy, performed one hundred days after initiation of therapy, demonstrated a fully quantitative restoration of spermatogenesis. There was no evidence of Leydig cell proliferation or successful ejaculation by the patient. This indicated that the ICSH content of Pergonal was insufficient for reparation of the interstitial tissue. Fifty-one days after initiation of combined Pergonal and HCG therapy, a measurable volume of seminal plasma was obtained in which the sperm count per milliliter was 60×10^6.

Heller[11] reported on a hypogonadotropic eunuchoid in whose treatment Pergonal was added after repair of the interstitial tissue with HCG. Eight weeks later, maturation of all the germinal elements was complete and ma-ture spermatozoa were found in the ejaculate. The microphotographic pic-ture of the biopsy taken after HCG therapy revealed, in addition to interstitial cell hyperplasia, a certain degree of germinal epithelium differen-tiation. It is therefore not surprising that complete restoration of spermato-genesis was obtained after a period of only eight weeks of Pergonal therapy.

Gemzell and Kjessler[8] have also successfully used gonadotropic extracts from pituitary glands for the restoration of spermatogenesis in one patient. Similar results on another patient, with pituitary FSH and HCG, have been reported by Davies and Crooke.[6] Since our previous reports by Mor et al.[20]

on three patients and by Lunenfeld *et al.*[18] on fifteen patients, we have increased our studies, which include 103 patients.

Patients, Materials, and Method of Investigation

In this study we investigated the effects of HMG (Pergonal) on testicular function in 103 patients. The patients were divided into three major groups:

I. Azoospermic patients 38
II. Oligospermic patients 48
III. Subfertile patients (subnormal sperm counts
     and/or impaired motility) 17

Group I was further divided into three categories according to the histological findings in the pretreatment biopsies. See Tables 15-VII, 15-VIII, and 15-IX. Group II was further divided into two categories: those with less than ten million sperm per milliliter (27 patients) and those with ten to twenty million sperm per milliliter (21 patients). See Tables 15-X and 15-XI. Group III contained patients with subnormal sperm counts (20-40 million-ml) and/or impaired motility (0-40). See Table 15-XII.

TABLE 15-VII
DOSAGE OF HMG (PERGONAL-500) ADMINISTERED AND RESULTS OBTAINED

Case	Age	Azoospermic - Group I-a* Amp of HMG (Pergonal-500)	Results
L.M./C-277	29	65	Viable sperm (preg.)
N.A./C-121	31	60	Viable sperm
S.N./C-208	35	70	Viable sperm (preg.)
G.A./C-422	26	60	Viable sperm
N.G./C-348	24	95	Viable sperm
M.J./C-398	29	40	Viable sperm (preg.)

*Group I-a: Azoospermic — small tubules (50-70 microns in diameter) with no lumen in *lobular* arrangement, containing Sertoli cells and cell elements up to spermatogonia, but with no signs of any spermatogenic or spermiogenic activity.

We selected only such individuals who had low or normal urinary excretion of 17-KS and low or undetectable urinary gonadotropic activity. None had a history of disease of the urinary tract or prostatic gland, or of infections of the reproductive system. Urological examinations of all the patients revealed no abnormalities. Deductions from the physical appearance of almost all the patients might be misleading since most of them had received symptomatic treatment with androgens or androgen-stimulating preparations before they were seen in our clinic. Due to this reason, we were restricted in evaluating the effects of gonadotropins by comparing the quality of the ejaculates before the treatment with that obtained after treatment.

TABLE 15-VIII
DOSAGE OF HMG (PERGONAL-500) ADMINISTERED AND RESULTS OBTAINED

Case	Azoospermic — Group I-b*		
	Age	Amp of HMG (Pergonal-500)	Results
D.S./C-138	33	72	Viable sperm
E.A./C-308	35	60	Viable sperm (preg.)
B.T./C-191	40	70	No change
G.Z./C-225	28	60	No change
B.I./C-310	26	72	No change
H.S./C-180	29	70	Viable sperm
J.J./C-365	32	65	No change
M.M./C-253	31	60	Viable sperm
J.S./C-433	37	40	No change
A.D./P-814	35	40	No change
S.N./C-217	36	40	No change
M.J./C-202	39	40	No change
B.J./C-298	23	50	No change
D.A./C-378	40	58	No change
C.S./C-501	38	60	Viable sperm

*Group I-b: Azoospermic — tubules of normal or near normal size with normal, moderate or thickened walls, containing spermatogonia and Sertoli cells and in some tubules also occasional spermatocytes. To this group were added those who had mixed forms, e.g. *some tubules* containing only Sertoli cells.

TABLE 15-IX
DOSAGE OF HMG (PERGONAL-500) ADMINISTERED AND
RESULTS OBTAINED

Case	Azoospermic — Group I-c*		
	Age	Amps of HMG (Pergonal-500)	Results
A.E./C-147	35	72	No change
G.I./C-219	23	60	No change
M.E./C-189	33	60	No change
G.M./C-31	30	90	No change
S.Z./C-114	39	60	No change
M.M./C-152	30	60	No change
G.M./C-197	28	60	No change
M.C./Z-111	29	50	No change
B.M./P-520	40	45	No change
Z.M./C-227	35	50	No change
A.J./B-118	26	65	No change
S.A./H-296	28	65	No change
S.J./C-243	34	35	Viable sperm
B.A./C-295	38	55	No change
C.S./Z-333	34	55	No change
H.S./C-456	34	60	No change
C.Z./C-492	42	60	No change

*Group I-c: Azoospermic — tubules of normal or near normal size with normal, moderate or thickened walls; *most of the tubules* contained Sertoli cells only.

A testicular biopsy was performed in all cases of azoospermic patients before initiating gonadotropic therapy, and a second biopsy was performed when the quality of the ejaculate indicated a definite change.

TABLE 15-X
DOSAGE OF HMG (PERGONAL-500) ADMINISTERED AND RESULTS OBTAINED

Oligospermia — Group II-a (less than 10 x 10⁶ sperm/ml)

Case	Age	Before Treatment Sperm Count x 10⁶	Per cent of Motility	Amps. of HMG (Pergonal-500)	After Treatment Sperm Count x 10⁶	Per Cent of Motility
M.N./C-351	40	3 – 6	10 – 50	69	12	2
K.J./C-305	50	<1	0	45	5	0
L.J./C-485	37	1 – 4	10 – 50	15	4	50
G.Sh./C-285	33	1 – 10	30	60	20	50 – 60
M.M./C-244	32	3 – 6	50	30	10	50
F.E./C-91	34	1	0	60	16	30*
K.H./C-317	31	2	30	60	20	40
G.A./P-580	29	<1	–	60	15	30*
BA.C./C-50	30	2	–	55	2	0
Ya.Ya./P-106	41	5	0 – 5	55	22	40
G.Z./C-154	50	5	30	60	5	30
T.M./M-111	26	2 – 4	0 – 5	40	25	40
D.M./R-111	51	1 – 10	10	30	58	15*
S.G./C-213	26	0.2 – 1	0 – 5	40	6	0 – 5
E.Y./P-471	30	<1	–	40	<1	0
A.S./C-118	21	<1	–	55	38	40*
L.Y./C-139	28	4	50	20	40	70**
S.Z./C-178	37	1	–	55	1	–
A.N./C-186	22	<1	–	55	71	70*
S.M./C-217	36	<1	–	40	<1	(twice preg. & abor.)
F.S./C-223	35	<1	–	30	65	60*
M.M./C-270	21	<1	–	30	<1	0
N.AW./C-316	23	<1	–	45	95	50*
M.M./C-345	33	<1	–	45	72	52*
P.E./C-415	22	<1	–	30	<1	–
E.M./C-141	28	5 – 10	0 – 5	30	40	65 – 70*
Ch.M./T-734	38	6	30	30	5 – 7	30

*Significant improvement.

TABLE 15-XI

DOSAGE OF HMG (PERGONAL-500) ADMINISTERED AND RESULTS OBTAINED

Case	Age	Oligospermia — Group II-b (10 - 20 x 10^6 sperm/ml)		Amps. of HMG (Pergonal-500)	After Treatment	
		Before Treatment			Sperm Count x 10^6	Per cent of Motility
		Sperm Count x 10^6	Per cent of Motility			
T.M./X-111	34	9 – 20	30	60	30	30
A.R./C-101	32	15	30	60	1	–
S.Sh./C-102	28	13	50	20	20	30
Y.D./C-273	32	12 – 22	20	55	6	60
A.Y./C-96	39	12	0 – 50	45	20	0
D.Sh./C-170	45	15	40	36	92	80*
D.Y./K-111	28	10	10	60	60	70*
S.A./C-131	27	15	30	45	40	60
Y.H./P-521	25	10 – 15	30 – 40	60	25	60
S.Y./C-245	36	9 – 17	30 – 40	45	37	60*
Y.Y./C-82	29	11	5	39	40 – 50	60 – 70*
M.A./C-299	34	15	30	34	40	30
P.R./K-113	36	10 – 12	30	45	20	55
L.C./B-111	38	10 – 15	30	30	30 – 40	50 – 60
V.A./C-81	34	15	40 – 50	60	5	50
A.S./K-281	29	15 – 19	35 – 40	30	56	60
E.Y./C-57	36	11	10	30	96	80
J.Y./C-220	28	12	50	35	35	50
Do.S./C-284	32	11 – 20	0 – 5	35	35	60
M.B./C-448	32	10	20	15	10	20
CH.D./C-497	33	16	40	60	39	70
B.J./T-787	32	13	50	55	10 – 15	50
S.G./P-113	33	10	20	30	9 – 11	30
S.B./H-111	25	5 – 15	20 – 30	30	37	70

*Significant improvement.

TABLE 15-XII
DOSAGE OF HMG (PERGONAL-500) ADMINISTERED AND RESULTS OBTAINED

Group III (Subnormal sperm count and/or impaired mobility)

Case	Age	Before Treatment		Amps of HMG (Pergonal-500)	After Treatment	
		Sperm Count x 10^6	Per cent of Motility		Sperm Count x 10^6	Per Cent of Motility
K.Y./C-360	35	30 – 37	15 – 20	43	63	60*
A.Y./C-320	50	12 – 30	20 – 30	60	55	60*
S.S./P-274	38	20 – 40	30 – 40	30	48	70*
A.M./K-112	32	30	40	45	42	70*
M.A./Po-111	32	20 – 30	20	20	31 – 42	10 – 25
T.D./C-70	34	30	40	45	64	60 – 65*
T.E./C-26	28	30 – 40	40	45	58	80*
D.A./X-110	30	20	20	60	68 – 73	70 – 90*
C.M./C-250	38	20 – 25	50	40	47	70* (preg.)
C.Y./C-65	30	22	10	23	20	10
P.C./C-89	42	20 – 23	40 – 45	60	24	50
T.K./C-130	26	20	40	40	38	50
A.S./C-201	39	10 – 35	0 – 10	45	20	20
Ch.M./C-254	45	42	50	35	82	70*
F.Z./C-297	28	27 – 30	35 – 50	60	28	85
N.A./C-309	33	10 – 30	10 – 30	25	29	35
M.Sc./T-771	28	10 – 70	1 – 40	20	60	DE

*Significant improvement.

Results

I. Azoospermic Patients

In twelve of the thirty-eight patients, viable sperm were found in the ejaculate after gonadotropic therapy. Six of these belonged to group a, 5 to group b, and 1 to group c. Tables 15-VII, 15-VIII, and 15-IX summarize the dosage of HMG (Pergonal) administered and results obtained in all categories of Group I.

In the six azoospermic patients belonging to group *a*, viable sperm were found in the post-treatment ejaculate. The gross morphological changes in this group showed significant increase in tubular size (from about 50 μ to 250 μ in diameter) after treatment all stages of spermatogenesis and spermiogenesis could be demonstrated.

In only five of the fifteen patients in group b, viable sperm were found in the ejaculate. There was no significant change in tubular size (from about 170 μ to 250 μ in diameter) before and after treatment, but in all cases which responded, all stages of spermatogenesis and spermiogenesis were found. Figures 15-5, 15-6, 15-7, 15-8, and 15-9 illustrate certain areas of the pretreatment and post-treatment biopsies of five patients.

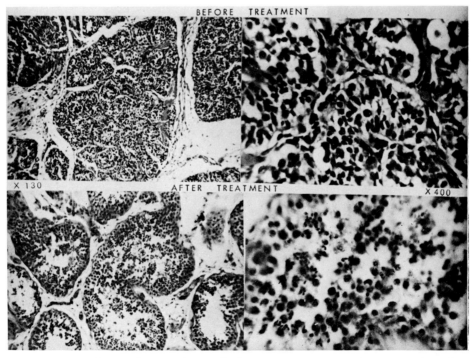

FIGURE 15-5. Testicular biopsy before and after HMG treatment of azoospermic patient of group a (see text).

The unresponsiveness of sixteen of the seventeen patients of group c might be explained by the fact that in the absence of cellular elements pertaining to the germinal line, no spermatogenic response can be expected. Since biopsy material might not represent the status of all the tubules, cases diagnosed as "Sertoli cells-only" syndrome might actually be mixed forms. In these cases gonadotropic therapy may either be beneficial from the therapeutic point of view or at least serve as a diagnostic tool.

It can be concluded that the treatment with HMG will activate spermatogenesis and spermiogenesis in patients with insufficiency of pituitary gonadotropins due to lack of production and/or release, whose testicular biopsy reveals tubules containing cells of the germinal line.

It can further be assumed from our results that to secure an ejaculate which contains viable sperm, treatment must be given to patients of Group I-a for at least eighty days. Treatment duration for patients of Groups I-b and I-c will be influenced, to a certain degree, by the histological findings of the pretreatment biopsy. The stage of the spermatogenic or spermiogenic

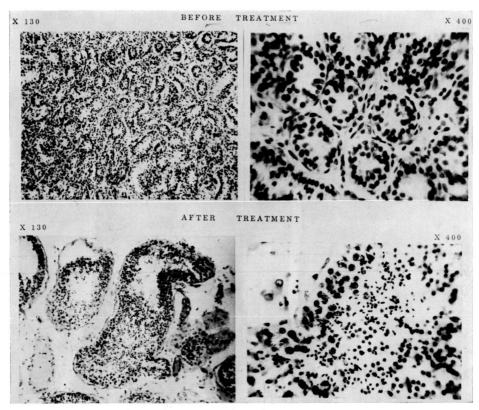

FIGURE 15-6. Testicular biopsy before and after HMG treatment of azoospermic patient of group a (see text).

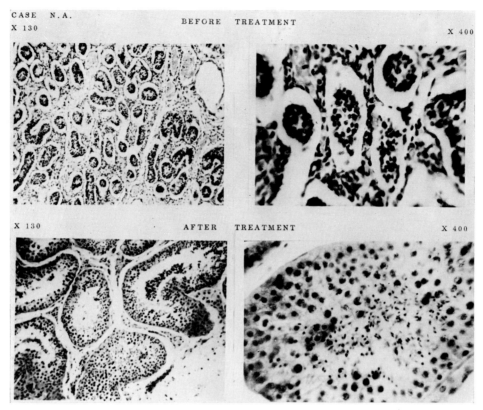

FIGURE 15-7. Testicular biopsy before and after HMG treatment of azoospermic patient of group a (see text).

arrest will determine the rapidity of response. It must be pointed out, however, that viable sperm did not appear in any of our patients prior to twenty-day treatment and, in most cases, a period of more than one hundred days was needed. The treatment schedule employed by us was chosen arbitrarily, and the optimal spacing and amounts of doses administered were not investigated at this stage.

A combined treatment with HMG and HCG should only be given to patients with insufficient ejaculate, less than 1.5 ml, or to patients whose testicular biopsy reveals a significant lack of Leydig cell proliferation.

II. Oligospermic Patients

In seventeen of the forty-eight oligospermic patients, a significant improvement was recorded. Eight of these seventeen, prior to treatment, had less than 10×10^6 sperm per cubic centimeter (Table 15-X), and nine had between $10\text{-}20 \times 10^6$ sperm per cubic centimeter (Table 15-XI).

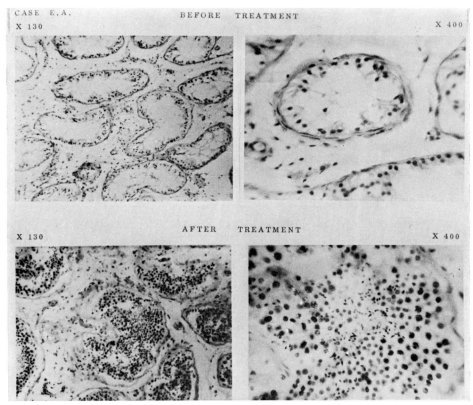

FIGURE 15-8. Testicular biopsy before and after HMG treatment of azoospermic patient of group b (see text).

III. Subfertile Patients

Nine of seventeen patients with sperm counts between 20-40 x 10^6, with 0-40 per cent motility after 1HR responded favorably to HMG treatment (Table 15-XII). Although one patient responded favorably after 20 amps (e.g. 40 days of treatment) and five cases after 30 amps (60 days of treatment), most of the other responsive patients in Groups II and III needed 40-60 amps (80-120 days of treatment) before significant sperm increase was noted. Also, in these groups one amp of Pergonal 500 was administered on alternate days. No attempts have been made, at this stage of our study, to investigate or correlate the dynamic processes taking place in the seminiferous epithelium with the amount, quality, and period of exogenous gonadotropic administration. Neither was the intertubular tissue investigated for possible functional changes in biosynthetic behavior. Such histological, histochemical, and steroid studies are being performed at the present time and will be reported at a later stage.

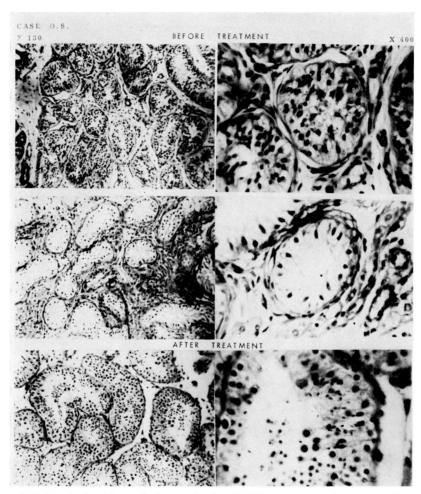

FIGURE 15-9. Testicular biopsy before and after HMG treatment of azoospermic patient of group b (see text).

REFERENCES

1. ALBERT, A., *et al.: Proc Mayo Clin, 16:*409, 1953.
2. ALBERT, A., *et al.: Proc Mayo Clin, 20:*557, 1953.
3. ALBERT, A.: *Recent Progr Hormone Res, 12:*227, 1956.
4. BORTH, R.; LUNENFELD, B., and DE WATTEVILLE, H.: *Experientia, 10/6:*266, 1954.
5. BORTH, R.; LUNENFELD, B., and MENZI, A.: In Albert, A. (Ed.) : *Human Pituitary Gonadotropins: A Workshop Conference.* Springfield, Ill., Thomas, 1961, p. 255.
6. DAVIES, A. G., and CROOKE, A. C.: *Proc Roy Soc Med, 58:*580, 1965.
7. GEMZELL, C. A.; DICZFALUSY, E., and TILLINGER, K. G.: *J Clin Endocr, 18:*1333, 1958.
8. GEMZELL, C., and KJESSLER, B.: *Lancet, March:* 644, 1964.
9. HELLER, C. G., and NELSON, W. O.: *J Clin Endocr, 8:*345, 1948.

10. HELLER, C. G., and CLERMONT, Y.: *Recent Progr Hormone Res, 20:*545, 1964.

11. HELLER, C. G. In PAULSEN, C. A. (Ed.) : *Estrogen Assays in Clinical Medicine.* Seattle, U. of Wash., 1965.

12. HOTCHKISS, R. S.: *Fertility in Man.* Philadelphia, Lippincott, 1944, p. 106.

13. HOWARD, R. P., *et al.: J Clin Endocr, 10:*121, 1950.

14. JOHNSEN, S. G.: *Acta Endocr (Kobenhavn), suppl 66,* 1962.

15. KOTZ, H. L., and HERMANN, W.: *Fertil Steril, 12:*375, 1961.

16. LORAINE, J. A.: *Vitamins Hormones (NY), 14:*305, 1956.

17. LUNENFELD, B.: Treatment of anovulation by human gonadotropins. *J the Int Fed Gynaec Obstet, 1:*155, 1963.

18. LUNENFELD, B., *et al.: Simposio-Internazionale, La Sterilita Femminile e Maschile,* Rome 14-16/5, 1965.

19. MacLEOD, J.; PAZIANOS, A., and RAY, B. S.: *Lancet, May:* 1196, 1964.

20. MOR, A., *et al.: Harefua, 69:*43, 1965.

21. NETTER, A., and BELLAISCH, J.: *Les Gonadotrophines en Gynecologie.* Paris, Masson et Cie, 1962, p. 197.

22. ZONDEK, B., and SULMAN, F.; *Vitamins Hormones (NY), 3:*297, 1945.

Chapter 16

THE INDUCTION OF OVULATION
WITH CLOMIPHENE

ROBERT B. GREENBLATT, IRMA PICO AND VIRENDRA B. MAHESH

An ANTIESTROGENIC agent with gonadotropin inhibiting and antifecundity properties was made available for clinical evaluation in 1960. This compound, clomiphene citrate, is an analogue of the synthetic nonsteroidal estrogen, chlorotrianisene (Tace®). It also has the basic stilbene structure of stilbestrol (Fig. 16-1). The original animal studies suggested that clomiphene might be a good contraceptive agent.[12,15] This hope, however, was soon abandoned when it was shown that it was an excellent ovulatory stimulation agent.* The first report of this action of clomiphene by my group[5] in 1961 was corroborated by numerous investigators throughout the world.[1,10,11,16,28,31] The original compound was a racemic mixture of two isomers which have now been separated and further studies are in progress with a trans and cis form of Clomid. This report deals with the pharmacologic, physiologic, and clinical experiences as observed by my group at the Medical College of Georgia.

SPECTRUM OF THE BIOLOGICAL ACTIVITY OF
CLOMIPHENE CITRATE

Estrogenic Action

Mild estrogenic action of clomiphene was observed in immature mice by an increase in uterine weight and cornification of the vaginal mucosa of treated animals.[4,12] In rats we were able to demonstrate such an action,[25] based on increase in the uterine weight of castrated female rats when treated with clomiphene (Fig. 16-2). In the human, however, clear-cut evidence of mild estrogenic activity could not be obtained.

Antiestrogenic Action

Clomiphene citrate has strong antiestrogenic properties, in experimental animals. This was suggested by a decrease in the uterine weight of clomiphene-treated intact female rats.[25] Further confirmation of the antiestrogenic effect was obtained by the counteraction by clomiphene of the uterotropic effect of estradiol in ovariectomized female rats[17,26] (Fig. 16-3). Clomiphene-

---

*A related compound Mer-25, was shown by Tyler (1960) and later by Kistner (1961) to have similar propensities. This compound was discarded because of toxicity.

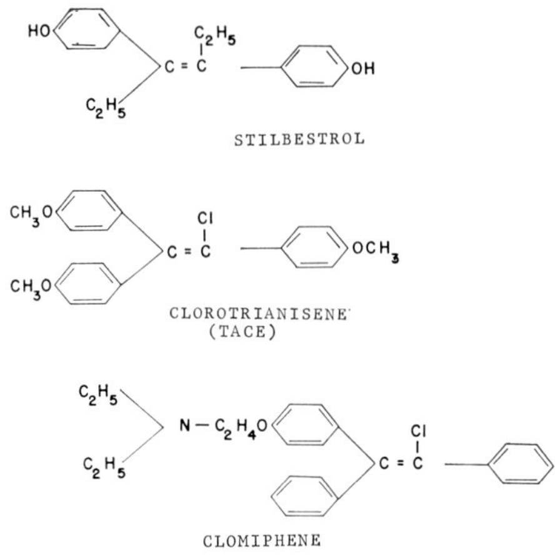

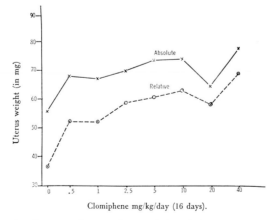

FIGURE 16-1. Structural formulae of stilbestrol, chlorotrianisene and clomiphene.

treated rats were injected with tritiated estradiol. Such pretreatment reduced significantly the uptake of radioactive estradiol by the uterus and the pituitary (Fig. 16-4). These observations suggest that the mode of action of clomiphene as an antiestrogen may indeed be by preferential binding and displacement of estradiol at the estrogen receptor sites.[27]

The antiestrogenic activity of this drug can also be readily demonstrated in the human. Clomiphene was found to be effective in bringing about regressive changes in the vaginal mucosa in precocious puberty.[8,24] Perhaps the best example of the antiestrogenic activity of clomiphene in the human is the counteraction of the ovulation inhibiting effect of 0.1 mg of ethinyl estradiol administered from day five to twenty-five to normally ovulating women[8,24] (Fig. 16-5).

FIGURE 16-2. Progressive increase in uterine weight of immature oophorectomized rats which received graded doses of clomiphene.

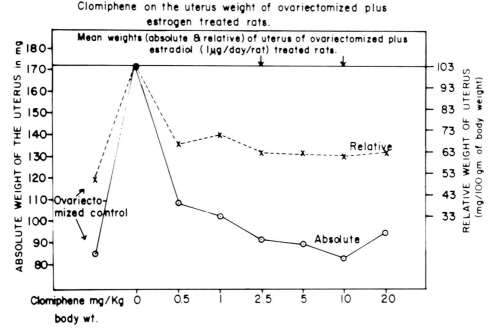

FIGURE 16-3. Progressive decline in uterine weight in estradiol benzoate-treated, immature, ovariectomized rats which had the same graded doses of clomiphene as were received by animals in Figure 16-2.

Effect on Gonadotropin Secretion

The urinary execretion of gonadotropins, estrogens, pregnanediol, 11-deoxy-17-ketosteroids, 11-oxygenated-17-ketosteroids, and tetrahydrocortico-steroids in a patient with classical Stein-Leventhal syndrome before and after the administration of clomiphene is shown in Figure 16-6. The results indicate stimulation of gonadotropin secretion by clomiphene. The increase in urinary gonadotropins after the administration of clomiphene to men and women has been observed by several investigators.[3,10,18,20,21,24] However, isolated reports of no changes in gonadotropin levels after clomiphene have also appeared.[19,29] There may be considerable variability in the responsiveness of different patients.[9] This may be illustrated by the urinary gonadotropin levels in two patients with classical Chiari-Frommel syndrome after a single course of clomiphene (Fig. 16-7). In one patient a release of pituitary gonadotropins occurred, while in the other there was no response.[6] This finding seems to refute the concept held by some of the direct action on the ovary.[19,29] Figure 16-8 illustrates the marked rise in urinary estrogens in comparison with controls in a patient who responded to Clomid therapy. The marked elevation of urinary estrogens is an excellent index that ovarian stimulation has taken place and that probably ovulation had occurred. Confirmation of probable ovulation was obtained by the rise in basal body temperature and a secretory endometrium. At laparotomy corpora lutea were found.

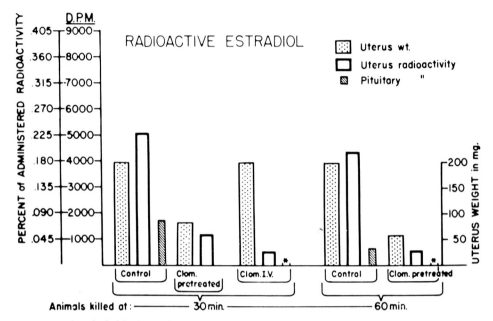

FIGURE 16-4. Diminished uterine and hypophyseal radioactivity, thirty and sixty minutes after the injection of radioactive estradiol in clomiphene treated rats. The uterine weight of animals that received clomiphene for six days (clomiphene pretreated) was decreased. Intravenous injection of clomiphene (Clom. IV) ten minutes prior to start of experiment did not alter uterine weight.

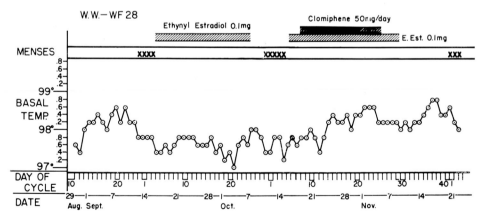

FIGURE 16-5. During the cycle in which ethinyl estradiol was administered there was failure of an ovulatory rise in BBT. Note that clomiphene counteracted the ovulation-suppressing effect of exogenously administered estrogen in the second cycle.

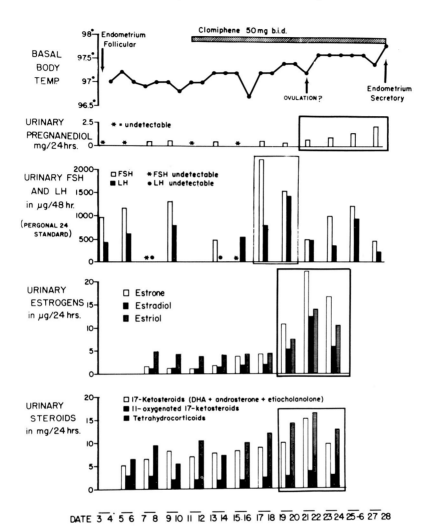

FIGURE 16-6. Urinary hormonal excretion patterns before and after induction of ovulation by clomiphene citrate. Square 1 shows rising urinary pregnanediol excretion. Square 2 shows initial rise in FSH followed by rise in LH. Square 3 shows elevation of estrogen excretion with peak values coinciding with, or twenty-four hours before, rise in BBT. Square 4 shows elevation of 17-ketosteroids and tetrahydrocorticoids coincident with ovulation.

CLINICAL USE OF CLOMIPHENE CITRATE

Induction of Ovulation

In 1961, we first reported the successful induction of ovulation in twenty-eight out of forty-three amenorrheic women by the use of clomiphene.[5] By 1964 our data showed that 257 women had received 1331 courses for the

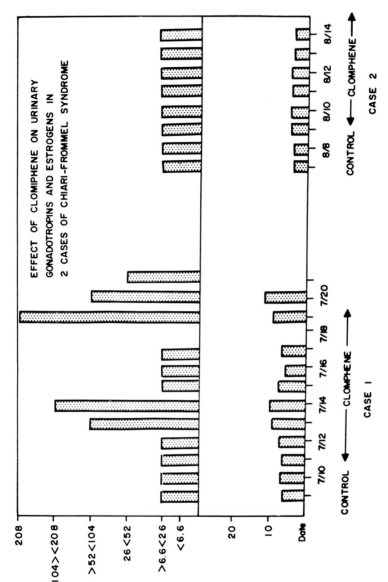

FIGURE 16-7. Urinary gonadotropin and estrogen assays in two subjects with Chiari-Frommel syndrome treated with clomiphene. Note that Case 1 responded by two surges in gonadotropin output accompanied by only a slight rise in estrogen secretion.

TABLE 16-I

Diagnosis	Patients Treated		Ovulation				Failure				Side Effects	
			With Menses		Without Menses		Without Menses		Anovulatory Cycles			
	No. Patients	No. Cycles	No. Pat.	No. Cycles	No. Pat.	No. Cycles	No. Pat.	No. Cycles	No. Pat.	No. Cycles	Cyst on the Ovaries	Hot Flashes
Functional amenorrhea	87	418	73	342	1	1	8	31	12	44	9	8
Secondary amenorrhea	75	465	47	275	7	22	19	81	19	87	9	8
Primary amenorrhea	18	109	5	26	–	–	12	51	4	32	6	4
Stein-Leventhal	42	165	36	149	–	–	3	4	3	12	11	5
Functional uterine bleeding	35	174	29	143	2	4	1	1	6	26	5	1
Total	257	1331	190	935	10	27	43	168	44	201	40	26

purpose of inducing ovulation.[7] Of these, ovulation occurred in 200 women (77%) in 962 cycles (72.7%) See Table 16-I.

Stimulation of ovulation may be expected in the majority of patients with dysfunctional uterine bleeding (Fig. 16-9), Stein-Leventhal syndrome, and those with oligomenorrhea and secondary amenorrhea.[2,3,14,22,23,30] Experience has shown that a moderately intact pituitary-ovarian axis is necessary for a positive response to clomiphene. In such patients, clomiphene may be considered preferable to human menopausal gonadotropin because of its availability, low cost, absence of differences in activity from batch to batch, and route of administration. Patients with primary ovarian or pituitary failure do not benefit from clomiphene therapy. However, successful results may be obtained in treating women with relative pituitary gonadotropin deficiency such as Chiari-Frommel syndrome[6] (Fig. 16-10).

The effect of a placebo on ovulation has not been overlooked. However, in our experience the incidence of the placebo-effect on ovulation was low. Figure 16-11 illustrates the ovulatory stimulating effect of clomiphene and failure of a placebo in one particular patient.

In a preliminary study of forty-one subjects to whom Clomid, trans-Clomid and cis-Clomid was administered, there was quite a variability in response. Some responded to cis-Clomid, not to trans-Clomid, or Clomid. On the other hand, there are those who responded variably to either one or all of the preparations, Table 16-II). The overall results suggest that cis-Clomid is equally as active or more active than Clomid per se in the induction of ovulation; whereas trans-Clomid appeared less active.

TABLE 16-II
COMPARATIVE DATA ON OVULATIONS INDUCED BY CLOMID,
TRANS C AND CIS C

Group	# Pts.	Clomid Cycles	Ovul.	Trans Clomid Cycles	Ovul.	Cis Clomid Cycles	Ovul.
1	9	18	13	14	5	—	—
2	4	11	5	—	—	14	8
3	7	—	—	15	4	15	6
4	21	51	23	31	12	28	22
	41	80	51.3%	60	35%	57	62.2%

Side Effects

The most common side effect associated with the administration of clomiphene was the development of ovarian cysts. Initially, ovarian enlargement was observed in about 15 to 20 per cent of patients when large doses of clomiphene were employed. The cysts regressed spontaneously in three to five weeks after discontinuance of therapy. At laparotomy the cysts resembled those produced by overstimulation with human pituitary gonado-

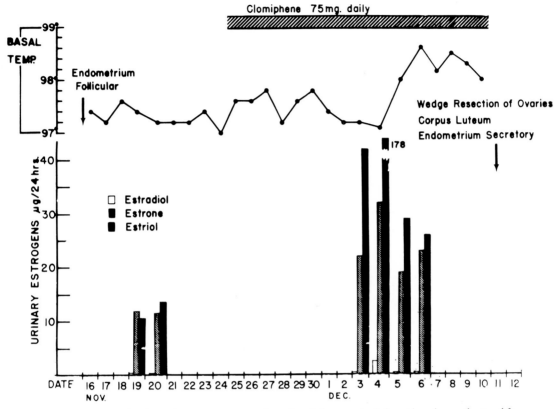

FIGURE 16-8. Rise in urinary estrogens after clomiphene administration in patient with Stein-Leventhal syndrome. Note estrogen peak coincides with time of ovulation.

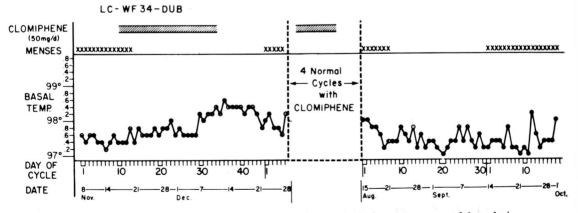

FIGURE 16-9. Dysfunctional uterine bleeding due to anovulation was corrected by administration of clomiphene. Cessation of therapy resulted in recurrence of dysfunctional uterine bleeding.

tropins. The incidence of cysts has lessened considerably by decreasing the dosage and duration of each course of treatment. Particularly prone are those with the Stein-Leventhal syndrome. The incidence of ovarian enlargement following a single course of clomiphene for three days or less was reported as 2.7 per cent; with multiple short courses of seven days or less it was 7.8 per cent.[13] A pelvic examination should be performed before the start of therapy; the drug should not be administered if an ovarian cyst is present. Patients should be observed closely if abdominal discomfort is a complaint while on medication, and the drug discontinued if cystic formation is apparent on palpation.

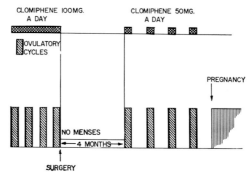

FIGURE 16-10. The administration of 100 mg doses of clomiphene resulted in cyclic ovulatory menses in patient with Chiari-Frommel syndrome. Surgery was performed because of massive ovarian cyst formation. Four months following surgery ovulation was induced again with smaller doses of clomiphene. Pregnancy followed a spontaneous ovulation at end of four courses of treatment.

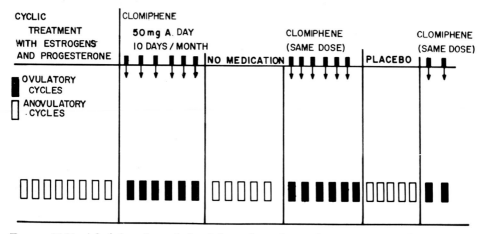

FIGURE 16-11. Administration of clomiphene brought ovulatory menses. Withdrawal of medication or substitution with a placebo resulted in anovulation. Ovulatory menses were restored following reinstitution of therapy.

Another untoward effect was the occurrence of hot flashes. Hot flashes are usually not severe and disappear promptly after treatment is discontinued. Occasional visual symptoms, described as either "blurring" or spots were reported by a few patients, as was temporary loss of head hair.

Periodic blood counts, serum transaminases, BUN, creatinine, cholesterol, protein-bound iodine, urinalysis, prothrombin time, coagulation tests, and slit-lamp examinations were found within normal limits.

Conceptions

In our series there have been 156 pregnancies in 135 women treated with clomiphene. The number of conceptions does not truly reflect the ovulatory-stimulating property of the drug, since many patients were unmarried or conception was not the goal. A high incidence of multiple births was observed by our group and by others (of 1450 pregnancies reported to Merrell Company, 129 were multiple pregnancies, of which two sets were quintuplets, six sets were quadruplets, eight sets were triplets, and 113 sets were twins). In the total Merrell Company series there were 344 abortions. The high incidence of abortion, initially noted in our own series, has been reduced drastically by the use of substituted progestational agents soon after conception was confirmed. There have been seventeen abortions in our first ninety patients; there were also two ectopic pregnancies, and in one patient with severe toxemia a therapeutic abortion was performed. As to congenital anomalies, there were three infants with congenital heart disease, one microcephalic monster, one case of undescended testes, and one set of twins with polydactyly.

Mode of Action

Considerable difference of opinion exists on the mode of action of clomiphene. Although the precise mechanism is still unknown, it is unlikely that a single property of the drug is solely responsible for the induction of ovulation. The primary effect appears to be release of pituitary gonadotropins attributed to the strong antiestrogenic action of clomiphene. This explanation, however, does not explain the ovulatory-stimulating effect of clomiphene in Chiari-Frommel syndrome in the presence of low endogenous estrogens. Therefore, in the majority of cases both antiestrogenic activity as well as gonadotropin-releasing activity may be considered responsible for the induction of ovulation. Suggestions have also been made that clomiphene may influence ovarian enzymes or serve as a potentiator of gonadotropin action on the ovary.

Clomiphene has some dangers if it is used in large or prolonged doses. Dosages should be individualized, given for short periods of time, and the

patient carefully watched for cyst formation. If such a complication develops, therapy is terminated. Cysts regress within a month or six weeks and
if a second course is attempted, the dosage should be greatly reduced. Low-
dosage schedules will not induce as many ovulatory responses, but it has
compensations in that the incidence of cyst formation and other untoward
effects are markedly reduced.

REFERENCES

1. BRET, A. J.: Induction of ovulation by clomiphene. *Gynec Obstet (Paris), 63:*489, 1964.
2. CHARLES, D.: MRL-41 in the treatment of secondary amenorrhea and endometrial hyperplasia. *Lancet, 2:*278, 1962.
3. CHARLES, D., *et al.:* Clomiphene in the treatment of oligomenorrhea and amenorrhea. *Amer J Obstet Gynec, 86:*913, 1963.
4. EMMENS, C. W.: Estrogenic, antiestrogenic and antifertility activities of various compounds. *J Reprod Fertil, 9:*277, 1965.
5. GREENBLATT, R. B., *et al.:* Induction of ovulation with MRL/41. *JAMA, 178:*101, 1961.
6. GREENBLATT, R. B., *et al.:* Ovulation and pregnancy in the Chiari-Frommel syndrome. *Fertil Steril, 17:*742, 1968.
7. GREENBLATT, R. B., and MAHESH, V. B.: Induction of ovulation with clomiphene citrate. In *Year Book of Endocrinology 1964-65.* p. 248.
8. GREENBLATT, R. B., *et al.,:* Induction of ovulation with clomiphene citrate. *Amer J Obstet Gynec, 84:*900, 1962.
9. GREENBLATT, R. B.; ZARATE, A., and MAHESH, V. B.: Methods available for the induction of ovulation. *Proceedings of the Sixth Pan American Congress of Endocrinology,* Mexico City, 1965, p. 129.
10. HEINRICHS, H. D., and ZANDER, J.: The excretion of hypophyseal gonadotropins in women with disturbances of ovarian function before and after treatment with clomiphene. *Klin Wschr, 42:*15, 1964.
11. HOCHULI, E.: Clomiphene, an effective substance to induce ovulation. *Geburtsh Frauenheilk, 6:*457, 1964.
12. HOLTKAMP, D. E., *et al.:* Gonadotropin inhibiting and anti-fecundity effects of clomiphene. *Proc Soc Exp Biol Med, 105:*197, 1960.
13. Investigators reports in physicians drug monograph on Clomid. Wm. S. Merrell Co., Cincinnati, Ohio.
14. KISTNER, R.: Further observations on the effects of clomiphene citrate in anovulatory females. *Amer J Obstet Gynec, 92:*380, 1965.
15. LERNER, L. J.; HOLTHAUS, F. J., and THOMPSON, C. R.: A nonsteroidal estrogen antagonist 1-(p-2-diethylaminoethoxyphenyl)-1-phenyl-2-p-methoxy-phenyl ethanol. *Endocrinology, 63:*295, 1958.
16. MAASS, H.; BETTENDORF, G., and SCHULTZ, K. D.: *Thirty-fifth Meeting of the German Society for Gynecology,* Munchen October 15, 1964.
17. MAHESH, V. B.; ROPER, B. K., and GREENBLATT, R. B.: Studies of the biological effects of clomiphene citrate. *Proceedings of the Second International Congress on Hormonal Steroids. Excerpta Med Int Congress Ser 111:*359, 1966.

18. MELLINGER, R. C., and THOMPSON, R. J.: The effect of clomiphene citrate in male infertility. *Fertil Steril, 17:*94, 1966.

19. NAVILLE, A. H., *et al.:* Induction of ovulation with clomiphene citrate. *Fertil Steril, 15:*290, 1964.

20. PAULSEN, C. A., and HERRMANN, W. L.: Increased pituitary-ovarian function in amenorrheic women resultant to clomiphene administration. *Clin Res, 11:*85, 1963.

21. PILDES, R. B.: Induction of ovulation with clomiphene. *Amer J Obstet Gynec, 91:* 466, 1965.

22. PUEBLA, R. A., and GREENBLATT, R. B.: Clomiphene citrate in the management of anovulatory uterine bleeding. *J Clin Endocr, 24:*863, 1964.

23. RILEY, G. M., and EVANS, T. N.: Effects of clomiphene citrate on anovulatory function. *Amer J Obstet Gynec, 89:*97, 1964.

24. ROY, S., *et al.:* Clomiphene citrate: Further observations on its use in induction of ovulation in the human and its mode of action. *Fertil Steril, 14:*575, 1963.

25. ROY, S.; GREENBLATT, R. B., and MAHESH, V. B.: Effects of clomiphene on the physiology of reproduction in the rat II. Its estrogenic and antiestrogenic actions. *Acta Endocr (Kobenhavn), 47:*657, 1964.

26. ROY, S.; GREENBLATT, R. B., and MAHESH, V. B.: Effect of clomiphene on the physiology of reproduction in the rat. I. Changes in the hypophyseal-gonadal axis. *Acta Endocr (Kobenhavn), 47:*645, 1964.

27. ROY, S.; MAHESH, V. B., and GREENBLATT, R. B.: Effects of clomiphene on the physiology of reproduction in the rat III. Inhibition of the uptake of radioactive estradiol by the uterus and the pituitary gland of immature rats. *Acta Endocr (Kobenhavn), 47:*669, 1964.

28. SUZUKI, I.: Ovulation induction with clomiphene. *Obstet Gynec Ther (Osaka), 8:* 379, 1964.

29. SWYER, G. I. M.: Induction of ovulation in the human—older and newer approaches. *Proc Roy Soc Med, 56:*39, 1963.

30. WHITELAW, M. J.: Clomiphene citrate: Newer aspects of its use in prevention and treatment of infertility. *Fertil Steril, 14:*540, 1963.

31. ZANDER, J., and BANTON, G.: Stimulation of ovarian function by clomiphene in patients without natural ovulation. *Geburtsh Frauenheilk, 23:*871, 1963.

Chapter 17

BIOGENESIS OF STEROIDS IN THE
HUMAN OVARY

KENNETH SAVARD

THE EXTENSIVE knowledge of steroidogenesis in the adrenal cortex and its control by the pituitary hormone ACTH stands as an imposing target for those concerned with the same process in the ovary. After many years of inattention and neglect (by biochemists), the ovary has very recently become the subject of intense study. It must be emphasized at the start of this review, that the investigation of the actions of gonadotropins in the ovary is usually complex for several reasons. In the relationship of TSH and the thyroid, ACTH and the fasciculata of the adrenal cortex or of gonadotropin and the testis, where the target tissues are relatively fixed (in the gross morphologic sense), the role of the tropic hormone is relatively direct. In each situation the particular tropic factor acts acutely to cause certain functional changes (depletion of cholesterol, ascorbic acid, activation of phosphorylase, respiration) which accompany the stimulation of the synthesis and release of the tissue's hormonal product. Under chronic conditions, the tropic hormone brings about a process of hypertrophy as the major morphologic change without changing the basic character of the tissue. This is not necessarily the case in the ovary. Here highly dramatic qualitative changes in morphology occur involving growth and maturation of follicles, and ovulation. Such changes as luteinization and formation of corpus luteum are morphologic processes unknown elsewhere in endocrinology. Many of these morphologic actions of the gonadotropins in the ovary have been studied since the inception of endocrinology but have not as yet been reduced to biochemical terms; e.e., there are no biochemical interpretations which describe the process of luteinization.

It becomes apparent that actions of gonadotropins on steroidogenesis in the ovary must be considered in the light of the ovarian structures present. Care must be taken to separate, if possible, the morphologic and histologic actions of the gonadotropins from the acute actions on the process of steroidogenesis in existing, preformed elements. In our approach to this problem, we have tried to avoid these complications by studying the acute action (three to four hours) of gonadotropins on preformed ovarian structures (corpus luteum, interstitium) under conditions where the ovarian compartment or structure has been dissected free from adjoining elements and placed in an *in vitro* incubation system. Details of the technique were first described[1] in 1961. These techniques permitted the study of the primary function of the corpus luteum, namely that of its production of progesterone, and the tropic factors which influence it.

It is somewhat surprising, to me at least, to be able to say that of the many species of experimental animals used in the study of ovarian endocrinology, the species in which we seem to have the most information is that of the human. It is my intention today to review this subject of steroidogenesis in the human ovary.

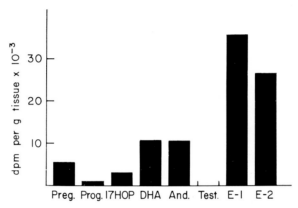

FIGURE 17-1. Profile of radioactive steroids formed *in vitro* from acetate-1-^{14}C by human follicular tissue. (From Smith and Ryan, 1961.)

THE FOLLICLE

Ryan and Smith[2] and Smith and Ryan,[3] in the first *in vitro* biochemical study of an ovarian compartment, described the nature of the steroids of the human follicle and their interconversions, and have shown that the major radioactive products formed from acetate-1-C^{14} are estradiol-17β and estrone (Fig. 17-1). This was the first thorough assessment of the formation of total steroidal product (in terms of seven individual steroids) that has been made in the ovary by the quantitative technique of reverse-isotope dilution, and showed the formation of pregnenolone, progesterone, 17-hydroxypregnenolone, dehydroepiandrosterone, 17-hydroxyprogesterone, 4-androstenedione as well as the two estrogens. Other studies by Ryan and Smith, employing radioactively labelled steroids, have established that two pathways of biosynthesis are involved in the formation of estrogens in the human follicle; these are shown in Figure 17-2. Both pathways occur in the two steroid-producing cell-types, the thecal cells and the granulosa cells (Petro and Ryan: *J Clin Endocr, 26:*46, 1966) .

In other species, steroid synthesis has been studied *in vitro* in the rabbit follicle,[4] but the radioactive products were not rigorously identified. In 1964 Short[5] reviewed his studies of the steroids present in the follicular fluid of the mare ovary where estradiol-17β was the steroid present in highest amounts. Ryan and Short[6] have shown that both the granulosa cells and the theca cells of the mare follicle are capable of estrogen synthesis from radioactive testosterone *in vitro*. Falck,[7] using transplanted rat ovarian segments, has shown that both theca and granulosa cells are necessary for estrogen production, assessed indirectly. In all of these studies, the action of gonadotropins on steroidogenesis in the follicle *in vitro* has, to date, not been explored. *In vivo,* Donini, Lunenfeld, and Eshkol and their associates (*Acta Endocr (Kobenhavn), 54*:91-95, 1967) have shown that highly purified human FSH from postmenopausal urine, while causing increased follicular size in the ovaries of immature mice, does not cause the production of estrogen. Combinations of FSH and LH or HCG cause both follicular growth *and* estrogen production; the latter was revealed by the increase in the weight of the uterus of the treated mice.

THE CORPUS LUTEUM

In the last few years, our laboratory in Miami began the study of the influences of pituitary and placental hormones on steroid production in

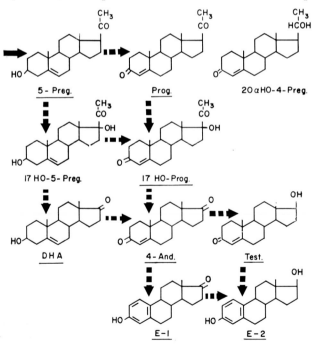

FIGURE 17-2. Route of steroid biosynthesis in gonadal tissue. The vertical pathway shown on the left is referred to as the $\triangle^5$-3β-hydroxysteroid pathway; the vertical pathway on the right is referred to as the $\triangle^4$-3-ketosteroid pathway.

various compartments of the ovary; this work has recently been reviewed in detail.[8] The approach which we employ is based on the assumption that the corpus luteum should be studied separately in order to determine the nature of the steroids biosynthesized. A further purpose has been to evaluate under *in vitro* conditions, which of the pituitary and other gonadotropins or tropic hormones are responsible for regulating the rate of steroid biosynthesis in the respective ovarian compartment. Up to the present, we have worked mainly with the corpus luteum of human and bovine ovaries. We have not as yet made any studies of follicular tissues or structures, although we have extended our studies recently to include steroidogenesis in the medulla or stromal compartment (interstitium) of the normal human ovary.

Our method of studying the corpus luteum consists of obtaining fresh specimens from normal ovaries *in situ,* or from the surgically removed organ. The corpus luteum is immediately chilled in physiological saline at 0-2°C and quickly transported to the laboratory. The corpus luteum is then sliced by hand into many thin (0.5 mm) slices which are weighed and distributed among a number of incubation vessels containing 5 ml of Krebs-Ringer bicarbonate buffer, pH 7.4, and radioactive acetate-1-^{14}C. Certain substances such as various gonadotropins or different amounts of the same gonadotropin are added to the beakers; suitable control vessels are also prepared. The vessels are incubated for two to three hours with shaking at 37°. Analysis for the amount of progesterone formed *de novo* during the incubation is then carried out.

Experiments with acetate-1-^{14}C and pregnenolone-7-^{3}H as radioactive steroid precursors have shown that bovine corpora lutea from pregnant and nonpregnant cows, synthesize only two major steroids,[1,9] progesterone and 20α-hydroxy-4-pregnen-3-one. The synthesis of these two compounds, particularly progesterone, by bovine corpus luteum slices *in vitro* is specially stimulated by anterior pituitary *gonadotropin preparations with luteinizing activity.* Thus luteinizing hormones (LH) of ovine, porcine, and bovine origin[1] have been found to be active in the cow corpus luteum. With the highly purified sheep luteinizing hormone (NIH-LH-S1), amounts as low as 0.01 μg per g of luteal tissue, or 10^{-10} molar concentration of LH, have given significant increments of progesterone synthesis *in vitro* in the cow corpus luteum.[10]

When this *in vitro* incubation method was applied to human corpora lutea obtained from patients in the luteal phase of the menstrual cycle or with ectopic pregnancy, it was found that in contrast to the corpus luteum of the cow, the human corpus luteum synthesized from acetate-1-^{14}C, at least seven radioactive steroids;[11] these are 5-pregnenolone, progesterone, 20α-hydroxy-4-pregnen-3-one, 17-hydroxyprogesterone, 4-androstenedione, estrone, and estradiol-17β. This tissue does not appear to synthesize radioactive dehydroepiandrosterone or testosterone from acetate-1-¹⁴C (Fig. 17-3).

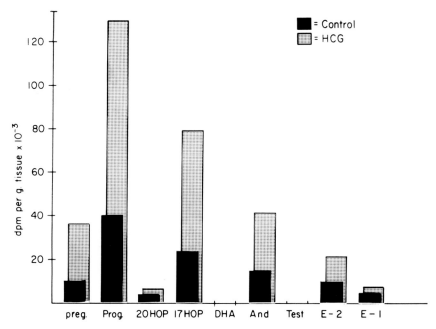

FIGURE 17-3. Profile of radioactive steroids formed *in vitro* from acetate-1-¹⁴C by human corpus luteum tissue. (From Rice *et al.*, 1964.) The bars show the radioactive labelling in the absence (black bars) and the presence (grey bars) of chorionic gonadotropin (HCG) in the incubation medium.

When human chorionic gonadotropin (HCG) was added to the incubating slices of human corpus luteum of pregnancy (ectopic), the incorporation of acetate-1-¹⁴C into *all of the above named seven steroids* was significantly increased; the synthesis of progesterone showed the greatest stimulation. Human chorionic gonadotropin showed a similar effect in slices of corpora lutea from women in the luteal phase of the menstrual cycle.[12]

Among various other tropic hormone preparations tested, human prolactin and human growth hormone do not stimulate steroid synthesis in the human corpus luteum.[12]

It is to be pointed out that both LH and HCG, in addition to causing increased biosynthesis of progesterone in the human corpora lutea of the cycle and of (ectopic) pregnancy, also cause increased synthesis of all other steroids including the two estrogens, estrone and estradiol-17β, suggesting that the corpus luteum may well be the source of the urinary estrogens excreted during the luteal phase of the cycle and in early pregnancy of the human. The hormone 17-hydroxyprogesterone, the synthesis of which in the corpus luteum is also augmented by both gonadotropins, may also be considered to be the source of urinary pregnanetriol reported to be increased during the late luteal phase of the cycle.[13]

It has long been suspected (from patterns of urinary steroid metabolites) that the human ovary secretes estrogen but no progesterone during the follicular phase of the menstrual cycle, and secretes both estrogen and progesterone (and recently discovered 17-hydroxyprogesterone) during the luteal phase. The origins of these steroids have been definitely established by the *in vitro* studies of steroidogenesis in follicular tissue (by Ryan and Smith) and in the corpus luteum by Huang and Pearlman[14] and by ourselves. Ryan (1963) has shown that the human corpus luteum involves only the $\triangle^4$-3-ketosteroid pathway of synthesis leading to estrogen (Fig. 17-3). The results of these *in vitro* studies are in excellent agreement with the existing concepts of steroidogenesis in the ovary derived from the study of urinary steroid patterns in women.

Our studies of human corpora lutea[11] reveal that this ovarian tissue synthesizes the same identical array of steroids throughout the luteal phase of the cycle, and that this pattern of steroid does not change when the life of the corpus luteum is extended by pregnancy. The finding that steroid synthesis (of all individual steroids) in all corpora lutea (of pregnancy and of the cycle) is augmented by both pituitary LH and chorionic gonadotropin[12] is entirely in accord with morphologic roles of pituitary LH in inducing luteinization and formation of corpora lutea and of chorionic gonadotropin in prolonging the existence and function of the corpus luteum in pregnancy.

THE STROMA (OR INTERSTITIUM)

Now I should like to turn to a consideration of another structure, or compartment, of the human ovary. This is the compartment which is anatomically distinct from the follicle and the corpus luteum, in which the nongerminal elements of the ovary are located. It contains interstitial cells, hilus cells, developing and atretic follicles, and a very large mass of cells that are referred to as the stroma. The name "stroma" suggests that it may be inert, acting solely as a supportive structure for the other elements. Consequently this portion of the ovary has been ignored. In the last two or three years it has become quite evident that the stroma is not merely a supportive structure. Recent histochemical studies by Scully and Cohen,[15] using a stain for the enzyme glucose-6-phosphate dehydrogenase, showed that the stroma of the normal ovary contained widely distributed cells of exceedingly high enzyme activity. The observation suggested that these may be steroid-producing cells. Of course they were unable to determine which steroids might be formed in these "enzymically active stroma" cells.

In our studies of the human ovarian stroma, we have used normal ovarian specimens obtained from women undergoing laparotomy for non-endocrine problems. The outer 2 to 3 mm cortical layer was discarded and the corpus luteum, when present, was dissected free and incubated separately. Large corpora albicantes were removed and discarded. The remaining tissue was used for the incubation.

Incubation with acetate-1-^{14}C was carried out in the usual way. The radioactive steroid products were analyzed by the reverse isotope-dilution technique. Figure 17-4 shows the profile of the radioactive steroids formed *in vitro* from acetate-1-^{14}C by the human stromal tissue from a patient with ectopic pregnancy. Identical patterns are obtained with stromal tissues from the ovaries of the menstrual cycle. The largest incorporation of radioactivity is in the three androgens, 4-androstenedione, dehydroepiandrosterone, and testosterone. Two estrogens, estradiol-17β and estrone, are formed in lesser, though significant amounts. Progesterone, the dominant steroid of the human corpus luteum (Fig. 17-3), is formed only in trace amounts in this portion of the ovary; 5-pregnenolone and 17-hydroxyprogesterone are formed in this tissue as they are also in the corpus luteum and in the follicle.[3] This radioactive steroidal pattern, with androgens as the major products, appears to be unique when compared with the patterns of radioactive steroids formed by the other two compartments of the human ovary (Figs. 17-1 and 17-3). The demonstration of the formation of radioactive

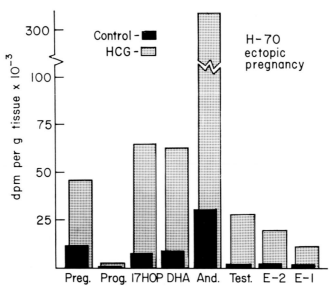

FIGURE 17-4. Profile of radioactive steroids formed *in vitro* from acetate-1-^{14}C by stromal tissue of the human ovary (From a patient with ectopic pregnancy). For explanation of diagram, see Figure 17-3. (From Rice and Savard, 1966.)

testosterone by stromal tissue slices[16] serves to fix the likely site of its synthesis in this compartment of the ovary. Ryan and Smith[1] report that little if any radioactive testosterone, compared to estrogen, is formed from acetate-1-^{14}C in the human follicle *in vitro*. We have sought this androgen among the radioactive products formed from acetate-1-^{14}C by human corpus luteum.[11,16] The results have shown that the corpus luteum, too, forms little or no radioactive testosterone. It seems, therefore, that the ovarian stroma would be the most likely source of plasma testosterone in normal women which reaches a peak at the time of ovulation.[17] Current studies reveal that both pathways of biosynthesis are involved in the synthesis of androgens in the stroma of the normal ovary [Leymarie and Savard, in press 1967].

We have studied the effects of several human gonadotropin preparations on steroidogenesis *in vitro* in human ovarian stromal tissue. Stimulatory effects on steroidogenesis such as those shown in Figure 17-4 have been observed with several anterior pituitary preparations of combined LH and FSH and with human chorionic gonadotropin. The specificity of this response to LH and HCG has not been ascertained as yet. The synthesis of radioactive 4-androstenedione seems to be the most sensitive index of response to the effect of gonadotropins. The synthesis of the other steroids, including that of the estrogens, is also increased when the synthesis of 4-androstenedione is increased. It would appear, as in the case of the corpus luteum, that the effect of the gonadotropin *in vitro* is to raise the level of synthesis of the entire steroidal product and not that of a single steroid or group of steroids.

These results, while they do not clarify the cellular source of the steroid formed in this stromal compartment of the human ovary, strongly suggest that the stroma as a whole, is a gland of internal secretion distinct from the follicle and corpus luteum, and that it is under influence of gonadotropins. The nature of steroids formed in this compartment resemble somewhat those which would be expected to be formed by the interstitial cells of a testis.

The exact contribution (in terms of micrograms of steroid) of the stromal compartment of the normal ovary to the systemic hormonal picture is not known at this time, and will no doubt be difficult to assess. It is likely that under the proper environmental conditions not only the stroma of the ovary possessing a matured follicle or corpus luteum, but also that of the contralateral ovary, will contribute to the total stromal steroid production. No doubt the absolute level of synthesis will rise and fall with the changing levels of pituitary and placental gonadotropins during the normal reproductive cycle. At the present time one can only speculate on the exact role of this "androgenic" compartment of the ovary. It may be considered possible that secretion of androgen into ovarian effluent is not its entire purpose or function. Androgens formed by the steroidogenic cells of the stroma[15] may not necessarily have to leave the ovary; they may exert certain morphologic influences on other proximal ovarian structures such as follicles, as noted by Payne and Runser[18] in their studies of the effects of androgens on the ovary of the rat.

It is, however, in certain anovulatory disorders where follicular maturation is impaired, or in the postmenopausal ovary, that the ovarian stromal compartment may be the major source, if not the only source, of steroid hormone. Under these circumstances and because of the nature of the steroids formed by the stroma, there exists a serious potential for virilism.

In this regard, we have briefly investigated the spectrum of radioactive steroids formed *in vitro* by ovarian tissue from one postmenopausal hyperplasia and from two patients with polycystic ovaries, under conditions identical to those used for the study of normal ovarian stromal tissue. The spectrum of radioactive steroids formed by each of these pathologic tissues under the conditions employed is similar to that of normal ovarian stroma.[9] The major steroids were 4-androstenedione, dehydroepiandrosterone, and testosterone. Small amounts of radioactive estrogens were formed, along with 5-pregnenolone, 17-hydroxyprogesterone, but no progesterone. These results suggest that the androgenic steroids found in these pathologic tissues (reviewed in Mahesh and Greenblatt[20]) reflect the basic nature of the tissue of which these pathologic ovaries are composed.

*　　*　　*

This study was supported in part by Grant No. CA-04004, National Institute of Health, U. S. Public Health Service.

REFERENCES

1. Mason, N. R.; Marsh, J. M., and Savard, K.: *J Biol Chem, 237*:1801, 1962.
2. Ryan, K., and Smith, O. W.: *J Biol Chem, 236*:705, 710, and 2207, 1961.
3. Smith, O. W., and Ryan, K. J.: *Endocrinology, 69*:869, 1961.
4. Gospodarowicz, D.: *Acta Endocr (Kobenhavn), 47*:293, 306, 1964.
5. Short, R. V.: *Recent Prog Hormone Res, 20*:303, 1964.
6. Ryan, K., and Short, R. V.: *Endocrinology, 76*:108, 1965.
7. Falck, B.: *Acta Physiol Scand, 47 (Suppl 1)*:163, 1959.
8. Savard, K.; Marsh, J. M., and Rice, B. F.: *Recent Prog Hormone Res., 21*:285, 1965.
9. Savard, K., and Telegdy, G.: *Steroids, 5 (Suppl 2)*:205, 1965.
10. Mason, N. R., and Savard, K.: *Endocrinology, 74*:664, 1964.
11. Hammerstein, J.; Rice, B. F., and Savard, K.: *J Clin Endocr, 24*:597, 1964.
12. Rice, B. F.; Hammerstein, J., and Savard, K.: *J Clin Endocr, 24*:606, 1964.
13. Fotherby, K. J.: *Endocrinology, 22*:ii, (abstract), 1961.
14. Huang, W. Y., and Pearlman, W. H.: *J Biol Chem, 237*:1060, 1962.
15. Scully, R. E., and Cohen, R. B.: *Obstet Gynec, 24*:667, 1964.

16. RICE, B. F.; HAMMERSTEIN, J., and SAVARD, K.: *Steroids, 4:*199, 1964.
17. LOBOTSKY, J., *et al.: J Clin Endocr, 24:*1261, 1964.
18. PAYNE, R. W., and RUNSER, R. H.: *Endocrinology, 62:*313, 1958.
19. RICE, B. F., and SAVARD, K.: *J Clin Endocr, 26:*593, 1966.
20. MAHESH, V. B., and GREENBLATT, R. B.: *Recent Prog Hormone Res, 20:*341, 1964.

Chapter 18

THE STIMULATION OF OVARIAN FUNCTION

(Panel Discussion)

W. INGIULLA, Moderator

D R. INGIULLA: After so many distinguished papers, a number of questions have been presented to this panel regarding both the biology and the clinical use of gonadotrophins and clomiphene. We are of the opinion that the various problems are especially related to two topics: the gonadotrophic activity during the cycle and the reaction of the ovary to the variation of endogenous gonadotrophins.

I think that we must follow the theory of the alternating increase of the two gonadotrophic activities. Probably the sequence of the two gonadotrophic activities is the expression of the normal hypothalamic-hypophyseal rhythm. We also appreciate the distinction made by Dr. Savard between the morphogenetic and the steroidogenetic activity in the ovary stimulated by the gonadotrophins. This could be the reason that in our *in vitro* experiments we obtained no significant modification in ovarian steroidogenesis with the use of HMG. I should like to ask Dr. Crooke's opinion on the subject.

DR. CROOKE: Most evidence seems to suggest that the gonadotrophins act at a very early stage in the synthesis of oestrogens. This is true *in vitro,* and it seems also to be true in *vivo.* Otherwise it is hard to understand how a single injection of FSH, which is rapidly removed from the circulation and excreted in the urine, can cause a progressive growth of the follicle and rise in production of oestrogens for the next ten to twelve days (Crooke, Butt and Bertrand, 1966).

Chorionic gonadotrophin and luteinizing hormone act also at a much later stage and are responsible for the rupture of the follicle. They may do this simply by increasing the osmotic pressure within the follicle causing it to swell until it bursts, but there may be other explanations. Whether the follicle ruptures as a result of hormone activity or is artificially punctured, the result is the same in terms of steroid synthesis. The synthesis of oestrogens is arrested at progesterone presumably because enzymes are lost with the cyst fluid which previously carried the synthesis further.

In the Stein-Leventhal ovary on the other hand the synthetic process is carried a stage further and is arrested at androstenedione. Here the follicle has failed to rupture and the enzymic failure is a function of time. After a period of about two weeks we have just shown that the follicle is no longer capable of producing oestrogens and reverts to the synthesis of androstenedione. Some dehydroepiandrosterone may also be produced by an alternate pathway.

DR. SAVARD: There are two important considerations which must be brought into this answer. The new concepts of molecular biology have given us a clearer understanding of the mechanisms whereby a primordial undifferentiated cell conceivably might have all the genetic information for all the hydroxylations, side-chain cleavages, dehydrogenases, et cetera, that are required for the synthesis of all steroids. As this cell differentiates morphologically, it retains its basic and most important capability to transform cholesterol into pregnenolone and progesterone. No matter whether the cell makes cortisol, progesterone, or estrogen, it must utilize a common pathway from cholesterol to pregnenolone. It is most likely that gonadotropin, ACTH, angiotensin, all of which are protein in nature, will act in the biosynthetic transformations which are common to all the cells. The message of stimulation is one that, I think, says, "Make more steroid." As this message is read into each cell, more cholesterol is converted to pregnenolone. Which individual steroid is formed is determined by the mosaic of enzymes present in the cell. Thus, in the corpus luteum the product will be progesterone; in the zone fasciculata it will be cortisol. It seems to me that the point of action should be at a common biosynthetic step in all these cells.

Therefore, to the question, Can gonadotropin increase the aromatization of androgen to estrogen in a certain type of cell? I would answer No, not in an acute fashion.

As to the follicular cysts, this is a very mysterious business. Dr. Crooke's associate in Cambridge, Dr. Roger Short, has often wondered about the true role of the cyst with regard to the secretion of steroids, because he has found very little relationship between the steroid content of the ovarian vein and the contents of the cysts. Therefore, I suggest that perhaps the purpose of the steroids in the cyst may be something that Dr. Dorfman has alluded to. We often think of the inhibitory action of the steroids as being directed to the pituitary, the hypothalamus. He has called our attention to their influence on certain steroid transformations: they may influence the rates of certain transformations. I also submit that perhaps within the ovary itself, steroids that are made in one compartment may have an inhibitory action on morphologic processes in other structures of the ovary.

DR. CROOKE: We are interested in the question of pure gonadotrophins. In 1963 we described the preparation of FSH which contained no biological LH activity in the maximum doses used in the assays and very low LH activity in the immunological tests (Butt, Crooke, Cunningham and Wolf,

1963). It also appeared to have no luteinizing activity in the hypophysectomized mouse (Kovacic, 1964.) It did contain some starch from the starch gel electrophoresis, and it contained some albumin. Some of it was ampouled by the Biological Standards Division of the Medical Research Council and is available for limited trials. Since then we have obtained material which contains no starch and no albumin, and we are now working on its chemistry (Amir, Barker, Butt, and Crooke, 1966.)

TABLE 18-I

	Pituitary FSH Percentage	HMG Percentage
Aspartic acid	7.8	6.3
Threonine	5.5	4.4
Serine	9.7	2.6
Glutamic acid	9.6	11.6
Proline	2.6	2.7
Glycine	4.9	2.8
Alanine	4.0	3.1
Valine	6.1	2.9
Isoleucine	2.4	2.7
Leucine	4.3	5.1
Tyrosine	3.8	3.9
Phenylalanine	3.7	3.7
Lysine	4.2	5.0
Histidine	2.1	3.4
Arginine	3.1	4.0
Cystine	0.5	4.1
Methionine	—	1.1
Tryptophane	1.0	—
Hexose	12.2	15.0
Fucose	1.7	—
N-acetylneuraminic acid	2.6	10.0
N-acetylhexosamine	8.3	11.0
	PSH potency per mg 1,000 IU	HMG potency per mg 12 IU

References:
  HMG amino acids:
    Segaloff, A.; Steelman, S. L.; Everett, C., and Flores, A.: *J Clin Endocr, 19*:827, 1959.
  Carbohydrates:
    Mourrillon, R., and Got, R.: *Acta Endocr (Kobenhavn), (Suppl 51)*:201, 1960.
  The analysis of pituitary FSH:
    Amir, S. M.; Barker, S. A.; Butt, W. R., and Crooke, A. C.: *Nature, 209*:1092, 1966.

Table 18-I shows the amino acid and sugar content of this preparation compared with a preparation of FSH from menopausal urine. We know that the latter is not pure, but it is surprising to find that the ratios of most of the amino acids are similar in the two preparations. Discrepancies in the others can probably be accounted for by the different methods of hydrolysis used. You will notice that the carbohydrates are not exactly alike and the difference in potency is quite extraordinary. It is possible that passage through the kidney or through the liver, in addition to the methods used for extraction, modifies the structure and reduces the activity.

We have been studying a whole series of reactions which affect activity and we know that quite small changes in the chemistry of the terminal groups can reduce this considerably. We know, for instance, that the terminal carbohydrate, N-acetyl-D-neuraminic acid is essential for biological activity.

Figure 18-1 shows the structure of N-acetyl-neuraminic acid. This material has the effect of enhancing FSH (Amir, Barker, Butt, and Crooke, 1966), but it also inhibits HCG (Amir, Barker, Butt, and Crooke, 1966.)

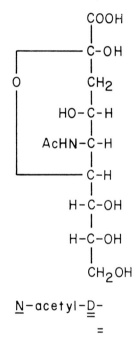

N-acetyl-D-

neuraminic acid

FIGURE 18-1. Structure of N-acetyl-D-neuraminic acid.

It is broken down in the body of N-acetyl-mannosamine; N-acetyl-mannosamine does not enhance FSH activity, but it still inhibits HCG. Some twenty closely related substances have been synthesized in the laboratory of the chemistry department of Birmingham University or obtained from other sources. These have been tested biologically, and we have found that the biological activity is very highly specific.

Table 18-II shows the results of some assays of FSH alone compared with FSH with added N-acetyl-neuraminic acid. The activity of FSH is enhanced 156 per cent in one and by 168 per cent in another.

Dr. Donini: Very briefly I should like to explain to those who perhaps have not been able to follow what was said previously on the importance of having available gonadotropic hormones perfectly separated from each other, that is biologically pure FSH and LH. Dr. Savard mentioned the possibility of studying steroidogenesis *in vitro,* not as has been done up to now by using mixtures of gonadotropic hormones containing both FSH and LH.

TABLE 18-II

AUGMENTATION OF THE ACTION OF FOLLICLE STIMULATING HORMONE (FSH, CP 1 FRACTION) BY N-ACETYL-D-NEURAMINIC ACID (D-NANA) IN UTERINE AND OVARIAN WEIGHT ASSAYS

Mixtures		Design of assays (no. of doses)		No. of mice	Potency (%) of mixture compared with that of CP 1 alone (95% fid. limits in parentheses)
CP 1 (μg)	D-NANA (mg)	Control	Mixture		
Uterine Weight Assay					
1	2	3	2	15	170 (109 − 260)
1	1	3	3	17	168 (108 − 256)
1	0.5	3	3	17	202 (133 − 314)
Ovarian Weight Assays					
1	1.5	4	3	20	156 (96 − 245)
1	1.0	4	3	21	168 (106 − 256)
1	0.67	4	3	21	110 (70 − 176)
1	0.44	4	3	21	93 (58 − 148)

*Reproduced from the *Journal of Endocrinology, 35:*425-526, 1966.

In order to be able to understand the exact mechanism of ovarian steroidogenesis, both in the humans and in animals, it is very useful to have these hormones available. In collaboration with Dr. Lunenfeld and Mrs. Eshkol, we have prepared in our laboratories biologically pure FSH and also LH practically free from FSH.

I was surprised to learn from Dr. Crooke — on the amino acid composition of FSH prepared from human pituitaries and urine — that the amino acid composition of one FSH preparation with a potency of 1000 IU per milligram was similar to that of urinary FSH containing only 12 IU per milligram. I think that the latter composition should reflect on the amino acids of the proteic contaminants and not on FSH.

Dr. Quinto: I should like to present two cases which will illustrate why we believe that a fixed dosage of HMG may not be convenient. For example, I present a case (Fig. 18-2) with low urinary estrogens and very low urinary gonadotropins to whom one vial of Pergonal-500 per day for eight days was administered. When the fern test became positive, a second vial per day was added and when the pyknotic index of the vaginal cytology indicated a preovulatory situation, we started HCG. Ovulation was evident by the notable increase of urinary pregnanediol, a biphasic basal body temperature, and modifications in the vaginal cytology. Menstrual bleeding followed fourteen days later.

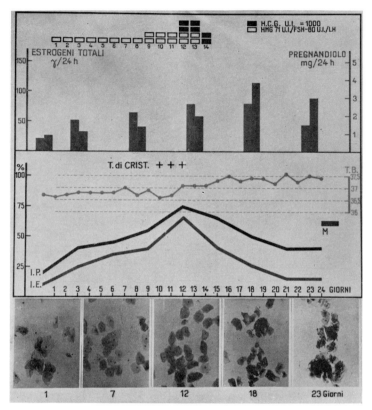

FIGURE 18-2. A case with low urinary estrogens and very low urinary gonadotropins to whom one vial of Pergonal-500 per day was administered for eight days.

In our opinion, it is not practical, from a clinical point of view, to follow patients continuously with hormonal assays; we believe that it is possible to follow them by the fern test and the karyopyknotic index.

I present a second case (Fig. 18-3), quite similar to the previous one from an endocrinological point of view (very low urinary levels of estrogens and gonadotropins), in which a considerably stronger dose of Pergonal-500 was necessary to achieve results. After three days of treatment with only one vial a day, there was no modification of the pyknotic index; accordingly, we increased the Pergonal dosage until we saw an improvement in the karyopyknotic index and the fern test. Medication was administered until the twelfth day when we added HCG. A clear indication was obtained that ovulation occurred, from the increase of estrogens and pregnanediol in the urine, as well as from a biphasic temperature curve and changes in vaginal cytology.

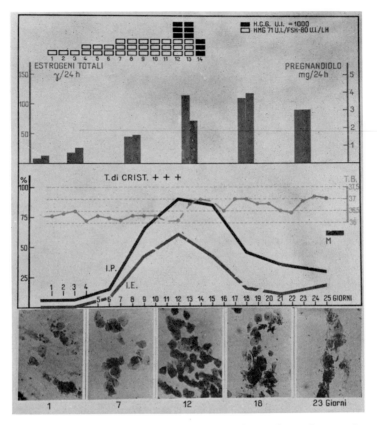

FIGURE 18-3. A case with very low urinary estrogens and gonadotropins to whom a much stronger dose of Pergonal-500 was necessary to achieve results.

It seems to me that, from these two cases, which are illustrative of a rather wide clinical experience, at least two conclusions may be drawn: (1) even in almost identical basal conditions of the endocrine imbalance there is, from patient to patient, a considerable individual difference in reactivity to Pergonal, so that a standardized scheme of therapy does not seem advisable and (2) whereas hormonal assays are of paramount importance to establish the endocrine imbalance at the beginning of the treatment, the Pergonal medication can be easily and safely assessed, even to reasonably high dosages, by means of the fern test and vaginal cytology.

DR. GREENBLATT: Dr. Quinto has made his point. The average gynecologist who will wish to employ human menopausal gonadotropins will not have all the sophisticated techniques to guide him. An intelligent use of such simple procedures as the fern test and the interpretation of vaginal smears and repeated pelvic examinations will usually suffice. Unfortunately, maturation of the vaginal mucosa may be slow in some instances, and as a result the patient may be overdosed. The vaginal cytologic index isn't foolproof; good spinbarkeit and ferning of the cervical mucus are more reliable.

What does one do if the patient has a high pyknotic index and good cervical ferning? In such patients I believe that the best we can do is to be cautious, administering two ampules of Pergonal per day for five to eight days, while daily pelvic examinations are performed to avoid excessive ovarian enlargement. When you think that the patient has received enough HMG, wait for two or three days, then give 4,000 to 5,000 units of HCG. If no untoward reactions are experienced and ovulation failed to occur, then the schedule of Pergonal and dosage may be changed to five vials every other day for three to five injections. Vaginal cytology and cervical mucus studies and repeated pelvic examinations are essential in following the patient.

DR. CROOKE: I think the questioner asked if one can rely on the fern test or on vaginal cytology to determine the correct dosage of FSH. We do not believe that any test carried out on one day can be relied upon to assess what dosage of FSH to give on the next day. The reason for this is, we believe, that a follicle once stimulated continues to grow spontaneously for ten to twelve days. In other words the maximum effect of a dose is not apparent until ten to twelve days later (Crooke, Butt and Bertrand, 1966.) This is not a criticism of the fern test or of vaginal cytology. These tests may be satisfactory for assessing whether a patient has responded to gonadotrophin or not, provided enough time is allowed to elapse between injection and sampling. They are unable to give the same quantitative information as that obtained from assays of steroid hormones, however, and a properly designed experiment is needed to compare them. This is now being carried out in three different centers in Britain under the auspices of the Medical Research Council where three commercial preparations from Serono (Pergonal), Paines and Byrne, and Organon are being compared with our own preparation of human pituitary FSH and the results assessed by a number of different parameters. We hope that this will give a complete answer to the question.

DR. QUINTO: I want to thank Dr. Greenblatt and to remind him that actually it is only when we have basal conditions which permit us to see the progressive modifications that we can use this data. It seems to us that they can have a certain importance, at least clinical and practical if in no other respect. If we find ourselves faced with a patient with amenorrhea who has adequate urinary estrogens, we employ HCG alone instead of Pergonal.

DR. INGIULLA: I believe that the evaluation of the dosage of HMG is still a problem. I would prefer strong doses at the beginning of the cycle to increasing doses during the cycle, but I understand that from a practical point of view, the problem is difficult to solve. Let us ask Dr. Greenblatt two other questions: What do you think about the use of clomiphene in male oligospermia? and Do you think there is a possibility of clomiphene effectiveness in Sheehan's syndrome?

DR. GREENBLATT: My associate, Dr. Jungck, has been interested in the problem of oligospermia. In one study with student volunteers who received 25-50 mg of clomiphene per day for six to ten weeks, sperm counts were evaluated at weekly intervals. He found in the normal male changes that were inconclusive. Some had an increase in the sperm count, others a decrease, and some no change.

However, in his treatment of oligospermic men, he found that about 25 per cent had an increase or a doubling of their sperm count in sixty to ninety days after the onset of clomiphene therapy. Though the quality of the sperm did not improve, the quantity did; and although some were successful in inseminating their wives, we are, nonetheless, not completely convinced of the role of clomiphene in therapy.

In order to use clomiphene, we must assume that there is a responsive pituitary ovarian axis. In the classical, full-blown Sheehan's syndrome, no evidence of ovarian stimulation was obtained. In such cases, a trial with HMG followed by HCG is their only hope.

DR. INGIULLA: We are now into the problem of clomiphene. As you know, we have sufficient experience with this very important substance. The results obtained by us are good in many cases of ovarian failure, in amenorrhea, Stein-Leventhal syndrome, and other such cases. At the present time we think that, from the clinical point of view, the first treatment of an anovulatory patient should be with clomiphene. Dr. Greenblatt, what is your experience in this matter?

DR. GREENBLATT: The anovulatory patient who does not have some obvious contributing endocrinopathy deserves a trial of clomiphene first. The patient with Sheehan's syndrome or Simmonds' disease and the patient with secondary amenorrhea and markedly elevated urinary gonadotropins are not candidates. The anovulatory female in whom urinary gonadotropins are normal or even nonmeasurable should be given at least three courses of clomiphene at monthly intervals before deciding that she is unresponsive. If we fail with clomiphene, then we might try clomiphene followed by an injection of 4,000 units of HCG. If that fails, then that patient is a candidate for HMG followed by human chorionic gonadotropin. Since gonadotropins are expensive and difficult to come by and we are not as fortunate as Dr. Crooke to have enough material to treat four hundred patients, we feel gonadotropins should be reserved for those who are nonresponsive to clomiphene or have definite hypogonadotropic hypoovarianism.

Dr. LUNENFELD: I fully agree with Dr. Greenblatt's approach. As I said this morning, clomiphene will act when there is a defect in pituitary release. In cases of primary amenorrhea, as you will remember from Dr. Greenblatt's data, very few positive results were obtained with clomiphene and, I believe, not a single pregnancy. In such cases, we start directly with gonadotropic treatment. In cases of secondary amenorrhea, I also think that the approach of Dr. Greenblatt is correct. We have published a paper with Dr. Greenblatt, on Chiari-Frommel cases, and good responses were obtained with either clomiphene or Pergonal (*Fertility and Sterility,* Vol. 17 (No. 6), 1966).

Dr. CROOKE: My position is very near to that of Dr. Greenblatt if only because of the question of cost. Obviously the cost of clomiphene is of a quite different order to the cost of FSH. I am also in agreement with his idea that it is worth while trying patients with secondary or even primary amenorrhoea on clomiphene first. We have had some that have responded to this treatment, but we have not had a high success rate, probably because of our inexperience.

I should like to make one comment on Dr. Greenblatt's choice of patients, based on their excretion of gonadotrophin. If I understand him correctly, he measures their gonadotrophin excretion once only. It is our custom to do three estimates in successive weeks, and we have found, particularly in women with anovular cycles, quite striking variations. If we get one high figure (say 100 mg first IRP) and two low (say 5 mg), we would consider the patient suitable for treatment. If we get two high and one low, we do three more estimations of gonadotrophins. If we get about an equal number of high and low figures, we find that these patients generally respond to gonadotrophins, and we have had pregnancies in such patients following treatment. This is quite contrary to what Gemzell used to say, and undoubtedly we are finding patients with enormous fluctuations in gonadotrophin excretion who respond well to treatment, but I believe that these patients quite often recover spontaneously.

Dr. GREENBLATT: Essentially, I am in agreement with Dr. Crooke. It is a matter of expedience that we obtain only one or two twenty-four-hour urine specimens for total gonadotropin assay. I believe these should be done more often; frequently, one or two assays are not sufficiently informative. I feel, however, that those who have extremely high values will prove unresponsive.

TABLE 18-III
HORMONE EXCRETION PATTERN IN A CASE OF
PROLONGED FOLLICULAR PHASE FOLLOWED BY PREGNANCY

Day of cycle	*(Occurrence of ovulation between days 40-45 of cycle)*					
	Estrone μg/24 hr	Estradiol μg/24 hr	Estriol μg/24 hr	Total estrogens	Ferning grade	Pregnanediol mg/24 hr
10	4.2	0.98	4.2	9.38	+	
18	5.1	3.9	6.48	15.48	+ +	
25					+ +	
30	2.88	0.96	3.6	7.40	+ +	
35					+ +	
40	9.42	3.5	9.6	22.52	+ +	$<$1
45						3.6
50	8.00	2.4	16.3	26.7	—	8.6
55	8.52	4.2	46.3	55.02	—	6.9
61	16.20	6.2	56.42	78.82		
68	P R E G N A N C Y		T E S T		P O S I T I V E.....................	

DR. LUNENFELD: Permit me to make some comments. Several years ago, Dr. Insler and I investigated two conditions: "Prolonged follicular phase" and "delayed follicular phase." The prolonged follicular phase is a condition of an ovulatory cycle, where the follicular phase may be prolonged up to one hundred days. Table 18-III illustrates such a case. On the other hand, in the delayed follicular phase, there is no significant ovarian activity until approximately ten days prior to ovulation. This is illustrated in Figure 18-4. During the "inactive" part of the cycle, the gonadotropic levels are sometimes high and may reach menopausal values. At a later stage, when ovarian activity begins, gonadotropic levels fall. This is the reason we carry our repeated gonadotropic assays before deciding on treatment.

DR. INGIULLA: Dr. Greenblatt, do you believe that clomiphene acts through its antiestrogenic properties?

DR. GREENBLATT: I am quite convinced that clomiphene has various modes of action. One may be at the level of the ovary. It may sensitize the ovary so that it is more responsive to endogenous gonadotropins.

There is another mode of action: it works at the level of the hypothalamic pituitary axis, permitting a triggering mechanism to take place in the release of gonadotropins. When gonadotropins are released and the ovaries are responsive, a rise in estrogen levels will result, particularly if ovulation has been induced. The antiestrogenic effect of clomiphene removes the steroid inhibition of gonadotropins, permitting their release to stimulate ovarian secretion of estrogens.

However, in the patient with Chiari-Frommel syndrome, clomiphene may exert its effects at the hypothalamic level. Because of the absence of endogenous estrogens in many such cases, it is obvious that the explanation cannot be based on clomiphene's antiestrogenic action. Since lactation is thought to occur as a result of isolating the pituitary from hypothalamic

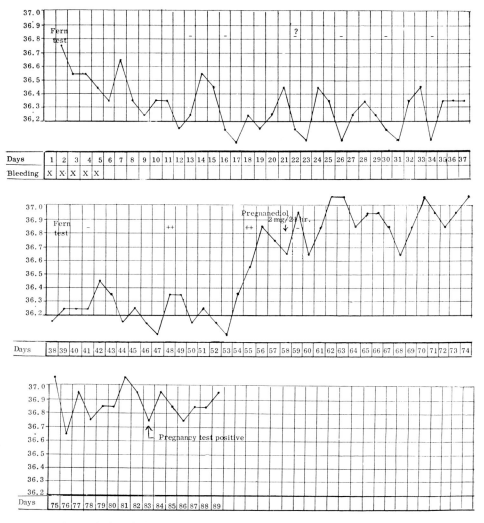

FIGURE 18-4. Ovulation followed by pregnancy in a patient with delayed follicular phase.

control, it is conjectured that clomiphene may be useful in some of these cases because it influences hypothalamic function. There probably are at least three modes of action of clomiphene in the human.

DR. LUNENFELD: May I propose a fourth possibility for mode of action of clomiphene, which I think that Dr. Greenblatt's group has demonstrated so well with radioactive material. It can be speculated that clomiphene, an antiestrogen, may alter the feedback mechanism and thus release gonadotropins.

DR. DONINI: Permit me to criticize what I have heard about gonadotrophin dosage, or rather about the utility of gonadotrophin carried out by the method of using the uterus of an immature rat or mouse. This is not a specific method, and in some cases such as those that must be studied for gonadotrophin or clomiphene treatment, we may find a relative or absolute imbalance between the FSH and LH factors. With the method using the uterus we have demonstrated that injecting biologically pure FSH into an immature mouse, absolutely no reaction was obtained. And I should like to say that many times, as far as I know, in routine work the determination of gonadotrophin is not always carried out according to the criteria that permit valid results. For example, I should like to ask Dr. Greenblatt if he has sufficient proof that clomiphene increases the amount of FSH. It seems to me that I saw a slide that showed an increase in FSH excretion determinated by a specific method, that is the Steelman-Pohley method, following clomiphene treatment. I seem to have seen — Dr. Greenblatt may correct me — that the determination of FSH was carried out on forty-eight-hour urine. Now I believe that with the Steelman-Pohley method it is not possible to find the dosage on forty-eight-hour urine. I believe that for a biologically correct dosage we must use at least two doses of the standard and two doses prepared from the titrated solution. I seem to remember that Dr. Dorfman showed a slide in which it was evident that injecting only two doses of the standard and one dose of the unknown preparation to be titrated, the possibility of error was 400 to 500 per cent. Now I wonder if the results that are obtained through biological dosages of gonadotrophins are always valid.

DR. GREENBLATT: I am in perfect agreement with Dr. Donini. He is perfectly right that you cannot draw conclusions from the few analyses we have performed on a few patients. It is true that in order to do meticulous gonadotropin assays, one should collect five- to seven-days specimens, ours were on forty-eight-hour specimens. The Steelman-Pohley assay technique was used for FSH, the ascorbic acid depletion test of Parlow for LH, and I am well aware that there are many pitfalls not only in performing the test, but also in their interpretation. Thank you, Dr. Donini, for once more emphasizing this very important point.

DR. INGIULLA: As you can see, each question returns to the difficulties of hormonal estimations by means of urinary assays. We have been following many patients with urinary total gonadotrophin assays simultaneously with LH determinations by an immunological technique. In many cases we have clear proof of the action of clomiphene at one of these two urinary parameters. At present we are trying to estimate both FSH and LH, by radioimmune assays, and we hope to present more significant results in a short time.

I believe that repeated analyses must be performed before treatment. After that, we use 50 mg of clomiphene for the first five days of cycle or all together on the first day to see if any variation in estrogens, pregnanediol, and gonadotrophin appears. We then can increase the doses up to 100 mg, and eventually, if LH is still low, add HCG. Only after that can we pass to the gonadotrophins, of course, with the exceptions considered by Dr. Greenblatt.

Now there is a question as to the danger of overstimulation with HMG. I should like to ask Dr. Lunenfeld to enlighten us.

DR. LUNENFELD: It is difficult to say which patients will be hyperstimulated and which will not. Dr. Jayle advised that before using gonadotropins, one should make a dynamic test with chorionic gonadotropins and see if the androgens are increased. This may determine at least one group of patients with increased stromal compartment (using the language of Dr. Savard). However, in other cases, as we have demonstrated, the hyperstimulation effect would only follow corpus luteum formation. We believe that, at least in some cases, hyperstimulation is due to a metabolic defect of the newly formed corpus luteum. This cannot be predicted beforehand.

I should like to draw your attention to the fact that Dr. Crooke, using his treatment schedule, also found hyperstimulation in some of his patients.

In all the cases we have studied, in which coagulability problems had occurred, the blood volume was strikingly decreased. Our treatment in such cases is to replace this loss either by blood transfusion or by causing a return of fluid into the vascular system by infusion of high molecular weight materials such as dextran or albumin. We have always added heparin to this treatment, in order to prevent any hypercoagulability.

DR. RICHTER: We have recently obtained a new compound Ferrosan, for clinical investigation from a Swedish Company. This substance has some structural similarity to clomiphene and, according to the preliminary observations of Persson in Upsala (*Acta Soc Med Upsal, 70:*1, 70, 1965), also has similar effects in the human female. It is called F-6066. Compared with clomiphene, this structure is modified in such a way that one carbon atom of the carbon-carbon double bond is already part of one of the three six-numbered rings. This particular ring is not an aromatic one, but a saturated one. I should just like to say very briefly that Persson found that F-6066 is very active; out of ten sterility cases six women became pregnant; nineteen out of twenty-seven anovulatory patients ovulated with treatment.

With regard to our own studies, I should like to offer a few preliminary results: no change of the urinary excretion of 17-ketosteroids and 17-hydroxycorticosteroid was found on treatment. As far as the estrogen excretion is concerned, it is of interest to mention that in all but one, the excretion of the estriol fraction was increased up to 50 per twenty-four hours shortly after the treatment was initiated; the excretion of the combined fraction of estrone and estradiol was less increased. However, under clomiphene treatment the increase in estriol excretion often was found to be less than the estrone excretion. The excretion of estrone was the highest of the three estrogens measured. Furthermore, the excretion pattern did not correspond to the excretion pattern normally observed at the time of ovulation or thereafter. Hence, we may assume that clomiphene has an effect on the bio-synthesis of the estrogens or rather on the metabolism of estrone-estradiol to estriol in the ovary or — more probable — in the liver. However, such an effect was not found following the administration of F-6066.

Various blood constituents (cholesterol, PBI, urea, creatinine, alkaline phosphatase, the transaminases) and the hemoglobin concentration were assayed before and during treatment. No significant change could be observed except for the cholesterol level which appears to be slightly de-creased. No change was found in the erythrocyte, leucocyte, and the throm-bocyte counts.

In twenty-two patients, we found no side effects even with daily doses as high as 600 mg. Ovulation occurred in long-standing amenorrhea cases as evidenced by biphasic basal body temperature curves and by the pregnane-diol excretion which increased to 4-6 mg. per twenty-four hours. Thus far, one patient with primary sterility became pregnant.

We think compound F-6066 is a promising new drug which appears to have some remarkable advantages over clomiphene.

(These studies have been performed in collaboration with Dr. M. Arnold, Dr. M. Berger, Dr. M. Keller, Dr. F. Roth, and Dr. O. Stamm.)

Dr. Ingiulla: We thank Dr. Richter for the presentation of this com-pound which we hope to study soon in comparison with clomiphene. Let us finish with the last question addressed to Dr. Greenblatt. Do you believe that we can use clomiphene in Stein-Leventhal cases where estrogens are not low?

Dr. Greenblatt: Clomiphene has proved effective in inducing ovula-tion in women diagnosed as Stein-Leventhal syndrome and in whom endo-genous estrogens were not low. The incidence of conceptions, however, was not as high as we had hoped.

CONTRIBUTORS AND DISCUSSANTS INDEX

AUTHOR INDEX

SUBJECT INDEX